ROBERT BOYLE ON
NATURAL PHILOSOPHY

by Marie Boas Hall

INDIANA UNIVERSITY PRESS
BLOOMINGTON   1965

ROBERT BOYLE ON
NATURAL PHILOSOPHY

An Essay with Selections
from His Writings

FOREWORD

This work was originally written to form part of a series which never began. The passage of years, however, has made the book seem more worth-while, not less, for interest in the history of science and in the work of Robert Boyle has markedly increased. It remains the case, as it was when this book was written and compiled, that books by Boyle grow scarcer and dearer with the years. A book of selections can never replace complete texts, but it can serve other purposes. Every attempt has been made here to give excerpts long enough to convey the character of the complete works from which they are taken. Readers and especially students will find these selections a useful and interesting guide; they may thereby be led to consult the handsome eighteenth-century volumes of Boyle's collected works, edited by Thomas Birch.

NORWOOD RUSSELL HANSON

PREFATORY NOTE

Most of the manuscript material used in the biographical study is to be found in the Miles Collection of Boyle Papers in the Royal Society; I have to thank the Council of the Royal Society for permission to study these papers, and the Librarians for aid. Some of the research on Boyle's work was undertaken while I was a fellow of the John Simon Guggenheim Memorial Foundation (1955–56).

The picture of Robert Boyle is reproduced by the gracious permission of Her Majesty the Queen from the portrait now in Kensington Palace. Figure 1 is reproduced by permission of the Trustees of the British Museum. The remaining figures are taken from *New Experiments, Physico-Mechanical,* the third edition, which includes the *First Continuation;* these were made available to me by the William Andrews Clark Memorial Library, Los Angeles.

The major portion of the material printed here is taken from *The Works of the Honourable Robert Boyle,* edited by Thomas Birch (second edition, London, 1772, in six volumes).

M. B. H.

Los Angeles, 1958
Bloomington, Indiana, 1963

CONTENTS

ILLUSTRATIONS

PART ONE
Introduction

[I]

Life

THE SEVENTEENTH-CENTURY tourist arrived in a foreign capital city armed not with camera and color film but with letters of introduction. An inquisitive tourist arriving in London in 1662, or any time thereafter for the next thirty years, would not fail to use his letters to visit the rooms at Gresham College occupied by the Royal Society, that galaxy of scientists, wits, "gentlemen free and unconfined," professional men and business men, the center of scientific learning in Great Britain. There he would see, as the Society's great showpiece, Mr. Boyle's air pump. If he arrived on a Wednesday he might be admitted to the weekly meeting of the Society, when members brought in new scientific facts and experiments, when aspiring scientists sent in accounts of their latest work, when new books were reviewed, and when the Curator, Robert Hooke, once Mr. Boyle's assistant, performed experiments of his own and others' devising. Perhaps Mr. Boyle himself might be there, affable and courteous, gentle and learned; if not, it was easy to meet the leading scientist of that brilliant assembly. The visitor would proceed at his convenience to the house on Pall Mall where Boyle lived with his brilliant and charming sister Lady Ranelagh, sure of gaining admittance, for Boyle was endlessly patient with visitors, a charming and agreeable host. Though he was somewhat stately and reserved, as befitted a great gentleman, he was condescending and friendly to those who sought the information he loved to impart.

3

In Boyle's laboratory lay many sources of delight for the curious, scientist or layman. There was an improved version of the air pump the visitor had already seen at Gresham College; in it he might witness an experiment on respiration, when birds or kittens were placed in the pump's glass receiver, which was then exhausted to ascertain the length of time they could survive without air. The creatures were usually revived for later experiments, though the tender-minded scientist often released them after their ordeal. Or the air pump might be used to show how air was generated from raisins. There were always chemical experiments in process, the great furnaces being kept hot for distillation or combustion. Best of all, Mr. Boyle was sure to show the visitor strange and curious experiments: how, by mixing two colorless liquids, a yellow solution or white solid might be formed; how a colorless liquid in a closed flask could turn bright blue-green when air was admitted; how silver might be turned into a white powder which blackened on standing; how air might be generated by pouring a liquid on iron nails. Or he would show samples of strange substances: the diamond that shone in the dark; the white powder he had prepared from pure water; the white solid, phosphorus, that shone in the dark and had to be kept under water, lest it burst into flame. All these things, Mr. Boyle assured the visitor, were far from magical and had a rational and simple explanation. And all his study of nature, he would also assure the visitor, led him every day more and more firmly to admire the wonderful contrivances of the Creator of the universe, a subject on which he discoursed with pious fervor. The visitor, entranced by what he had seen and heard, left feeling that he had indeed been in touch with the great man of English science, and he could return home to boast with great content of his intimate acquaintance with the leading member of the Royal Society.

And he was correct; for Boyle was indeed the leading English scientist and the most influential member of the Royal Society. Though he refused all honors and would not, after the first year of its life, even be President of the Royal Society, he yet dominated the scientific scene of the day. When the Royal Society had a problem of science or scientific method, the members turned to Boyle; when they sought influence at Court, they turned to him equally. Impecunious scientists sought his patronage and obtained it freely, as dedications show. The touchy Robert Hooke, though occasionally offended by a casual word, was a constant visitor to Boyle's house and laboratory, and never forgot what he had learned in his youth as his patron's laboratory assistant. The arrogant Newton, admitted to the Royal Society, talked with Boyle at meetings, sent warm, friendly, and respectful messages, and even, at his request, ventured upon some hypotheses. Wherever one went, Boyle's work and the attitude toward science which he embraced were regarded as official English scientific policy. His work and that of the Royal Society were regarded as one, and just as Newton's name came to mind when the Royal Society was mentioned in the early eighteenth century, so Boyle's did during the first thirty years of the Society's existence. And this in spite of the galaxy of scientific talent that glittered in and about London at this time.

Nothing fades faster than a reputation which is based mainly upon a scientific attitude. Boyle, however, was not only a leader of scientific thought in his own times, but a distinguished and original scientist. He made his first public reputation through his work on the physical nature of air, and "Boyle's Law" still, justly, commemorates his name, though we no longer speak, as his own age did, of the Boyleian vacuum. The work on air, which he continued throughout his life, is masterly. But so was his work on the mechanical philosophy, that blend of an attitude toward the world and a rational explanation of it which underlies the best work in natural philosophy throughout the seventeenth and eighteenth centuries. He was also a notable chemist, one of the first to make chemistry truly scientific, a masterly designer of chemical experiments. And, as a rich and private gentleman, he had the leisure and means to pour forth a string of works—not less than one or two a year—in which he displayed his knowledge and promoted the new science for the benefit of the world at large.

Unfortunately, Boyle's writings are not readily available today, though they contain so much to interest the modern reader. For all his popularity—each work went through several English and Latin editions in his lifetime—seventeenth-century copies of his books are today very dear, and even the Latin editions, which few people can now read, are highly priced in the booksellers' catalogues. The eighteenth century produced two collected editions of Boyle's works, but these are cumbersome and increasingly expensive. For long the only available single work was *The Sceptical Chemist,* a polemical work of propaganda that has mysteriously kept its reputation when the controversy is forgotten; it is one of his most difficult books. There is, it is true, another reason why Boyle is so little read: quite simply, he wrote too much. Over the years he wrote book after book without pausing to revise or to organize, and his works fill some 4,000 pages of the large quarto edition of 1772. His aim was a familiar and easy style, but what was easy for the seventeenth century is distressingly prolix for the twentieth.

If Boyle is to be appreciated and enjoyed as he deserves, and if his true importance for the history of science is to be recognized, then something must be done to make his ideas available to the modern reader. In the present volume the selections have been chosen with a view of presenting Boyle's main achievements and ideas in a comprehensible manner, without the frequent repetition which he felt to be essential. The one thing that has proved impossible is to give a really adequate illustration of the enormous wealth of experiment with which almost all his works are filled, and which made his books popular even with his opponents. It is difficult to read long accounts of complex experiments in the language of a bygone science without so much gloss that the experiment is lost in the explanation. But in reading what is set out here one should remember that the bulk of every book is made up of a mass of experiment, designed to illustrate and confirm the theory. For Boyle was, above all else, an experimental scientist—in the words of Henry Oldenburg, publisher of the *History of Cold* and secretary of the Royal Society, an "exquisite searcher of nature."[1]

Robert Boyle was born on January 25, 1626/7 (the fact that England still used the "old style" calendar let contemporaries note that he was born in the same year that Francis Bacon died), the fourteenth child of the Earl of Cork, at Linsmore Castle in Munster, Ireland.[2] As he himself said, he was above all things lucky in his birth. Son of "the Great Earl," an Elizabethan adventurer who by ability, ruthless greed, charm, and luck had raised himself from a penniless younger son into one of the richest and most powerful men in Ireland, he had the assured background of position, family, and wealth. Yet as a younger son, with four older brothers, he did not need to concern himself with public affairs or the promotion of family interest. As he chose to grow up studious and disinclined to anything that might distract him from intellectual pursuits, his position was invaluable to him, for he was dependent upon nobody, yet had the support of a large and influential family.

It must always be one of the surprising things about the
past that families of this size managed to develop any
affection or common interest in an age when babies were
put out to nurse with peasant foster parents for three or
four years, for the sake of wholesome country air, and
when children left home by the age of twelve or so, girls
to the families of their future husbands, and boys to be
educated by "governors." But they often did, and Robert
Boyle grew up devoted to half a dozen of his brothers and
sisters. The Boyles were a singularly energetic and talented family; a contemporary wrote, a little overemphati-
cally, "believe me, ould Cork could not begett nothing
foolish,"[3] and at least half the family did indeed make a
notable stir in the world. This talented half came to form
a very congenial group, differing markedly in age but not
in interests. Eldest was Katherine, Lady Ranelagh (born
1614/5); of her husband, contemporaries could find
nothing good to say except that he was not often at home.
She was a clever and beautiful woman, with charm, learning, and piety, a friend of the poet Milton and of the leading
Puritan intellectuals of the day, exercising much influence
over the family group. The other members of this group
were nearer of age: Roger, Baron Broghill, born 1621, was
the idol of his youngest brother; he shared his father's
political talents, glittered in the social world—the stir he
made in his youth is commemorated by Suckling's "Ballade
upon a Wedding"—and found time for writing plays and
romances. Mary, born 1624, was the family rebel, who
insisted, contrary to her father's commands, on marrying
an impecunious younger son for love; convention won out,
for he became Earl of Warwick, and the match proved as
unhappy as those of her obedient sisters; she solaced herself with a repellently strict and mystic religious faith,
described at tedious length in her diary.[4] The other members of this circle were the two youngest boys, Francis,

later Lord Shannon (born 1623), overshadowed in his boyhood by his younger brother and in his manhood by his elder brother; and Robert, who in the end outstripped them all.

Like all boys of gentle family, Robert Boyle began his education at home, learning, besides the rudiments, French and Latin. He seems, by his own account, to have displayed even in boyhood a disarming and ingenuous goodness and piety which should have made him priggish, but somehow did not, in spite of much family spoiling. This singular temperament stood him in good stead when he accompanied Francis to Eton, to which sons of gentlemen were just beginning to be sent for their formal education. Robert, at nine, was far too young for the school, and was given much freedom but little learning. The experiment was not a success for the brothers, and in 1638 they were packed off to Switzerland under the care of a citizen of Geneva named Marcombes, who had been educating the older Boyle boys, and was later to educate Broghill's sons. In Geneva the boys were kept busy at their studies by their father's express command. Conscientiously, Marcombes made sure that they were thoroughly grounded in rhetoric (Latin grammar) and logic, the formal elementary subjects of the day, though they bored teacher and pupils alike. They all preferred mathematics (which meant arithmetic, geometry, astronomy, and fortification), geography, and history. Natural philosophy was not neglected; it was in Geneva that Boyle read Diogenes Laertius' *Lives of the Philosophers*, where he learned of the atomic theory of Epicurus, and also Seneca's *Natural Questions*, which interested him in the problem of earthquakes. When Marcombes asked permission to take the boys to Italy he urged its value not only for learning the language, but also for astronomy and architecture. They were in Florence in the winter of 1641–42, when Galileo died; while there Robert read in his newly improved Italian what he later called "the new paradoxes of that great stargazer Galileo, whose ingenious books, perhaps because they could not be so otherwise, were confuted by a decree from Rome."[5]

Years later Boyle confessed that he always found May Day inauspicious, ardent rationalist though he might be; and it was on May 1, 1642, that he first heard news of the Irish rebellion.[6] The Earl wrote that he would be unable to send any more money for his sons' support; they should return to fight in Ireland, or else join the Dutch wars, where Protestant volunteers were also needed. Francis, too old at twenty-one to be still in tutelage, readily set off for Ireland and fought there with his father and brothers. Robert, feeling too young at sixteen, appealed to Marcombes for aid, explaining to his father that he needed "repose" before he could "gather some force and vigour to serve and defend my Religion, my King and my Country according to my little powers."[7] This "repose" lasted for two years; with the death of his father Boyle finally decided to return to England. Here civil war had broken out and he intended to join the King's army in the family tradition. He always said that it was by mere chance that he found out where his sister Katherine was living; she welcomed him affectionately and, a convinced Parliamentarian herself, soon dissuaded him from his intention of fighting for the King. Instead, she introduced him to what he called "several persons of power & interest in the Parliament and their party," who helped him secure the estate bequeathed him by his father.[8] The manor of Stalbridge in Dorset was sufficient to maintain him in comfort, and he could now lead the life of a leisured country gentleman if he chose.

Though he soon went to Stalbridge to put all in order, it was some time before he settled there. He went to France briefly, perhaps to repay Marcombes; he visited Broghill and his sister Mary; he stayed with friends and made new acquaintances. Within a year he was settled in the life he was to lead for the next half dozen years: long periods of quiet at Stalbridge interspersed with London and country-house visits, mainly to members of the family group. Lady Ranelagh kept both her favorite brothers interested in the Parliamentarian side. With the Irish rebellion temporarily suppressed, Broghill planned to join the Royalist forces overseas; Lady Ranelagh talked of him to Cromwell, who persuaded him to serve Parliament instead, first in Ireland, later in Scotland and England, and Broghill became one of the Lord Protector's staunchest followers. While providing Broghill with an active Parliamentarian life, Lady Ranelagh was equally able to provide an intellectual Parliamentarian life for her studious youngest brother Robert, by introducing him to a circle which he found most congenial, and which was to provide the stimulus that turned his thoughts from the literary pursuits encouraged by Broghill and Lady Ranelagh into more nearly scientific interests.

This intellectual circle centered around Samuel Hartlib, whose principal occupation was the promotion of schemes, mainly educational or religious, for the public good.[9] Hartlib came from Prussia, where his father had been a well-to-do merchant, and presumably came to England partly to escape religious persecution. Settled in London, he became an active philanthropist. He assisted Protestant refugees from Catholic German states, was in close touch with Puritan and Parliamentarian projects for the welfare of mankind, and was associated with bringing the Czech educator Comenius to England in the 1640's. Above all, Hartlib was an "intelligencer," a peculiarly seventeenth-century profession (or avocation). He had an enormously wide acquaintance in intellectual and theological circles, which he continually widened, and he maintained a truly huge correspondence even for that age, gathering and exchanging news of all kinds. What he lived on is something of a mystery; Parliament several times gave him grants of money, but these were presumably to recompense expenses incurred in his public benefactions. He had multitudinous interests, many directed toward that favorite seventeenth-century notion of a Utopian society or college of learning, half Baconian *New Atlantis*, half Puritan monastic retreat. There are many books which deal with such schemes, and a number of them were directly influenced by Hartlib's encouragement of the author. Hartlib himself was especially interested in the "Pansophia" of Comenius, which offered the universal road to light and truth: universal knowledge should be collected in universal books, taught in universal schools, written and spoken of in a universal language, all of which would result in a universal truth, a universal peace, and a Christian Commonwealth on earth. It was partly in pursuit of this ideal that Hartlib tried to persuade Parliament to set up an "Office of Public Addresse" in 1648; this was to combine charitable, commercial, and informational purposes.

It was Hartlib's interest in the promotion of knowledge, especially useful knowledge, that appealed to Boyle. Also, the studious, serious, earnest young man, well connected and well off, was a valuable recruit to Hartlib's circle. He was soon on intimate terms with Hartlib and his friends, and had begun that extensive correspondence from which so much of our knowledge of the group is derived. Boyle was soon writing to his friends of the intellectual stimulus he was finding in contact with what he called the "Invisible College" or "our new philosophical College." *

* Some confusion has arisen because Thomas Birch, Boyle's eighteenth-century biographer and editor, assumed that Boyle, who was later such a prominent member of the Royal Society, must have been a member from its first tentative beginnings, which date from 1645; Birch therefore assumed that the Invisible College was identical with the group of scientists meeting at Gresham College. But aside from the improbability

Its Comenian nature is indicated by what he wrote Hartlib in May, 1647: "You interest yourself so much in the Invisible College, and that whole society is so highly concerned in all the accidents of your life, that you can send me no intelligence . . . that does not (at least relationally) assume the name of Utopian."[10] The guiding principle was that the members of this Society "valued no knowledge, but as it hath a tendency to use," which gave them very wide scope for interest. Boyle at this time described them, with youthful enthusiasm, as "men of so capacious and searching spirits, that school-philosophy is but the lowest region of their knowledge; and yet, though ambitious to lead the way to any generous design, of so humble and teachable a genius, as they disdain not to be directed to the meanest, so he can but plead reason for his opinion; persons that endeavour to put narrow-mindedness out of countenance, by the practice of so extensive a charity, that it reaches unto every thing called man, and nothing less than an universal good will can content it. And indeed they are so apprehensive of the want of good employment,

---

that the leading scientists of England would include in their discussions a lad of eighteen with no special scientific knowledge, there is no mention of him in John Wallis' account of those early meetings, written when Boyle was the most famous of living English scientists. Wallis would surely not have forgotten had Boyle in fact been a member in 1645; his memory would rather have erred in the other direction. It seems certain that Boyle's "Invisible College" was Hartlib's Comenian group. On this see Rosemary Syfret, "The Origins of the Royal Society," *Notes and Records of the Royal Society*, 1948, amply confirmed by Boyle's correspondence with Hartlib (in *Life* and in *Works*, Vol. VI). Cf. also Hartlib's *Ephemerides*, extracts of which have been published by Turnbull in "Samuel Hartlib's Influence on the Early History of the Royal Society," *Notes and Records*, X (1953), 101-30. It is now in Sheffield University Library. Turnbull believes that Hartlib was actively involved with the Gresham group, but his evidence mainly applies to the later 1650's. More evidence in support of the Syfret thesis may be found in my *Robert Boyle and Seventeenth-Century Chemistry*, Chap. I.

that they take the whole body of mankind for their care."[11] This universal Comenian philanthropy, coupled with the fashionable intellectual position of the day, the rejection of traditional, "bookish" learning in favor of an appeal to "things," to knowledge learned from experience, was exactly calculated to appeal to the young, high-minded, serious kind of man that Robert Boyle then was.

In spite of Boyle's encomium, these men were not, themselves, especially talented in the fields they desired to promote, but most of them were sufficiently active in public affairs to have left some record, and except for John Dury, the divine, were interested and active in science. There was John Pell, a good mathematician, though best known as Cromwell's political agent to the Swiss Protestant cantons; and Theodore Haak, also a German, who led a life very like Hartlib's, though his interest was primarily in science and his correspondence with the leading scientists in France. With Dury, Pell, and Haak, Boyle seems to have had little or no direct contact. He was closer to the younger men, many of whom appeared to have been his patrons in science, while he was their patron in worldly matters./ Among these was Benjamin Worsley, surgeon to Cromwell's Irish expedition, and later Surveyor-General in Ireland, the member of the group for whom Hartlib seems to have felt most esteem; after 1647 there was the young William Petty, later Worsley's adversary and successor in Ireland, already a brilliant and talented youth, later a public figure of note, and writer on political economy; after 1650 a number of chemists, mostly rather mystically inclined: Hartlib's son-in-law, Frederick Clodius, widely accused of being an alchemist; Robert Child, Puritan divine, also an alchemist; George Starke, who called himself "philosopher by fire"; minor inventors like Cressy Dymock; agronomists, like John Beale, who wrote on orchards and cider, and Gabriel

Plattes; and miscellaneous writers like Gerard and Arnold Boate, who wrote both *A Natural History of Ireland* and an anti-Aristotelian tract called *The Reformation of Natural Philosophy*. They were almost all more important for their promotion of established ideas than for any genuine originality and were perhaps all the more suited to Boyle's developing interests for that.

Boyle was still very young when he settled at Stalbridge, and began to devote himself to study and writing. One must not think of him as a hermit or recluse, however; he led a normal country-house life, shooting, fishing, dining with his neighbors, looking after his estate; what differentiated him from others was his eager curiosity which led him to try to learn husbandry from the ploughman, and the fact that he was more apt to amuse himself with books than with wine. He became increasingly engrossed by his studies, and began a little to resent intrusions by visitors, as he was to do all his life; though, essentially gregarious, he never avoided their interruptions—merely complained of them. But country pleasures and interruptions still left him time to read omnivorously—especially chemical and travel books—and to write enormously. In the family tradition he wrote ethical and moral reflections; there are some fragments of a treatise on ethics still extant, and he wrote his "Free Discourse Against Customary Swearing" at Broghill's suggestion. He even tried his hand at romances, some very bad fragments of which remain. Theological reflections attracted him; he combined two literary styles by writing a theological treatise in the form of a romance under the title *Some Motives and Incentives to the Love of God, Pathetically Discoursed of, in a Letter to a Friend*, a cumbersome title which he and everyone else shortened to *Seraphic Love*. This was begun at Stalbridge and finished in the summer of 1648 during a long visit to his sister Mary at the Earl of Warwick's castle at

Leighs in Essex.[12] Though this had lately been besieged by
Royalist forces it was quite habitable, striking testimony
to the relative mildness of civil war strife compared to
modern rigors. One cannot help regretting the practice
Boyle acquired during these years in writing on many
topics, for it gave him a wicked facility that soon turned
into prolixity.

But though Boyle might act as if ethical and theological
philosophy were his chief concerns, an interest in natural
philosophy persistently asserted itself. Urging the superior-
ity of divine over human love, he could not help drawing
his moral from the study of nature; as he wrote, "when
with bold telescopes I survey the old and newly discovered
stars and planets, that adorn the upper region of the world;
and when with excellent microscopes I discern, in otherwise invisible objects, the unimitable subtility of nature's
curious workmanship; and when, in a word, by the help of
anatomical knives, and the light of chymical furnaces, I
study the book of nature, and consult the glosses of
Aristotle, Epicurus, Paracelsus, Harvey, Helmont, and
other learned expositors of that instructive volume: I find
myself oftentimes reduced to exclaim with the Psalmist,
How manifold are Thy works, O Lord! in wisdom has Thou
made them all!"[13] He made a kind of transition from
theology to natural philosophy by writing (though with
many interruptions for chemical experiments) a series of
essays intended for his sister Lady Ranelagh (ostensibly
addressed to her son, in the final version) on "the theological use of natural philosophy." In spite of interruptions, he
did, in fact, complete these essays by 1649; they were
eventually published in 1663 as the first four essays of the
first tome of *Considerations Touching the Usefulness of
Experimental Natural Philosophy*. But as he himself confessed, it was chemistry that "bewitched" him and occupied his time.[14]

The initial impulse to the study of chemistry came from the motives of the Invisible College, for chemistry, when it was not alchemy, was a useful art or craft in the mid-seventeenth century, concerned with the preparation of medical drugs. Boyle desired to test and try chemical remedies both for the benefit of mankind, and for his own use. In the seventeenth century, home doctoring was common and normal; everybody with pretensions to learning was an amateur doctor, with his own pet remedies which he tried on himself, his family, and his friends; unlearned people also doctored themselves, though more commonly with herbs than with chemicals. The letters and diaries of the seventeenth century testify to a profound and widespread interest in the diseases that people had or fancied they had; the wonder to a modern is that our ancestors survived the heroic purgings and blood-lettings which they unanimously felt to be essential to good health. Boyle was no exception. He enjoyed the ill health he claimed to suffer from, and indeed became so hardened to it that real illness interfered with his usual pursuits surprisingly little. He appears to have begun collecting remedies from philanthropic motives, with the desire to collect and publish the best available remedies for all possible diseases. Thus he wrote, rather quaintly, to Hartlib in 1647:

For your bedfellow's receipt for the stone (which certainly wants a parallel, if it be not more easy than effectual) I beseech you to return her (together with the present of my humble service) most humble thanks, which I mean very shortly, God willing, to pay you in an epistle I have drawn up to persuade men to communicate all those successful receipts, that relate either to the preservation or recovery of our health.[15]

Actually, he delayed and it was not until 1649 that he finished "An Invitation to Communicativeness," which eventually appeared under the rather complex title, "Epistolical Discourse of *Philaretus* to *Empiricus,* written by a Person of singular Piety, Honour and Learning, inviting all true Lovers of Vertue and Mankind to a free and generous Communication of their Secrets and Receits in Physick" as part of the *Chymical, Medicinal and Chyrugical Addresses, Made to Samuel Hartlib* and published by him in 1655.[16]

By 1649 Boyle was no longer purely philanthropic in his medical interests, for his own ill health required attention. He suffered from a "Quotidian Ague" (malaria), with a severe cough, for which a Dr. Davies prescribed a mild diet, a cough syrup, and the inevitable "physick."[17] Soon he was also suffering from kidney stone, as so many men did in the seventeenth century, and this plagued him all his life. So did a "weakness" in his eyes for which he consulted the famous Dr. Harvey; this made it difficult for him to read by candlelight, but nothing could altogether stop his reading, and in fact his eyesight lasted remarkably well. Petty, himself an M.D., once twitted Boyle with making his health worse than it was by too much self-medication and impairing his eyesight by an excessive devotion to books.[18] Boyle certainly enjoyed his ill health; we can jeer, like some of his contemporaries, at his keeping "chemical cordials" each one of which was appropriate to a particular state of the wind, but we cannot easily reprove, as they did, his refusing to approach physicians who had just been in contact with smallpox cases, nor his consulting a thermometer before deciding what clothes to wear.[19] But even serious illness never entirely prevented Boyle from working, and like many hypochrondriacs he seems, in fact, to have had a fairly tough constitution.

At Stalbridge Boyle acquired the knowledge and the experimental technique requisite for a scientific career, interesting himself in almost every branch of physics, chemistry, medicine, and natural history. He began to plan a tremendous series of essays touching upon nearly every aspect of nature, and drew up new lists every year on such topics as "Of Time and Idleness," "Of the Vanity and Partiality of Fame," "Of Natural Philosophy and Philosophers," "Of Chymistry and Chymists," "Of Atoms," "Of Authority in Opinions," "Of Cold," "Of Mechanics," "Of the Weapon-salve and Occult Qualities"—the last, presumably, stimulated by discussions with Kenelm Digby, that rather mysterious figure who at one moment was lecturing on the wonderful effects of his weapon salve, which cured wounds when rubbed on the weapon, and the next moment was lecturing on the relations between respiration and combustion. At the beginning of every year Boyle began what he called "Memorials Philosophical"—a kind of philosophical diary, a collection of fact, ideas, and recipes in a glorious jumble, which amply attest to the wide variety of his interests. Like most of us he never persevered very long at this industrious practice, and each Memorial lapses after a few weeks, not because he did not continue to collect information, but because he could not bring himself to note it down in methodical fashion. How familiar he became with the chemical literature is amply shown in a little work he wrote about this time called "An Essay of Turning Poisons into Medicines," with reflections on God's mercy to man because of this provision of nature, and of the usefulness of chemistry to man's welfare, together with a great many medical remedies.[20] It shows a very competent skill in the usual chemistry of the day, though no great originality.

In 1652 there came a great change in Boyle's life, which ended once and for all his seclusion at Stalbridge, and threw him ultimately into the scientific world. Cromwell's pacification of Ireland was now reasonably complete, but ten years of strife had left land ownership in a nearly hopeless muddle, and if Boyle wished to secure title to the Irish estates bequeathed him by his father he had to take active legal steps. Reluctant as he was to become embroiled in public affairs, family interests demanded that he do so, and obedient to them he left his quiet and peace for two years' legal involvement, which meant residence in Ireland a good deal of the time, and constant travel to and from England and Ireland, and within Ireland. He complained much of being cut off from books, experiments, and intellectual companionship; yet he found time to study anatomy with Petty, also now in Ireland; to survey mining and metallurgical practices; to talk to artisans; and to observe natural history.

Perhaps it was this interruption which convinced Boyle that a new life had to be begun if he were really to make that progress in science on which he had set his heart. Certainly in 1653 he was inquiring from one of the leading scientists of the day (Wilkins) for a likely young man to serve as a laboratory assistant. And he was considering a move from the quiet of Stalbridge to the bustle of Oxford, then by chance the scientific center of England. (In fact, his affairs delayed him, and it was a year before he settled in what, with the usual interruptions, became his chief place of residence until 1668.) The reason that Oxford attracted him was the presence there of the major part of that group which had begun meeting in London usually at Gresham College, about 1645, with the sole purpose of discussing and advancing the "new learning." John Wallis, the mathematician, describing these meetings when he was a very old man, remembered that they discussed

Philosophical Enquiries and such as related thereto; as Physick, Anatomy, Geometry, Astronomy, Navigation, Staticks, Magneticks, Chymicks, Mechanicks, and Natural Experiments; with the state of these studies as then cultivated, at home and abroad. We there discoursed of the Circulation of the Bloud, the Valves in the Veins, the Venae Lacteae, the Lymphatick vessels, the Copernican Hypothesis, the Nature of Comets, and New Stars, the Satellites of Jupiter, the Oval Shape (as it then appeared) of Saturn, the spots in the sun, and its Turning on its own Axis, the Inequalities and Selenography of the Moon, the several Phases of Venus and Mercury, the Improvement of Telescopes, and grinding of Glasses for that purpose, the weight of Air, the Possibility or Impossibility of Vacuities, and Nature's Abhorrence thereof, the Torricellian Experiment in Quicksilver, the Descent of heavy Bodies, and the degrees of Acceleration therein; and divers other things of like nature.[21]

These discussions, in fact, comprised the whole compass of the new philosophy—with inspiration drawn from Galileo and Bacon—and reflected a point of view and scientific approach which exactly suited Boyle.

Among the men who made up the original group, with almost all of whom Boyle later became intimate, were mathematicians, like John Wallis and John Wilkins; physicians, like Goddard, Ent, Glisson, and Merret; astronomers, like Foster, then Gresham Professor. Within a few years this group, which had been meeting weekly under formal rules, broke up, and many of them found their way to Oxford. Here were Wilkins, now Warden of Wadham College; Wallis, Savilian Professor of Geometry; Seth Ward, Savilian Professor of Astronomy; Goddard and Willis, physicians; William Petty, until he went to Ireland. In 1651 this group organized themselves with formal rules. By the time Boyle arrived, in 1654, there were several additional members, bright young undergraduates and graduates, including Laurence Rooke, later Gresham Professor of Astronomy; Christopher Wren, a very precocious scientist before he turned architect; and Robert Hooke, still an undergraduate, but already known for his mechanical ingenuity and interest in natural philosophy. Exactly how Boyle first came to know members of this group is unclear; the first evidence is a letter from Wilkins in September, 1653, introducing an unnamed young man who, as Wilkins thought, might suit Boyle as a laboratory assistant, referring to previous correspondence, and hoping that Boyle really intended to make good his expressed plan of settling in Oxford.[22] But Wilkins, a divine and academic, married to Cromwell's sister, had such a wide acquaintance in London Parliamentary circles that it would have been surprising if he and Boyle had not met. Once they had met, Wilkins would obviously assume Boyle to be an eminently proper person to be invited to join the Oxford group, where, in addition to scientific attractions, there was ample opportunity to pursue a subsidiary interest, the study of the Biblical languages.

The move to Oxford was a wise one for Boyle. Here at last he found himself in a stimulating atmosphere, meeting and talking every day with his scientific equals, sharpening his mind against other, even keener minds, and forced to abandon the amateurish dilettantism proper to the Stalbridge days. The Oxford group recognized Boyle as a brilliant natural philosopher, one dedicated to the same ideals that they upheld, familiar with contemporary work, addicted to the new learning as espoused by Bacon and Galileo. He was not, as many of them were, an accomplished mathematical scientist; but in spite of the deprecating remarks he later made on many occasions (part of his old pose as an amateur, a lover of learning but an uneducated one) he was well read in the mathematics of the day and well able to appreciate the mathematical work of Wallis, as the latter himself publicly proclaimed in a preface of dedication.[23] (Of course a patron was always flattered; but Wallis did not need to choose a work in technical mathematics to dedicate to Boyle, unless he thought that Boyle would, in fact, appreciate it.) The amateur role was a useful one when it came to controversy, and the younger son of a great family could never quite forget that he was a gentleman before he was a scholar.

Nevertheless, Boyle did become a professional scientist. He had in the Oxford period a number of assistants, "laborants" as he called them. These varied in skill from unknown artisans, through minor chemists like the Englishman Greatorex and the German Peter Stael (he later gave public lectures at Oxford, which Anthony à Wood attended, as did John Locke; but in spite of Wood, Boyle was better able to teach Stael than the other way around),[24] to the talented Robert Hooke, who probably became Boyle's assistant about 1657, and who learned much from his patron. With these men to help him Boyle was able to perform an enormous number of experiments on various topics, experiments which became the nucleus of his later life's work. For there is no doubt that he planned and wrote the major part of a large number of books in this period, on a wide range of subjects. He was particularly concerned to persuade the Oxford group that chemistry had an importance above and beyond its usefulness in medicine, and to this end designed and began writing a number of books dealing with the borderline between chemistry and physics. He also wrote much on various aspects of scientific method.

As these works were later published, no complete copies of the original manuscript versions, designed for circulation within a limited circle, now exist, except for a chemical work, a preliminary version of *The Sceptical Chymist*, copied out about 1660 by Henry Oldenburg.[25] (Oldenburg was then tutor to Boyle's nephew, son of Lady Ranelagh, to whom Boyle was to address a number of his early works; Oldenburg was a friend of Hartlib's and later for many years Secretary to the Royal Society.) This was entitled, cumbersomely, "Reflexions on the Experiments vulgarly alledged to evince the 4 Peripatetique Elements or the 3 Chymical Principles of Mixt Bodies"; it was a mature though brief work, later entirely incorporated into the published treatise. In 1657 Boyle's research received a new direction with the news of Otto von Guericke's invention of the air pump, and he eagerly and fruitfully turned to pneumatic experiments, which he pursued in addition to all the other branches of natural philosophy that already occupied his attention.

By 1659 the world was changing, and the Oxford group was deeply involved in the change. Wilkins went to Cambridge; then, with the death of Cromwell, others migrated to London. London was a whirling center of political intrigue; Richard Cromwell, Oliver's son, was so clearly unfit to govern that even loyal Cromwellians like Lord Broghill began to think of, and then to plan, a royal restoration. Boyle had little taste for what he called "the disturbances of this troubled time," and, feeling even Oxford too close to the press of affairs, withdrew to a friend's country house.[26] There, with leisure and no opportunity for making further experiments, he turned to writing up those he had previously made with his new air pump; this he did in the form of a letter addressed to Viscount Dungarvan, son of Boyle's eldest brother, the Earl of Cork, a staunch Royalist who had alternately fought the Irish and stayed quietly on his Irish estates throughout the Civil War.

His reason for deciding to publish these experiments is somewhat obscure—almost as obscure as his failure to publish anything earlier. He had never been secretive. He was known to be engaged upon scientific pursuits; he had allowed Nathaniel Highmore to dedicate to him his *History of Generation* as early as 1651; he had circulated many essays in manuscript; in 1659 he had signed his name to a broadside proposal in favor of a Dutch anatomist (part of Hartlib's eternal plan to get Parliament to support learning).[27] Yet it was not until 1659 that a full-scale work of his actually appeared in print; this was *Seraphic Love,* whose publication was, in a sense, forced upon him. A stationer was asked to print a pirated copy, and, with sensible cunning, asked the author for a more perfect copy. Perhaps it was this which made him decide to publish some scientific works as well, a thing he had apparently been promising, for in the dedication to *Seraphic Love* he mentioned that he was aware that the learned world rather expected "some treatises relating to Experimental Philosophy" than a work on theology. Very likely he wanted to show the world some examples of the influence and importance of the Oxford scientists during the 1650's. At any rate, as soon as he had finished writing about pneumatics (though by no means all the work done with the air pump was included), he sent it to be printed; it appeared in 1660 under the title *New Experiments, Physico-Mechanical, Touching the Spring of the Air and its Effects,* and created immediate and widespread interest. It was followed in 1661 by *Certain Physiological Essays* (physiology in Boyle's time was equivalent to natural philosophy, the study of nature) and *The Sceptical Chymist;* and every year thereafter saw the appearance of either a new work, or the revision of an old one, so that the absolute lack of publicity of Boyle's early days was suddenly replaced with a spate of books of such a high standard as to make Boyle's reputation sure and certain.

In spite of his professed disinclination, Boyle was by no means averse to taking some part in public affairs once it was certain that the restoration would take place smoothly and peacefully. He appears to have gone briefly to Holland, presumably to present his services to the King—at least he obtained a safe conduct from Pepys for that purpose[28]—and he was much in London with his sister.

⌈After King Charles' triumphant entry into London he was often at court, in the dual role of a representative of a great family and a representative of the world of science. Boyle's brothers, whether Royalist or not, were all given peerages—Charles II wisely rewarded the loyal and bribed the disloyal—and Boyle was offered honors varying from a peerage to a bishopric, all of which he refused, insisting that he preferred to remain a private gentleman. His friends, however, worked for him and secured rich lands in Ireland, forfeited estates of those too outspokenly and actively disloyal to be pardoned. Boyle accepted the lands, and decided to use their income for what he considered the public good—the promotion of the Protestant faith in Ireland and in the New World. Because of these missionary interests he was appointed by the King governor of the Corporation for Propagating the Gospel in New England, a position which he took most seriously, as correspondence with John Eliot amply testifies. Boyle remained interested in the propagation of the gospel among the Indians all his life, and in his will left money to both Harvard College and William and Mary College for the education of Indian missionaries; the scheme was never very successful, and after the Revolution the money was transferred for the same purpose part to Canada and part to the West Indies. When the King offered Boyle an appointment to the Board of Directors of the East India Company he accepted in large part because of the hope that he could assist the Company in missionary activities there, though an equally important reason for accepting was the desire to hear the reports of the Company's men after their return—an ideal way, he thought, of learning curious facts about the natural history of India. The King remained Boyle's patron, even though he could not make him into a professional courtier, and in 1664 Boyle was made a member of the Company of

Royal Mines.[29] He was a public figure and an influential
one.

Boyle's favored position at Court was of much assistance
to the scientists of England. Many of the Oxford group,
scattered in the preceding years, had come together again
in London by 1660. Wren was now a Gresham Professor,
and the scientists began to meet at his rooms there, as,
fifteen years before, they had met at Foster's. The original
group, with its Parliamentary slant, was joined here by a
number of Royalists, many of whom had been in France
for years. On the neutral ground of natural philosophy
Royalist and Parliamentarian could find a common interest,
and all agreed that the new monarchy offered a fair chance
to secure aid in promoting the new learning. At the end
of November, 1660, to repeat the well-know account, there
met in Wren's rooms a large group including Boyle, Wilkins, Goddard, Petty, Rooke, and Wren, all former members of the Oxford group, and, among Royalists, Lord
Brouncker, Sir Robert Moray, and John Evelyn; and that
night they decided to organize an association "for promoting experimental philosophy."[30] Not content with a private
association, they determined to secure a charter from the
King, and possibly financial aid. The Royalists and Boyle
used their influence, and the Royal Society received its
first charter in 1662, though its founding is usually dated
from 1663, when a more detailed charter was granted.

Boyle was, naturally, a member of the Council appointed
by the King under the charter of 1663, as he was to be
many times thereafter, when the Society elected its own
Council. He was President in the very early days when
Presidents served only for a month at a time. He supplied
the Society with its two professional officers, Henry Oldenburg Secretary until his death in 1677, and Robert Hooke,
the Curator or Demonstrator, whose job was to provide

experiments at the weekly meetings. This was a most important position, for the Society was clearly and distinctly devoted to experimental learning. Their motto was *"Nullius in verba"* and they tried strenuously to live up to it, refusing to believe as true what they had not seen with their own eyes (though always eager to consider reports of strange events). As Hooke wrote, "The business and design of the Royal Society is to improve the knowledge of natural things and all useful Arts, Manufactures, Mechanic Practices, Engines, and Inventions by Experiment (not meddling with Divinity, Metaphysics, Morals, Politics, Grammar, Rhetoric, or Logic)."[31] It was exactly Boyle's aim, and his books, which appeared with such regularity year after year, were rightly taken to be exemplars of this design. This, if nothing else, would have made easy the identification of Boyle's work with that of the Royal Society; but in fact he was always and constantly associated with it.

Though often at Oxford until 1668, Boyle came to the weekly meetings of the Society whenever possible, and when he could not attend in person he sent notes, articles, queries, comments. He kept in touch by having both Oldenburg and Hooke write him detailed accounts. When he came to live in London he still did not always attend the meetings, partly because he was in such constant communication with his friends, but he was eager to keep in touch and to meet new members like Newton, with whom he conducted occasional correspondence, and whom he stimulated in formulating certain general ideas. As he grew older, however, he came increasingly to avoid responsibility, and took no official part in the Royal Society's management. He even refused the office of President, to which he was elected in 1680, on the ground that it might involve his subscribing to religious tests, a matter on which his conscience was, as he said "tender"—that is, he would not swear to religious convictions which deviated, however slightly, from those he actually held.[32] But he always regarded the welfare of the Royal Society as of paramount importance for the welfare of science.

And the welfare of science—the promotion of scientific discovery, whether his own or others—was his unceasing avocation. Until 1668 he maintained his residence and his laboratory in the relative peace of Oxford, though he was often in London, where he attended the meetings of the Royal Society; discussed the progress of science with Hooke, Evelyn, and others; performed experiments on cold in his sister's house in Chelsea, during the frosty weather; discussed missionary work in Ireland and overseas; attended court; and entertained visitors. During the worst of the plague in 1665–66, he retired to an isolated village a few miles away, once again to practice country enjoyments, as at Stalbridge, and, deprived of the means of experimenting, wrote up many old notes. In 1668 he seems to have decided that the travel involved in this way of life was excessive, so he moved to London and settled in Pall Mall with his sister Katherine. Here he was besieged with visitors: his friends; idle and curious fashionable ladies and gentlemen, who expected him to show them amusing and instructive experiments (of which he always had a store); scientists from overseas, like Huygens and Duhamel (Secretary of the French Academy of Science); tourists, like Duke Cosmo of Tuscany—no one felt that he had had any personal contact with English science unless he talked with Mr. Boyle. Even Boyle's affable temperament began to feel the strain, especially as ill health plagued him more and more—genuine ill health now, like the severe paralytic attack of 1670, which, though at times it rendered him almost helpless, could not prevent his continuing to think about scientific problems. Eventually he was driven to post a board outside his house, giving visiting hours, so that he could be sure of having some part of every day free for uninterrupted work. This must have seemed a shocking action on the part of a man who was not a professional scientist, architect, physician, man of affairs, politician, or courtier, but merely a rich gentleman. But the fashionable world still came to his laboratory and still found a wealth of intellectual entertainment.

There was another sort of visitor who came to see Boyle: young scientists, anxious not only to meet the great English natural philosopher, but to work with him. This is common enough nowadays, particularly when most scientists have academic appointments, but it was something of an innovation then, when there was no idea of research training, and when most scientists learned experimental technique by trial-and-error methods. Boyle had, especially in the 1670's, a number of people working for him who were research assistants, rather than laborants, in much the same position as Hooke had occupied in the years between 1657 and 1660. Denis Papin, who had already worked with Huygens in Paris on pneumatic experiments, spent some time in Boyle's laboratory, partly conducting experiments under Boyle's direction, partly developing his "digester," the earliest version of the pressure cooker. This he demonstrated to the Royal Society in April, 1682, by preparing for them a "philosophical supper," including beef-bone jelly, fish with the bones in, also reduced to jelly, and pigeons, which John Evelyn reported to be the best of all. Papin was a skillful experimenter and able scientist, and Boyle entrusted to him the composition of a compilation of pneumatic experiments, some made by Papin, some by others, which appeared in 1681 as *A Continuation of New Experiments Physico-Mechanical. The Second Part.*

The other young scientists who worked in Boyle's laboratory were chemists. Perhaps most important was Guillaume Homberg; he had traveled throughout Europe to acquire a thorough scientific education, which he did not regard as complete without some years spent working with Boyle (at about the same time that Papin was also in the laboratory); he took readily to Boyle's radical view of the proper subject matter of chemistry and became an ardent advocate of Boyle's theoretical approach, so much so that when he returned to Paris and became a member of the Academy of Science he set himself to reform French chemistry, with considerable success. His own researches upon salts, an important chemical contribution, form an extension of some of Boyle's work. Quite a different sort of chemist was J. J. Becher, a German mystic and the real originator of the phlogiston theory; he also worked in Boyle's laboratory at one time, but the knowledge he acquired there did little to influence his chemical viewpoint though one can find traces of Boyle's influence in some parts of Becher's work. Besides all these, there were lesser men who worked, not as aspiring young scientists, but as artisans, like the Hanckwitz brothers, who, after Boyle's death, set up a chemical supply trade, partly on the basis of recipes learned in Boyle's laboratory.

Boyle had another role to play in regard to struggling young scientists, the role of patron. He was one of the few wealthy scientists, and to secure permission to dedicate a book to him meant both money and glory to the author. There are dozens of dedications, ranging from the appreciation of competence from an equal like Wallis to the quaintly adulatory "to the most noble and famous Robert Boyle, brother to the illustrious Earls of Burlington and Orrery, chief of scientists" of Walter Needham in his *Disquisitio anatomica de formato foetu* (1667). And every indication is that rising young scientists who sought his company received great attention and encouragement from Boyle.

Boyle's later life was increasingly uneventful, though nothing changed his main preoccupations, science and the spread of the Protestant religion. Active to the last, he continued to publish, on both new and old subjects of investigation. But he was undeniably growing old, and his health was certainly poor, though ill health, even at the end of his life, made little change in his manner of working. In the summer of 1691 he made an elaborate will, leaving much of his wealth for the furtherance of Christianity in the New World and of Protestantism in Ireland; he also established the Boyle Lectures, a series of sermons to be preached, as he put it, "for proving the Christian religion against notorious Infidels." As it happened, Richard Bentley, who preached the first series, established the eminently suitable tradition that much of the evidence for religion should be drawn from the study of nature, and they became a series of treatises on natural religion. Bentley's *A Confutation of Atheism* and William Derham's *Astrotheology* are famous and influential examples of these sermons.

Boyle died on the 30th of December, 1691, after a very brief final illness, only a week after the death of his sister Katherine, to whom he had been so closely tied by affection and with whom he had shared so much of life. Characteristically, when he died he had several books almost or quite ready for the press, so that his yearly publication ceased only several months after his death. The regrets of his contemporaries were prompt and sincere. As John Evelyn noted in his diary, "This last week died that pious admirable Christian, excellent philosopher, and my worthy friend, Mr. Boyle, aged about 65—a great loss to all that knew him, and to the public."[33] And indeed, scientists everywhere commented upon his death and mourned that he would contribute no more to the new philosophy, even when, like Huygens and Leibniz, they regretted that he had never composed any complete system of philosophy. (A generation later, the Newtonian mathematical physicist Colin

Maclaurin praised him for the very thing that Huygens regretted, and regarded him as one who had carried out the
survey of nature intended by Bacon.) Bishop Burnet, a
personal friend, declared in his funeral sermon,

He had the purity of an angell in him, he was modest and
humble rather to a fault. He despised all earthly things; he
was perhaps too eager in the pursuit of knowledge, but his
aim in it all was to rouse in him a higher sense of the wisdom
and glory of the Creator, and to do good to mankind; he
studied the Scripture with great application and practised uni-
versall love and goodness in the greatest extent possible, and
was a great promoter of love and charity among men and a
declared enemy to all bitterness and most particularly to all
persecution on the account of religion.[34]

This is interesting as showing that there still was, in the
minds of nonscientific divines, a feeling that there ought to
have been some conflict between science and religion, even
when, as in Boyle's case (as indeed of most other scientists
of the age) there was none. The most enthusiastic summary
of his scientific fame is undoubtedly that of Abraham de la
Pryme of St. Johns College, Cambridge:

Alas! who can refrain from tears, what learned man can but
lament at the sad newse that came the other night, viz. the
death of the famous and honourable Mr. Boyle, a man born
to learning, whose death can never be enough lamented and
mourned for. England has lost her wisest man, wisdom her
wisest son, and all Europe the man whose writings they most
desired, who well deserved the character that the ingenious
Redi gives him, who calls him, "Always worthy of the highest
praise." He was a mighty promoter of all pious and good
works. He was a mighty chemist.[35]

[II]

The New Learning
and its Methods

ALTHOUGH Boyle had written little of scientific importance when he settled in Oxford in 1654, his attitude
toward science was already clearly formulated. He had
eagerly accepted the new learning; he had thought out the
appropriate methods for pursuing it; and he had developed
his own areas of exploration. His adoption of the new
experimental mechanical philosophy was his great bond
of interest with the Oxford scientists, from whom he
differed only in the branches of natural philosophy which
he thought were most profitably investigated by its
methods. The friendly atmosphere in which, as in the
modern graduate school, friends met almost every day
to discuss the work on which they were engaged, when
ideas, experiments, news, and the latest books were freely
exchanged at both formal and informal meetings—all this
exactly suited Boyle's gregarious nature and his somewhat
casual methods of working.

It also suited his disinclination to publish. Working as he
did primarily for his own interests, in close touch with the
most distinguished English scientists, he did not need to
write up the results of his work in anything but an informal
manner, suitable for circulation in manuscript. Certainly
he wrote down enough so that his friends could appraise
his ideas; but why bother to publish when all the men who
mattered were content with manuscript copies? Besides,
publication involved much hard work; in particular it
meant producing order out of the chaos of almost desultory

scientific investigation which Boyle loved, and he saw no reason for making that effort. Perhaps one day he would have accumulated enough material so that he could write a really important work, a great work on the mechanical philosophy or on theoretical chemistry, that would make the principles of these sciences clear and would totally confound the older views of the "school" philosophers and the "spagyrical" chemists. That would be well worth while; meantime there was no hurry; better to wait, to collect experiments and ideas, and to see how far he could provide experimental evidence for the theories which he believed to be true and solid, but which he would not venture to proclaim as true to the world in general until he could offer irrefutable evidence.

Though he had written so little by the time he arrived in Oxford, Boyle had already decided which topics most interested him, and had established a definite pattern of work. This is hardly surprising, since in 1654 he was nearly thirty, a much more mature age then than now. He had never felt any inclination to restrict his work to one subject at a time. In Stalbridge days, indeed, he had dabbled in an impossibly varied series of topics; as time went on these diminished in number, though not so very much in range. Had he continued to draw up lists of essay titles they would have grown fewer, and what had seemed possible to encompass in an essay would now have been seen to require a book. But he never confined himself to any one topic; when he thought of an experiment he was impatient to perform it, whether it belonged to the topic he was just working on or not. It would surely fit somewhere into his scheme of things, and its results as much as anything would finally determine to which of the many projects he had in hand it did, indeed, belong.

This method of thinking and experimenting necessarily produced a peculiar method of recording his experiments.

Though it was only later in life that he began systematically to record his experiments on loose sheets of paper, so that no one could steal his notebooks (presumed, erroneously, to contain important and valuable alchemical processes), he never had a methodical scheme of grouping experiments under topics in a notebook as he made them. Rather he wrote them down in a jumble of topics, and only later on "reviewed" them and indicated by a few letters scrawled in the margin to which treatise they should be assigned. Many sheets of this sort still exist in the Boyle papers located in the library of the Royal Society. Thus, for example, there are some leaves in Boyle's handwriting, perhaps dating from the early 1660's, appropriately headed "Philosophical Entrys & Memorials (of all sorts) Here Confusedly throwne together; to be Hence transferr'd to ye severall Treatises whereto they belong." Another sheet is headed "NOTES & EXPERIMTS belonging to my Papers about the History of Qualities among which they are to be inserted in their proper place." Usually such notes begin with the remark, "Remember to show" such and such a thing—as for example "Rʳ the troublesome Truths mention'd in the same Paper and make NN argue nearer to the purpose, than the Witty Fools that his Friend opposes."[1] Or they may contain brief accounts of experiments which, upon review, Boyle found could be used in one or more of the books he had in hand. It is, in fact, abundantly clear that his lack of method was tempered by a very cautious desire to lose no idea or experiment, and that equally when he came to write up a topic he did his best to include every relevant experiment available.

When a sufficient mass of notes had accumulated in its appropriate pigeonhole Boyle either prepared or resurrected a suitable outline of an essay which should make adequate use of the experimental material available— though it should be kept in mind that these were not topical outlines specifically invented to fit the material, but rather fragments of a larger whole. A few of these outlines, prepared in advance and never used, still exist; the most notable is that for "The Requisites of a Good Hypothesis," frequently referred to in his published works, but never completed to his satisfaction (cf. Part Two, Section I, no. 3). There are also brief outlines of such diverse topics as a consideration of the Cartesian theory that beasts are but machines, and an attempt to explain completely the nature of fire and flame. When he had both the material and the outline, still Boyle might not write the required essay unless he had leisure and the spirit moved, or his friends urged him on. The occasion might be his making a stay in the country, where he would be cut off from the means of experimenting, as in the confusions of the months before the Restoration, late in 1659, or during the period when the plague raged so fiercely in 1665-66. Or the writing of a book might be the result of some exigency in the nature of the work, as the approaching winter made him hasten to publish his experiments on cold so that his friends could try them out during the very short and variable period available in an English winter.

He is very ingenuous in exposing his rather idle distaste for bringing order into his notes, as one can see from his letters (cf. Part Two, Section I, no. 7) and even in the prefaces to his printed works (cf. Part Two, Section II, no. 13). Boyle confessed his faults in the preface to almost every work—candidly, he said; boastfully, one might think, as if he thought it praiseworthy to work, think, and write in no methodical order; perhaps, indeed, he did have some lingering feeling that this method better suited a gentleman. The publishers' notes to the reader are one long wail of exculpation: it is not their fault that the book comes forth late or lacking in material, but that of the author, who had mislaid, lost, or delayed essential experiments and observations. With such a method of writing (or lack of it) it is no wonder that treatises appeared in no obviously significant order, that some never appeared at all, that parts of treatises were maimed by the loss of papers, or that a book was often based upon experiments performed many years before.

On top of all other causes for chaotic confusion, there was Boyle's increasing infirmity of sight, which made it difficult for him to read and write much, especially, as he noted, by candlelight. This weakness of sight of course had certain advantages—it made a good excuse, either for errors in his own works or for neglect of other people's— but it was not only an excuse. To avoid much writing he took to employing amanuenses, about whom little is known. Most wrote badly and showed their ignorance of subject matter by their misspelling of technical words—spellings which Boyle usually corrected in the end, for he dictated the first draft only; he later read through every manuscript and added minor corrections. Sometimes he corrected fact, sometimes he changed a word, sometimes he added capital letters, which, as he wrote Oldenburg, he used "to point out Emphaticall Words."[2] Indeed, for all his pose of the idle amateur, he had very high and exacting standards of how his work should be best presented to the public.

Boyle's style is peculiarly his own, and clearly reflects both his education and his intent. All that juvenile interest in literature—romances, ethical tracts, theological works, occasional reflections—had given him a dangerous facility with words, a facility which increased when he came to dictate. Clearly he liked to retain the pretensions to literary taste which he had established in his youth in admiring imitation of his brother Broghill, and the literary taste of the times leaned toward prolixity. There was as well the fact, which he never forgot, that he was a gentleman writing primarily for other gentlemen—for though he moved in the scientific world, and found his greatest admirers there, he always hoped to be able to do what Galileo had so brilliantly done: make the latest advances in science available to the layman. Natural philosophy should be the concern not only of scientists, but of all educated men, "gentlemen free and unconfined," as Sprat remarked in his *History of the Royal Society*. In fact, natural philosophy should be, as it always had been, one of the liberal arts, a proper part of the education of all free men. It was, besides, a study guaranteed to elevate the mind, as he had thought since his very youthful days, and would offer a wholesale alternative to the riotous life so tempting to young men of wealth and position. Hence, in part, Boyle's device of addressing many of his books to "Pyrophilus," well known to be Richard Jones, son of his sister Katherine, a wild young man whom Henry Oldenburg had the dubious pleasure of watching over in a tour of France from 1657 to 1660. No doubt Boyle genuinely hoped to influence his nephew in natural philosophy; no doubt too there were motives of family feeling involved, such as had made him earlier dedicate books to his brothers and sisters, and later to another nephew. But it is very clear that this was in some measure a convenient device, which, he hoped, would remove the severe formality normally associated with scientific works from his own books and make them easier and more attractive reading for the lay audience he hoped to capture.

As an alternative, inspired both by his literary pretensions and his early admiration for Galileo, he tried his hand at dialogues; unfortunately he had none of Galileo's skill in debate, and the attempt was not a success. *The Sceptical Chymist* is, fortunately, the only work published in this form, but others were planned, notably the "Requisites of a Good Hypothesis," of which some fragments still remain. All these literary trimmings were, in part, a device for presentation to the world at large, and it may be that Boyle's conviction of the necessity to present his work in a literary dress was one of the factors which caused his delay in publication. Such early manuscripts as survive intact reveal a simple, straightforward style very different from the elaborations of his first published books. The opening essays of the *Usefulness of Natural Philosophy* (cf. Part Two, Section I, no. 4) were straightforward enough, and they appeared very much in the form in which they were initially written, as a copy of one of them in Oldenburg's notebook indicates, and as Boyle claimed. The early version of *The Sceptical Chymist,* the "Reflexions on the Experiments Vulgarly Alledg'd to evince the 4. Peripatetique Elements or ye 3. Chymical Principles," as Oldenburg copied it, is quite straightforward piece of expository argument, with no literary flourishes. That was, however, written "to gratify an ingenious gentleman," not for publication, and apparently when Boyle gave way to the urging of his Oxford friends, who insisted that the subject was too important not to be made public, he felt that he had to dress up the argument in what is now an ineffably tedious style. The modern reader can be grateful that, in later years, Boyle's avocations, preoccupations, scientific fertility, and increasing bodily infirmities made him conform more nearly to the "plain and unadorned" style advocated by the Royal Society, though he never entirely lost his prolixity.

Some of that prolixity, however, was deliberate, as indeed he indicates, intended to lead the reader insensibly into the discussion and, as well, to convince by the very wealth of argument and experimental evidence. Boyle, and the seventeenth century in general, had no objection to bludgeoning the reader into informed acquiescence. It must not be forgotten that experimental science was still a new and exciting discipline, whose techniques had not been fully explored even by its most ardent advocates. It was desirable to be conscious of the difficulties of experimental facts and their interpretation, as well as of the experimental method in general: gentlemen had to be convinced that the experimental method was worth their while, and shown how to use it; opponents of the new discoveries had to be shown that fact and theory rested on irrefutable experimental evidence; opponents of the method had to be shown that it would obtain results better and more securely than rational argument; and sympathetic readers had to be shown in detail how every experiment had been done, partly so that they could appreciate the masterly experimental technique involved, partly so that they could, in the spirit of the Royal Society, repeat the experiments themselves rather than take them for accurate on Boyle's word alone.

There was a further consideration as well, a distaste for secrecy. Natural philosophers were coming to distrust men who kept their experimental techniques secret, which was, or so it was beginning to be felt, an offense against the truth as well as an offense against the well-being of mankind. Boyle was not the only man who wrote against the practice of keeping medical remedies secret. Part of the reaction against alchemy in this period came from a growing belief that if you wished to claim a scientific accomplishment, you must expect to tell the world how you arrived at it. If you failed to tell your method, it might well be because you had not achieved your vaunted result. This growing skepticism was very important in the development of chemistry particularly. Boyle was proud of his ability to guess the method of preparation of Glauber's salt (sodium sulphate) or of Helmont's *ens veneris* (a confused mixture of salts rather than the "coppery substance" its name implies) and unlike the original authors, he described the preparations in detail. Like other proponents of the new learning, Boyle felt strongly that natural philosophy had no place for secrets. All should be open, clear, evident, and manifest; and if this made for prolixity of style and tediousness of description, these were minor disadvantages which must be accepted for the sake of the enormous advantages they carried with them.

Boyle's nonmathematical and almost nonscientific style is but one aspect of his professed desire to emulate Francis Bacon in promoting the new learning. To be a Baconian meant many things to Boyle. It meant, first of all, being a propagandist of the new philosophy, a spokesman of Baconian scientific groups like the Oxford group and the Royal Society. As a publicist, Boyle felt that he must appeal to the widest possible audience. That making science intelligible was no light task is amply apparent from the remark of Pepys after reading Boyle's *Experiments and Considerations touching Colours* while being rowed up the Thames: he found it "so chymical, that I can understand but little of it, but enough to see that he is a most excellent man."[3] This desire to democratize science meant an emphasis on experiment as well as on a simple style, for all men could perform experiments. Yet Boyle knew, as Bacon did not, what a very great deal of skill is required to perform even simple experiments so that they give useful information, and how much more skill is required to make sure that the experiment is suitable for the purpose for which it is intended. It is sometimes forgotten that many Peripatetics, school philosophers, and chemists claimed an experimental basis for their theories, *a priori* though they really were; Boyle knew well, better in fact than the modern historians, that it was not only a question of performing experiments, but it was necessary to teach the world the true and proper manner of applying experiment to confirm theories, or to provide the basis upon which true theories could be built. Or, indeed, to convince men that it was necessary to build theories upon experimental evidence; many men agreed with Leibniz that "Mr. Boyle spends too much time, to be truthful, drawing from an infinity of splendid experiments no other conclusions than those which he could have taken for principles of nature . . . which one can certify to be true from reason alone, whereas experiments, no matter how numerous, cannot prove them."[4] But even Leibniz praised the experiments, and indeed much of Boyle's continental reputation rested upon his superb experimental technique, which scientists of quite different theoretical persuasions readily recognized to be masterly. Thus, for example, the Dutch scientist Christiaan Huygens, though a professed Cartesian, as Boyle was not, admired Boyle's experimental work enormously, read his books avidly as they came off the press, and cited his experiments without reservation, though he might draw rather different conclusions. Those who disagreed with Boyle most vehemently were quite ready to pillage his books for useful experiments, since it was certain that they were reliable—and Boyle frequently complained of the way others used his experiments without credit, whereas he tried to be scrupulous about acknowledging his sources of information.

It was tempting to steal from Boyle, for he not only described experiments, he taught the world how to write up experiments so that they could readily be repeated, as, for example, by noting the very necessary but often overlooked precautions that must be taken with almost any experiment. Indeed, Boyle went further; he often described precautions that should have been taken and were not, and some of his erroneous conclusions could be readily corrected by following the advice he gave but had been too careless or lazy to follow himself. Thus his experiments remained of use for a century, and some of the corrections which Lavoisier made to Boyle's work could have been made earlier had anyone cared to follow Boyle's directions.

A very clear exposition of Boyle's philosophy of experiment is to be found in the Proemial Essay to *Certain Physiological Essays;* this, which is entitled "Some Considerations Touching Experimental Essays in General," was written in 1657 and published in 1661 (Part II, Section I, no. 1). It thus was one of the works from which contemporaries derived their notion of what Boyle's purpose might be. Here he is at his most Baconian, boldly denouncing "systems," and almost implying that they have no value—but never quite going so far, for he was at heart a theoretical scientist. The systems he thought evil were the so-called *a priori* theories that were still so commonly advocated, theories based not on experimental fact but on preconceived principles, purely speculative, as we should say. It was necessary to show that pure experiment was superior to pure theory, though of course a combination of experiment and theory was superior to either alone. If the emphasis was particularly on experiment, that is because the battle for the experimental method was still being fought, for to many people, from philosophers like Leibniz to laymen like Charles II, experiment was an idle playing about with nature that could be of little aid in the attempt to gain true theoretical knowledge.

Because Boyle was a publicist for the winning side, it may seem that he was overstating his case; but in fact the battle was a real one, and needed fighting. And it should be noted that Boyle never meant to write, even here where he was at his most vehement, as if random experiment were desirable or useful. He was no advocate of experiment for its own sake, even though he once had contemplated writing a continuation of Bacon's *Sylva sylvarum,*[5] which would have been a mere collection of experimental facts. He was temperamentally incapable of performing an experiment without trying to understand the meaning of the results obtained, and most of his own experiments were devised to answer questions rather than to satisfy simple curiosity. But he insisted that an investigation must begin with experiment, and that experiments alone were worth reporting even if they were not the basis for a complete system of philosophy. Not only because complete systems of philosophy were things which he regarded with, at best, skepticism, but also because the satisfactory progress of science demanded that men should report their work to others before it had reached the stage where it could be used as the basis for a tolerably complete theory.

Boyle had the scientific modesty which admits that one man alone cannot undertake to explain the universe. He was glad to offer other men material which they might use in framing hypotheses. More than that, he thought it a worthy thing to call attention to a subject which needed investigation, and he always generously hoped that others would explore where he had shown the road. This was, perhaps, laziness; he lacked the patience for detailed, systematic investigation. But it was more a devotion to science for its own sake, a conviction that the great need was to understand nature, and that many hands and heads were needed in that difficult task. Hence, if someone else took up a subject he had begun, he promptly dropped his investigations and pursued them no further. Thus he interested Hooke in the problems of capillary attraction, and ceased to investigate them himself. He had intended, as he indicated in the *Experiments and Considerations touching Colours,* to investigate light and colors more fully than in that treatise, but when the obviously superior work of Newton on light and colors was sent to the Royal Society (Boyle was one of the referees who approved its publication)[6] he gave up his own investigations and left the field to younger men. The only subject which he continued to pursue, after it had once become of interest to others, was pneumatics, and this was peculiarly his own subject, and was, moreover, a subject in which he showed himself to be far more inventive than were other scientists.

With all his rejection of systems, Boyle by no means intended to reject theories or even hypotheses. Systems to him were rigid bodies of philosophy, based upon a few hypotheses which were, themselves, commonly *a priori* principles, as he believed. Hypotheses need not, however, be *a priori;* they might be based upon experiment. Generally Boyle (and the seventeenth century as a whole) recognized the difference between an hypothesis—which even if based upon experiment was not satisfactorily proved by experiment—and a theory, which was to be regarded as proved, and proved preferably by much experimental evidence. Boyle was no such pure empiricist as some of his writings in praise of experiment might suggest; he knew well that science must be theoretical if it were to progress, and that necessarily involved the framing of hypotheses.

Indeed, he was so much interested in the conscious process of balancing hypothesis and experiment that he went so far as to plan the writing of a book on the subject. There are many references to the "Requisites of a Good Hypothesis" in the published works, although only fragments now remain: a few introductory pages in the form of a dialogue, a list of desiderata for "good" and "excellent" hypotheses (cf. Part Two, Section I, no. 3); and a few notes with "RGH" scrawled by Boyle in the margin, to indicate their ultimate destination. This is a pity, for it represents a very interesting type of philosophy of science, as well as deep conviction on Boyle's part. What remains can be extended by casual remarks scattered through other works, in particular the preface to the *Mechanical Origin and Production of Qualities*: "For the use of an hypothesis being to render an intelligible account of the causes of the effects, or phaenomena proposed, without crossing the laws of nature, or other phaenomena; the more numerous, and the more various the particulars are, whereof some are explicable by the assigned hypothesis, and some are agreeable to it, or, at-least, are not dissonant from it, the more valuable is the hypothesis, and the more likely to be true. For it is much more difficult, to find an hypothesis, that is not true, which will suit with many phaenomena, especially, if they be of various kinds, than but with a few."[7] This is, in effect, a summary of the properties of a good hypothesis; but one of the more important points made in the "Requisites of a Good Hypothesis" is that to be really good —excellent, Boyle said—an hypothesis should offer predictability. This, of course, is exactly what one demands of a good scientific theory or law today, that it not only describe the observed data—phaenomena, as Boyle called them—but that it predict what will be observed under given conditions in the future. Boyle's Law, for example, is such an hypothesis, and it was as an hypothesis that he described it.

When Boyle first, as a very young man, began to apply himself seriously to the pursuit of experimental natural philosophy, he was inclined to apologize to his sisters, because it took him away from ethical and theological studies. His apology is a measure of his sober and devout turn of mind. Theology was always, to him, a subject of supreme importance, and one which he pursued with assiduity. He soon found that he could combine natural philosophy and theology, for natural philosophy had, as he wrote to his sister (cf. Part Two, Section III, no. 14), its "theological use." Indeed, this was an excellent reason for studying nature, that it led to devout reflections.

The earliest of all Boyle's essays which were later published are the first in the *Usefulness of Experimental Natural Philosophy* (published 1663, though written 1647-48), those which treat of the usefulness of natural philosophy "in reference to the mind of man." Natural philosophy insensibly leads to truth, and as the highest truth is that of religion, philosophy and theology are inseparable. No one, Boyle was sure, could contemplate nature without remembering that the natural world is a divinely created work, so that the more one understands the wonders of nature the more one is led to admire the wonder and omnipotence of the Creator of nature. In this, as in so much else, Boyle was typical of the English scientists of the period, who never could understand why their opponents regarded as atheistic a study which, for them, merely confirmed the great truths of religion.

Boyle, like other scientists, still regarded theology as the queen of sciences, and he published several purely theological works during his lifetime; modern readers tend to find these tedious stuff, for we no longer share the seventeenth century's passion for long sermons. To us it seems odd that a scientist should devote so much attention to theology; though it was common enough then, even Boyle's contemporaries seem to think that he ought to concern himself wholly with natural philosophy, in which his contributions were notable, rather than spending time on theology, in which other men were equally skilled. This is apparent from the apologetic tone of the Preface to *The Excellency of Theology Compared with Natural Philosophy (as both are Objects of Men's Study);* as if to make amends for publishing a work of pure theology, Boyle let the publisher add a treatise of natural philosophy, "The Excellency and Grounds of the Mechanical Hypothesis" (cf. Part Two, Section I, no. 4, and Section II, no. 9).

Generally, as a matter of fact, Boyle wrote not on pure theology, but on the relation between the study of natural philosophy and the belief in a divinely created universe. This is the main theme of the first "tome" of the *Usefulness of Experimental Natural Philosophy,* which also explains Boyle's view of the nature of the universe. The attributes of God, he thought, were amply displayed in the structure of His universe. For surely, in spite of the Epicureans, the universe was too complex and wonderful a thing to have been made by the fortuitous concourse of atoms. Indeed, the order and harmony of the universe, together with the manifold wonders of living beings, all proved the existence of God—and the more one understood these, the more one admired the majesty and supreme wisdom of God. For the universe was a wonderful and intricate mechanism, governed neither by chance nor by mystic and occult forces, but by rational laws framed by the Creator in the initial construction of the world. God did not work in wholly mysterious ways; the ways in which God designed the universe to work could be understood by man, if man would but try.

There was no need to assume living forces, but rather laws of mechanics. We should not be like the Chinese, who, Boyle insisted, when first shown a watch thought it must be alive; we should rather be like those same Chinese, who, once they had been assured that the watch was the work of a man, were able to understand—and yet still admire— the skill of the watchmaker. So with the natural philosopher: the more he understands the working of that machine or great piece of clockwork, the universe, the more he is struck with the marvelous power and ingenuity with which God framed it to run according to immutable laws. When Boyle thought of the universe as a great clock, what he had in mind was the most famous cathedral clock in Europe, that of Strasbourg, which not only told the time of day and gave an annual calendar, but had numerous automata, the most famous being the iron cock that crowed and flapped its wings every day at noon, in commemoration of St. Peter's denial of Christ; this was a complex mechanism worthy of being compared with the universe, when one considered the difference in kind between the creator of

FIG. 1 HABRECHT'S MODEL OF
THE STRASBOURG CLOCK (1589)

The lowest level contains a calendar ring which shows days,
months and years, as well as
the phases of the moon and the
position of the sun in the zodiac.
The next level, supported by
two moving cherubs, shows the
quarter hours; at its center is a
map of the world. The top dial
shows both mean and astrologi-
cal hours.

Above these are four levels of
automata: the first shows the
seven days of the week in the
guise of the gods after whom
they are named; these pass before the starry heavens. The
second shows angels passing before the Virgin and Child every
hour. The third shows the four
ages of man, each of which
strikes one of the quarters. On
the fourth, Death strikes the
hour bell, while on the left
Christ comes forward every
two minutes.

On the very top is the cock
which flaps its wings and crows
every hour.

All this, complicated as it is,
is simpler than in the original.

the clock and the Creator of the universe. As Boyle so continuously insisted, it was, to him, more wonderful that God had designed matter with laws of motion built in, so to speak, than it would have been had God had to interfere continually and push matter about, or if He had to make use of occult spirits and forces to keep the world going in the way in which He had intended it should from the beginning.

Since God created the universe, there is clearly design in its form, and one of the roles of experimental natural philosophy is the search for this design. Hence final causes should not, in spite of Bacon, be totally banished from natural philosophy; it was abundantly permissible to inquire into the end for which a thing was made, because everything, being made by God, was made for a specific purpose. This is particularly true when investigating physiology, plant or animal; we owe to Boyle the information that William Harvey (whom Boyle consulted for his eyes) was led to the discovery of the circulation of the blood because he tried to understand the purpose of the valves in the veins, a fact which Boyle regarded as adequate justification for his own faith in final causes.[8] When it came to physical science, Boyle seems to have meant by "final causes" the laws which govern the universe, which in some sense "explain" the reason why things behave as they do. In general, natural philosophy shades insensibly into natural religion precisely in the consideration of final causes, which is thus beneficial to both subjects.

The notion of the universe as a machine implied no derogation of the dignity of God, then, and it made the processes of science much easier. To understand a machine one commonly analyzes the action of the parts, by taking it to bits and putting it back together again, when (if, of course, one has understood its working aright) it will run as well as the maker designed that it should. So if one wants to understand that great piece of clockwork, the universe, one must try to understand how its parts work, in accordance with the laws governing machinery (i.e., mechanics, the great seventeenth-century physical science); the equivalent of taking a clock to pieces is to investigate the universe by experiment. The experimental method has divine sanction; for God would not have made the universe as it is unless man were intended to understand it, which he can do only by experiment.

It is doubtful whether Boyle ever noticed how hypothetical the concept of the world machine really was. It certainly defied one of his rules of what a good hypothesis should be, for it was not the only hypothesis which could explicate the phenomena; otherwise he would not have had to attack his opponents—Peripatetic or Epicurean—so fiercely and in such detail. It did, to be sure, offer a certain kind of predictability, namely the prediction that the natural world was indefinitely intelligible. And it was a useful hypothesis and a consistent one, which contradicted no known phenomena and did explain many things. Boyle thought of it less as an hypothesis than as a theological doctrine, and though he was the very opposite of dogmatic in natural philosophy—indeed, rather too prone to avoid committing himself to a position—it did not seem to him that the same attitude was desirable in matters of religion. It appeared to him, in fact, to be not merely a plausible argument, but the clear truth, that a direct road to a devout faith in God could best be reached by a study of His works, a study which, however, must be undertaken in the method and spirit of the new experimental philosophy.

Its usefulness to the mind of man was but one aspect of the usefulness of natural philosophy, and Boyle by no means overlooked its usefulness "for the relief of man's estate," as Bacon put it. Both Baconian and Comenian impulses inclined him to consider practical uses of natural philosophy. This was an interest begun in very early days, and continued into the period of the founding of the Royal Society, when Boyle's influence added to the general intention of the Fellows, and helped stimulate that interest in compiling histories of trades (accounts of technical processes) which was so marked a characteristic of the Society throughout the seventeenth century.[9] The motive for the study of agriculture, mining, soap making, dyeing, glass making, and various chemical crafts was twofold in this period. There was first the conviction that the study of technical processes might benefit the scientist; who knew what empirical knowledge the artisan might possess which would totally escape the natural philosopher if he was only book learned? Secondly, there was the belief that if the scientist thoroughly understood the problems of technology he would be able to use his knowledge of nature to aid in solving these problems, so that science might be applied to the benefit of mankind.

Neither of these aims was very well realized in this period, though it was certainly to the advantage of science to be aware of the needs of technology, and occasionally (as with the new technique of "salting out" in soap making) the interest of the scientist served to spread the knowledge of empirically discovered techniques. It was a controversial point of view, and one that Boyle, who accepted it wholeheartedly, felt the need for defending as late as 1671, when the "second tome" of the *Usefulness of Experimental Natural Philosophy* was published. There were still two different classes of people to convert: there was the gentleman philosopher who did not like to associate with vulgar craftsmen (though such a feeling was, obviously, uncommon among the fellows of the Royal Society), and there was the craftsman himself, fearful lest he lose his livelihood when trade secrets were exposed (cf. Part Two, Section I, no. 5).

Actually, as Boyle pointed out, the craftsman had more to gain than to lose by the natural philosopher's interest in trades. For it was the philosopher who both invented and demanded the production of new scientific instruments. The sixteenth-century instrument maker might derive his income from the manufacture of instruments for navigation and surveying; the seventeenth-century instrument maker clearly manufactured his products mainly for the scientist and virtuoso, making telescopes, microscopes, air pumps, and so on. The glassblowers especially profited from the demand for new and improved forms of glass jars, air-pump receivers, glass tubing; though, as Boyle among others complained, their skill was not equal to the scientists' hopes. Boyle's air pump called for the manufacture of receivers, and a fair amount of the work connected with the air pump (for example, the studies on fermentation and putrefaction, which, so Boyle hoped, would lead ultimately to new methods of preserving food fresh for long intervals) was directed toward perfecting new trades. This was an influence that the artisan could not escape; when the philosopher tried to improve crafts directly he had little influence, and trades proceeded by traditional methods until revolutionized in the late eighteenth century by new craft inventions rather than by scientific discovery, which, however actually relevant, seemed too theoretical to interest the relatively unlettered tradesman.

It has been sometimes noted that, except for his work in pneumatics, Boyle appears to have remained outside the main stream of scientific thought of the mid-seventeenth century, since this was so largely concerned with mathematical physics, or at least with experimental physics whose results could be expressed in mathematical terms. This is partly the result of misinterpretation; Boyle's mechanical philosophy is not mathematical, but no more was that of Descartes. It is also partly the result of ignoring an interesting though minor aspect of his interests (as regards the amount of space and time he devoted to it), an aspect illustrated best by the *Hydrostatical Paradoxes* (Part Two, Section I, no. 6). This was presented to the Royal Society in 1664 as a kind of review of Pascal's *Treatise on the Equilibrium of Liquids*, particularly a critique of Pascal's experimental method. Boyle thought Pascal's approach was only pseudoexperimental, since he could not have performed most of the experiments he offered as supporting evidence for his theorems, for some were quite impossible of performance (like the series which had to be made under water) and some were either extremely difficult to perform or involved apparatus difficult to construct. Boyle wished to show that he could provide experiments to illustrate the same or similar problems which could be performed easily and successfully; in a sense this is a treatise on the correct use of the experimental method, and shows how difficult it was in the early days of the experimental philosophy to devise useful and correct experiments. It also contains a justification of Boyle's avoidance of the currently preferred mathematical approach. He later (in Tome II of the *Usefulness of Experimental Natural Philosophy*, published in 1671) printed an early essay on the "Usefulness of Mathematics to Natural Philosophy" (it had circulated in manuscript ten years before it was printed), which shows a fairly wide reading in standard mathematical works; this justifies Wallis' praise of Boyle's skill in algebra and applied mathematics as well as in theology, languages, public affairs, experimental philosophy, medicine, and chemistry. He was not himself a mathematician, but he understood the mathematical approach to science and valued its elegance and succinctness.

But he felt that it had grave disadvantages as well, of which the most serious was that it limited the audience for a scientific work to a very small portion of the educated public. Boyle wanted, always, to appeal to as many kinds of people as possible; both gentlemen and tradesmen would benefit more from an experimental treatise than from a mathematical one. Besides this, Boyle felt that the insistence on a purely mathematical approach was a limitation; even hydrostatics was not a perfect mathematical science. The mathematician had contributed much, but he perforce avoided those problems which would not readily lend themselves to mathematical expression; it was time that the natural philosopher showed what could be done to advance such fields by purely experimental means. In his heart, indeed, Boyle believed experimental proof to be far more convincing than mathematical proof; mathematical proof was a bit too close to the method of reasoning from *a priori* principles to appeal to him, and he was far more interested in the real world revealed by experiment than in the ideal world of mathematical law. One would like to know if he ever discovered how successfully Newton had blended the two approaches in the *Principia*—but for all the friendly interest which the elder scientist took in the younger, there is no record of what, if anything, Boyle thought of that great work.

[III]

The Mechanical Philosophy

BOYLE's insistence on the doctrine of the world machine was but one aspect of his acceptance of the mechanical philosophy. This doctrine, as he was willing to call it (though he fervently denied that it was a system), involved not only the attiude implied in the emphasis on the mechanical nature of the working of the universe, but a "mechanical" theory of matter as well. It was, in fact, a complete and well developed theory, founded upon experiment, adequate to explain all the properties of matter, and both rational and empirical; it was the exact antithesis of either the Peripatetic (Aristotelian Scholastic) or the Spagyrical (chemical) doctrine of matter. For Boyle, the explanations of both the Aristotelians and the Spagyrists were not only untrue, they were unsound and even vicious, being occult, outmoded, and mystic, dealing in mere semantic images, whereas the corpuscular philosophy (as he liked to call it), was true, reasonable, modern, and rational, making use only of real and factual entities, and based upon experimental evidence rather than logical argument. The older explanations implied a world not to be easily understood, certainly incomprehensible without recourse to occult forces. ("Occult properties," which the Peripatetics used for mysterious forces like magnetism, became a phrase of scornful derogation to the new philosophers of the seventeenth century.)

The newer, mechanical explanations implied a world totally explicable in everyday, common-sense, empirical

terms. Just as it was a poor philosopher who could not
understand the workings of a clock without recourse to
metaphor and occult or mystic forces, so it was a poor
exponent of the new learning who could not understand
the universe, that great piece of clockwork, without recourse to "Aristotelian forms and hypostatical principles."
(Hypostatical principles are those concerned with the
essence or substance of a body, its elementary nature, in
fact; they usually refer to the chemical rather than to the
Aristotelian elements.) These were undesirable not only
because they were mere words, signifying nothing in actual
observed fact, but because they were occult, implying as
well the existence of such mystic forces as sympathies,
antipathies, attractions, repulsions, sociabilities, and
nature's aversion to a vacuum. The rejection of these forces
and the passionate advocacy of the mechanical philosophy
was one of Boyle's most influential contributions to the
science of his day, especially because it encouraged experimental investigation of the physical and chemical
properties of bodies, a comprehension of which in mechanical terms was of enormous advantage to physical science.

Although he had received an unconventional education,
Boyle was thoroughly familiar with the orthodox and
scholastic attitude toward the nature of matter; indeed no
one could read as widely as Boyle had done in the natural
philosophy of the early seventeenth century without gaining a complete knowledge of the doctrine of forms and
qualities. The theory of substantial forms and real qualities
was derived from Aristotle's emphasis on the importance
of the formal cause, the explanation to the question "why
is this substance what it is, rather than being some other
substance?"—that is, why is it wood and not stone? This,
for Aristotle, was a philosophically important problem,
but not a profound scientific problem. Later Aristotelians,
the Peripatetics, exploring aspects of physics (and chemis-

try) little discussed by their master, elaborated a theory of forms which reached its climax of complexity in the early seventeenth century. The formal cause of fire is heat, Aristotle had said (because heat is the most essential property of matter); heat is a form, said the Peripatetics, and so are color and solidity and taste and odor and fluidity and volatility and density and light and indeed every chemical and physical property perceived by the senses. Gold is yellow and dense and malleable and heavy and nontarnishing, we say; gold contains the forms of yellowness and density and malleability and ponderability and incorruptibility, said the Peripatetics, and these forms, being really in existence, can reasonably be expected to be implanted in some other metal, and so gold be made. As Boyle put it (in an unpublished essay on "Occult Qualities"), "If you ask a Vulgar Phylosopher the cause of the fire burning, he will presently answer you, that the fire burns by the quality of heat that is most eminent in it: but if you further ask him what that heat is, and how it enables the fire...to performe the various effects we dayly see produced by fire; he will if he *be* ingenuous, confesse to you in plain terms that he cannot tell, and though he *be not*, he will but in a confused & unintelligible Discourse give you cause to conclude as much." By the end of the seventeenth century, Boyle's attitude had become so much a commonplace that Molière could make fun of the doctor who explained that opium acted as a narcotic because of its dormitive power—he might as well have said because of its dormitive form or quality.

The greatest stimulus to the investigation of forms came from chemistry, especially from the new school of medical chemistry. The medical chemists or Spagyrists adopted the Peripatetic theory to their needs, combining Aristotelian forms with Paracelsan elements; indeed, one of their number, Daniel Sennert, reconciled forms, elements, and atoms

—and was quite willing to combine with all this the doctrines of Galen. (His best known book was indeed called *On the Agreement and Disagreement of the Chemists with Aristotle and Galen.*[1]) This combination seemed ideally suited to the study of chemical reactions, where change of "forms" was most commonly the result of subjecting substances to a chemical process, as when one mixed a solid and a liquid and acquired a liquid, or two solids heated together gave a liquid. To suppose that one had merely removed certain forms, and replaced them with others, was a perfectly adequate "explanation" provided that one was satisfied with a predominantly verbal explanation. This method had its experimental basis too: salt, which replaced the Earth of the Aristotelian elements for the chemist, retained the form of solidity, so if one had a solid, it must be solid because it contained salt, and if a liquid solidified in the course of a reaction that was the result of the addition of salt. Similarly, mercury carried the forms of fluidity and of metallicness, sulphur of yellow and inflammability. And so on. It was only natural that, the doctrine of forms and qualities being long established, chemists should attempt to explain new phenomena in the old terms, even though to do so caused ever greater complexities.

One reason for this is a sound principle of science, that one should try to accommodate new facts to established theory whenever possible. There was also the fact that there was little for even the most violent anti-Aristotelian to offer in place of the elaborately developed doctrine of forms. Seeking the cure in the origin of the disease, anti-Aristotelians began by trying to revive the atomism of the ancients. In Aristotle himself one could read of the atomic theory of Democritus; and one did not need to be convinced by Aristotle's attack. In Diogenes Laertius' *Lives of the Philosophers* one could read Epicurus' own account of his atomic theory (as Boyle had done as a boy in Geneva). Lucretius' great Latin poem *On the Nature of Things* was very popular in literary circles from the fifteenth century, in spite of the pronounced atheism which made Boyle distrust even the Christianized Epicureanism of Gassendi (1592-1655), the French contemporary of Descartes. There were medical atomists mentioned by Galen, and there was the simple physical atomism of the Greek mechanician, Hero of Alexandria. These were all eagerly read, and many minor writers tried, like Gassendi, to adapt these ancient, nonoccult philosophies to the new natural philosophy of the early seventeenth century. But though they were mechanical and nonoccult, they were too simple to be readily adaptable, and it really did not help advance physics to know that air differed from fire because of the mere size and shape of its particles, when neither of these could, as far as anyone knew, ever be determined experimentally: for even the newly invented microscope did not actually make the particles of bodies visible, though it did make their existence much more credible.

The new method of explanation of the properties of bodies, a method which effectually drove forms and qualities quite out of scientific discourse, was derived from that most successful new science of the early seventeenth century, dynamics, the branch of science which deals with bodies in motion. The development by Galileo of the mathematical and experimental foundations of dynamics is the primary reason for the enormous respect in which the terms "mechanics" and "mechanical" were held by seventeenth-century natural philosophers. Once this had been successfully achieved for the macroscopic world it was not difficult to see that it might also be achieved for the microscopic world; and if the particles of bodies were in motion, this might, as Galileo pointed out, account for the properties of bodies we know. Material particles of various sizes and shapes moving at various rates of speed could easily affect our organs of sensation to produce the qualities of bodies so familiar to all—as heat did, for example. This was a notion which Galileo tossed out in passing in the course of a famous polemic, the *Saggiatore* or *Assayer*.[2] Galileo was by no means the only person to arrive at the same conviction, which was soon to become elaborated into the general theory of the mechanical philosophy.

It was the dynamic mechanical philosophies of Bacon and Descartes which had the greatest influence upon Boyle, and indeed upon the later seventeenth century generally. Bacon was well read in classical atomic theory and, like Galileo, recognized the potentialities of trying to understand the properties of bodies in terms of matter and motion. This was the "discovery of Forms" for which Bacon campaigned so ardently, and of which he proclaimed: "From the discovery of Forms therefore results truth in speculation and freedom in operation."[3] Bacon was a linguistic conservative and so he retained the *word* "form" while rejecting the *thing*; he wanted mechanical explanations of the old forms and qualities, that is, explanation in terms of matter and motion. A great part of the *Novum Organum* is concerned with an elaborate dissection of the nature of heat; the method of inquiry is tediously and needlessly detailed, but the result is irreproachable: "Heat is a motion, expansive, restrained, and acting in its strife upon the smaller particles of bodies."[4] Bacon hoped that, once he had shown the way with his analysis of heat, others would follow and by experimental analysis determine the cause of whiteness, putrefaction, magnetism, and other occult forms. It was this vision of a new field of investigation of natural philosophy which inspired the young Boyle to plan a great work on the mechanical philosophy; in a sense, all his works were devoted to this subject.

Though it was Bacon who mainly inspired Boyle, he was influenced by Descartes as well. Descartes was the first to develop a complete mechanical philosophy, systematic and complex, based on the notion of the universe as a machine, whose mechanism could be understood if the method of reasoning rightly were applied to physical principles of the nature of matter and laws of motion; this is exposed in its entirety in his *Principles of Philosophy* (1644). God divided the matter with which the world was originally filled by endowing it with motion, so that it split up into particles. These were not atoms; for there was no particle so small that it could not be at least mathematically divided. Nor were these particles surrounded by a vacuum, as true atoms are. Descartes denied the possibility of a vacuum, because he defined matter as characterized by extension. Now if matter is extension, there can be no such thing as "empty" space, for space and matter are one, and if the matter is removed the space can no longer exist. One can, however, empty space of ordinary matter; in this case the ether (subtle matter) is still left behind, and fills up the space. (This was how the Cartesians explained what happened in Boyle's air pump.) Since space was filled with matter, all motion proceeded by impact, and so Descartes' laws of motion were mainly laws of impact. Actually, he did not believe that ordinary matter was endowed with motion; ether was, and it was the motion of the ether that moved matter. Thus gravity was caused by the pressure of the ether, which is in motion about the earth; when a stone is removed from the earth, the motion of the ether forces it back. Light is a pressure through the ether; heat is caused by the motion of the ether acting on the particles of matter, the ether being in turn agitated by fire or friction. There was no need for occult forces or qualities, when all properties could be explained by the action of the ether.

Logically, since matter is extension, physics is geometry, and Descartes should have been able to express his ideas on the nature and properties of matter in mathematical terms; in fact, this was not so, nor did later Cartesians do much in this way. As the ether was devised by Descartes from logical rather than empirical considerations, his was not in any sense an experimentally based form of mechanical philosophy. Nor were the Cartesian explanations of the properties of bodies ever subjected to thorough experimental verification even though many later Cartesians, like Hooke, were able experimenters. Cartesian philosophy had all the merits of a consistent, logical, complete, and systematic doctrine but it lacked the one ingredient which Bacon's tentative and inchoate speculations possessed, that is, the conviction that the best method of establishing reasonable and satisfactory mechanical principles was by basing them squarely upon detailed experimental evidence.

When Boyle in his youth espoused the Cartesian concept of the world machine, he very naturally accepted as well the theory that the universe was constructed of matter and motion; "those most grand and Catholic principles," as he called them, took the place of the wheels and gears of the clock. Too devout to be an Epicurean (in any case his convictions were already set by the time Gassendi's complete system appeared in the *Syntagma Philosophicus* of 1658), too much the empiricist to be a Cartesian, Boyle was forced to evolve his own theory in an attempt to combine the best features of both Cartesianism and Epicureanism. This was possible because they were agreed in their fundamental outlook; as he put it, "The Atomical and Cartesian Hypotheses . . . agree with one another and differ from the schools in this grand and fundamental point, that not only they take care to explicate things

intelligibly; but . . . explicate . . . phenomena by little
bodies various figured and moved . . . and both parties
agree in deducing all the phenomena of nature from
matter and local motion."⁵ It was on the basis of this agreement, and the desire to explain all things intelligibly, in
terms of matter and motion, that Boyle devised his own
corpuscular philosophy and planned to write a "History
of Qualities," which was to be a complete survey of the
whole field, that discovery of forms which Bacon had
demanded.

The "History of Qualities" was, in fact, never written.
Beginning in the Oxford days Boyle did write a series of
separate essays, one to each form or quality, which circulated in manuscript and were later published in various
formats. These assumed a theory, and were mainly concerned to show that his explanation of every form was
grounded on experiment, and could be supported by
experiment, for which purpose he found chemical experiment the most efficacious. The earliest published essay on
this topic is one contained in *Certain Physiological Essays* (published in 1660), rather grandly called "A Physico-Chemical Essay, Containing an Experiment, with
some Considerations Touching the Differing Parts and
Redintegration of Saltpetre"—usually referred to by Boyle
as the "Essay on Nitre." This contained a single experiment, or rather a single series of experiments: saltpetre or
nitre (potassium nitrate) was analyzed into its component
parts by fire to give "fixed nitre" and "spirit of nitre,"
which would combine to give saltpetre again. What he
actually did was to use charcoal for the fire, so that the
"fixed nitre" was mainly potassium carbonate (potash);
spirit of nitre is nitric acid. This, Boyle thought, could be
explained only in corpuscular terms, because he did not
believe he had added anything; he considered the question
of whether the charcoal was involved in the reaction but

decided that it was not, because so much more fixed nitre was formed than seemed to him consonant with the amount of charcoal used. This essay is almost entirely experimental, because its theoretical value was indicated in the preface, entitled "Some Specimens of an Attempt to Make Chemical Experiments useful to Illustrate the Notions of the Corpuscular Philosophy" (Part Two, Section III, no. 15). And, as an afterthought, he added two more experimental essays, those on fluidity and on firmness.

These four essays (for the preface is almost an essay in its own right) attracted a good deal of attention because of their novelty; for the attempt to expound a corpuscular philosophy in empirical terms, with a wealth of relevant experiments, was indeed novel. But it was, as the title of the preface indicated, only an attempt to illustrate the philosophy; it did not really set forth its tenets with sufficient persuasion. It might, Boyle felt, confirm those predisposed to the mechanical philosophy in their convictions, but it was not suitable for winning converts, as he ardently desired to do. The same disadvantage lay with the *Experiments and Considerations touching Colours* (published in 1664) and the *Experimental History of Cold* (published in 1665); in each of these Boyle assumed the corpuscular philosophy but, wishing to gain the widest possible audience for his important new experiments, tried to impose his philosophy as little as might be.

Instead of completing his long-intended account of qualities, Boyle was forced to compromise, and to write a series of theoretical discussions side by side with the experimental ones. So in 1666 he published *The Origin of Forms and Qualities, According to the Corpuscular Philosophy; Illustrated by Considerations and Experiments. Written formerly by Way of Notes upon an Essay on Nitre,*" his first real declaration of the details of his doctrine. This was followed in 1674 by *The Excellency and Grounds of the Corpuscular or Mechanical Philosophy* (rather quaintly annexed to the *Excellency of Theology*) and is printed in its entirety below (Part Two, Section II, no. 9).

Another sort of theoretical treatise on the corpuscular philosophy was that in which, rather than setting forth his own doctrine persuasively, he was more concerned to demolish the alternative doctrines of the Aristotelians and the chemists, particularly the latter. This he did by showing experimentally that their forms, elements, and principles are unreliable, uncertain, transmutable, and imaginary. Treatises of this sort are *The Sceptical Chymist* (1661); the *Producibleness of Chymical Principles* (1679); *Of the Imperfection of the Chymist's Doctrine of Qualities* (1675). But the bulk of Boyle's work continued to deal with individual properties of matter, explicated in great experimental detail; the most complete example of this is the collection entitled *Experiments, Notes &c. about the Mechanical Origin or Production of Divers Particular Qualities* which contains essays on heat, cold, taste, odor, volatility, fixedness, corrosiveness, corrosibility, chemical precipitation, magnetism, and electricity, as well as an interesting preface (see below, Part Two, Section II, no. 13) explaining his intention and his method.

The Excellency and Grounds of the Corpuscular or Mechanical Philosophy is one of the best, as it is certainly one of the briefest, expositions of the basic tenets of the corpuscular philosophy and of the reasons for its adoption. As usual, and especially in a proselytizing work, Boyle was concerned to show that the corpuscular hypothesis was entirely consonant with religion; for him, God created the world out of matter and motion and it is by the motion of matter (divided into corpuscles) that individual substances come to be endowed with their characteristic properties, as intended by the Divine Creator. (This is utterly opposed to the Epicurean theory, with its world formed by the fortuitous concourse of atoms.) And, equally, he was concerned to show that his philosophy, unlike that of the Aristotelians and Spagyrists (Paracelsan chemists), was clear, rational, intelligible, and simple. Besides all this, the corpuscular philosophy could explain each and every property, merely by using the facts of matter and motion, without recourse to imaginary occult forces or undetectable principles, like elements, spirits, attractions, and so on. Matter and motion are facts, experimentally detectable; they are intelligible, and their use to explain the properties of bodies makes the world intelligible as well, and the power of the Creator even more wonderful.

In many of his works (as in the *Excellency of the Mechanical Philosophy*) Boyle was more concerned to explain that matter and motion accounted for the properties of bodies, and how they did so in specific cases, than he was in devising a detailed theory of the structure of matter. But if he was often somewhat uninterested in describing at length a theory of the structure of matter, it was by no means because he did not have one. His reluctance was partly policy—he hoped to gain more converts by making his discussion as widely applicable as possible; partly innate temperament—his curious inability ever to present a formal and complete development of any subject; and partly conviction—the fact that any theory of the intimate structure of matter must be based upon logical rather than experimental considerations. Besides, it was the gross structure of matter, almost experimentally detectable, with which he was primarily concerned, for it was this which actually figured in chemical and physical investigations.

Nevertheless, Boyle did have a fairly detailed theory of

how the simplest particles fitted together to make matter as we perceive it. Matter, Boyle claimed, had originally been divided by God into very small particles (or perhaps, indeed, matter was originally created in very small particles); these were too small to be individually detectable by any means. They were not, strictly speaking, atoms, since it was impossible, Boyle thought, to imagine a particle so small that it cannot be mentally divided, and God, being omnipotent, could in any case divide any particle, however small it might be, if He chose; yet these least particles are normally never divided, remaining small, solid objects of a definite size and shape. These naturally occurring least particles tend to combine to form coalitions or clusters, which are so compact that they will normally persist unchanged through many vicissitudes. Since these clusters have a continuous existence, it is they which are the important units for chemistry and physics; they have definite size, shape, and motion, and it is these which determine the nature of the substance which they compose. In many ways, especially in chemistry, it is possible to alter the size and shape of such a coalition or cluster, and if this is done, the substance is changed. In general, however, chemical reactions involved rather the association and dissociation of primary clusters, which thus are rather like modern molecules.

More important even than the size and shape of the primary clusters—which one could never actually determine—was the motion of the clusters, for a change in motion altered many chemical and physical properties of the substance involved. Motion was especially useful in explaining what looked like occult forces, the result of attraction or sympathy—for what really happened is that motion (which was not mysterious) brought the molecules close together. Thus, Boyle deprecated the prevailing theory (supported by Cartesians and chemists alike) that salts deliquesced in air because there was a sympathy between the salt and water; he preferred to say that the air, which was in constant motion, continually brought dissolved water particles in contact with the salt, and since the pores between the salt particles happened to be the right shape to admit water particles, deliquescence was the natural result. This was clearly a successful example of the application of the concept, for no one could deny the constant motion of the atmosphere.

This was a theory of matter highly suitable to physical explanations, but perhaps less so to chemical ones. Indeed, Fontenelle, Secretary of the French Academy of Science, and a Cartesian, once publicly complained that Boyle was far too rational and too little mystic ever to be a proper chemist. Chemists at this time usually embraced some form of physical theory of matter, but their demands were for explanations such as the physicist's theory— whichever theory it might be—was not intended to provide. Consequently, they commonly superimposed upon the physical a chemical theory of principles, hypostatical or elementary they were usually called. (Indeed, this mixture remained fairly standard throughout the eighteenth century.) Thus, the earliest chemical atomists combined atoms with forms and qualities, and many combined particles (often Cartesian) with elements, which were so designed as to take the place of forms and qualities. The Aristotelian elements carried with them certain forms which were inalienable, and the source of identification— the dryness of earth, for example, or the fluidity of water. The *tria prima,* the Paracelsan or Spagyrical principles, salt, sulphur, and mercury, took on the attributes of the Aristotelian elements, so that each became just a little more crowded with properties than was requisite when there were four elements. For this reason, and for experimental reasons, many later chemists expanded the *tria prima* to four or five, adding phlegm, spirit, oil, etc. as fancy and chemistry dictated. Salt, for example, took on some of the attributes of the Aristotelian earth, and was the "cause" of solidity and equally of chemical precipitation; the presence of sulphur caused a body to be inflammable, and alkaline, and oily, and yellow, etc.; mercury conferred fluidity and weightiness.

All this Boyle, naturally enough, found no more rational or useful than Peripatetic forms or occult qualities. He was sure that sea salt, brimstone, and quicksilver were not elementary, nor even slightly impure forms of the chemical principles: they were compounds or clusters of corpuscles, like all substances. On both philosophical and experimental grounds Boyle insisted that no substance could be truly elementary, because all were made up of particles. But he was not content to reinterpret the chemical theory of elements, he denied it altogether. Aware that to do so meant undermining the foundations of ordinary chemical thinking, Boyle devoted much space and many experiments to the problem, first in *The Sceptical Chymist* (a dull book, but a mine of interesting experiments) and then in the *Producibleness of Chymical Principles*, as well as incidentally in other places. These are experimentally based books, which endeavor to refute the supposedly empirical basis of the theory of elements and principles, for *a priori* though the theory of elements was, it was allegedly founded on observation.

The chemists claimed that analysis revealed the presence of elements in all substances, not that they had tried detailed analysis of all substances, but that they believed that one typical experiment could be used to justify the claim for all. Boyle called Jean Beguin, an influential textbook writer of the early seventeenth century, the leader of the Spagyrical sect, and it was Beguin who set the fashion for demonstrating the existence of elements by analysis by fire: when a green stick was burned, it gave off fiery smoke, which was sulphur; a liquid sap, which was mercury; and there remained ash, which was salt. Where Beguin saw the *tria prima,* others saw the four Aristotelian elements, and still others saw five or six principles—and were equally content to find the same elements in all bodies, first organic bodies (which on destructive distillation do indeed give off a bewildering variety of solids and liquids) and then inorganic substances. Boyle, skeptical for other reasons, saw the fallacy in this and insisted first, that the oils, spirits, earths, and so on were by no means identical, and second, that most common chemical substances obstinately refused to yield the correct number of elements when heated.

For these reasons, Boyle flatly denied that elements or principles had any real existence.[6] This is rather a shock to the modern reader, who knows that there are, in fact, over a hundred elements recognized by chemistry. And it is especially a shock if one reads Boyle's definition of an element rather quickly, when it sounds deceptively modern. As Boyle says, he defined elements as most chemists did, as substances found in all bodies, and into which all bodies may be ultimately reduced. The literal interpretation of this statement is the correct one: *every* substance contains *all* elements, properly speaking, every substance contains salt, sulphur, and mercury, or earth, air, fire, and water, or whatever the preferred principles may be. Hence all common substances are compounds; and hence too if one wishes to talk about the composition of a substance (like sal ammoniac, or silver) one can only do so in terms of the elements. But elements, by definition, cannot ordinarily be obtained in a pure state, and so no chemical analysis could do more than indicate the presence of elements, which by definition were already known to be there—that is, experiment could only confirm what one knew on rational grounds, as it could not explain the composition of substances in any but elementary terms. Boyle thought the doctrine of elements not only untrue, but confusing, and he devoted much effort to pointing this out. Elements, principles, forms, and qualities, far from being the immutable basis of matter, were highly unstable and impermanent, and very easy to transmute one into another. He was delighted when he found that organic oils, like turpentine and oil of aniseed, gave a tarry solid residue on prolonged heating, for this was a manifest change of form, and perhaps a change of one principle into another.

Even better in this regard was the experiment in which, so he believed, he had succeeded in transmuting water into earth. He included this in the *Origin of Forms and Qualities* as part of his attempt to refute all opposing doctrines while at the same time advocating the corpuscular philosophy (Part Two, Section II, no. 12). If one accepts the corpuscular hypothesis, all substances should indeed be transmutable, though with varying degrees of ease; all that was required was to rearrange the corpuscles, or at worst to break bits off to make new corpuscles, together with some change in the motion of the corpuscles —and there was no reason why prolonged heating and repeated distillations should not accomplish this. (This is why all the most rational mechanical philosophers regarded the transmutation of base metals into gold as a theoretical possibility, though most thought it not very probable.) In his delight at this discovery, a delight that made him discuss it at inordinate length, Boyle triumphantly announced it as a proven fact that water had been changed into earth. And yet, even so, he was too good an experimental scientist not to enter a note of caution, and to explain exactly why he might be mistaken, and exactly what steps to take to correct his mistakes, if he was indeed mistaken. He saw well enough that the "earth" might be merely fragments of glass dissolved by the water, and he realized that he should have tested it to make sure that it was not glass. But he failed to do so. Undoubtedly, this failure was, in part, because he preferred to think that a real transmutation had taken place. Partly it was the result of that generous temperament which made him enjoy tossing out suggestions for others to work at. (He would have much enjoyed being a modern academic scientist, with plenty of graduate students appealing to him for suggestions for Ph.D. topics.) There is little doubt that he would have been more pleased than distressed at the work of Lavoisier, which showed conclusively that no transmutation had in fact taken place, though surprised that it had taken over a century to settle the problem.[7]

One of the things which most clearly distinguished Boyle's corpuscular philosophy from other mechanical philosophies was its close attachment to experiment. Boyle was not a man to frame hypotheses independent of the empirical facts; it was his boast that his philosophy was solidly grounded in experiment. This meant, or so he hoped, not that his explanations were confirmed by experiment after he had invented them on rational grounds, but that the explanation was the result of much experimental evidence, patiently gathered together. Hence the majority of his works are experimental essays, which present a mass of experiment dealing with some particular property or quality, experiment which usually, at the conclusion, serves as the basis on which to present the mechanical explanation of the particular quality under consideration. Boyle never tired of exploring occult qualities or of finding further experimental data relevant to qualities which he had already discussed. The most complete presentation of this kind of work is the *Mechanical Origin and Production of Qualities*, in which some dozen qualities, physical and chemical, were explained and interpreted in the light of the corpuscular philosophy in what Boyle clearly hoped, as he ventured to indicate in the prefatory "Advertisements," was a definitive manner (Part Two, Section II, no. 13).

Mechanical explanation involved consideration of the size and shape of the corpuscles, which could be determined only on rational grounds, but it also included consideration of the motion of the corpuscles, which was closer to being a property that was experimentally determinable. The relation between heat and the motion of the particles was what above all made the motion of particles seem so likely to be of great consequence for the properties of matter, and heat was itself a "quality" which Boyle considered in great detail, in more than one experimental treatise. His discussion is admirably clear and exact; particularly good is his recognition that what would move a macroscopic body, like a nail, would also move microscopic bodies, like the particles of the nail, so that a hammer striking a nail produces motion in the nail or heat in the metal of the nail by exactly the same mechanism. Hence it is clear that no occult force can be involved. Hence, too, as heat is the result of the violent agitation of the particles, cold is mere absence of such agitation, and the slower the motion of the corpuscles the colder will the object appear to be; so cold is not a positive quality needing an explanation of its own, but merely a special case of heat.

Magnetism was another quality which, like heat, could be mechanically produced; here again, Boyle saw no need to regard this as an occult quality, since it could so easily be explained in mechanical terms: magnetism was the result of a special alignment of the particles, an alignment that could be produced either by the action of a magnetic field, or by mechanical rearrangement. Thus no occult force like attraction needed to be considered. Having so neatly explained magnetism in mechanical terms, Boyle naturally tried to do the same thing for electricity, but electrical attraction he found more difficult to deal with, and the results are less happy: electric bodies when rubbed give off effluvia which form themselves into elastic strings, whose stretch and relaxation account for the attraction of light bodies. This amply indicates the weakness as well as the strength of the mechanical explanation.

Boyle's ideas on the nature of light, color, and fire are of especial interest, since they were problems of such importance for the time, and since this work shows both the best and the worst of Boyle's amalgamation of experiment and theory. The *Experiments and Considerations touching Colours* is an ambitious work, dealing with whiteness, blackness, color in general, and color in solutions, which led him to a number of important chemical discoveries and conclusions (cf. below, on chemistry). The work on colored light, which included some experiments with a prism, are the least successful aspect of Boyle's work on colors, and perhaps explain in part why he did no more experiments on color after the publication of the ideas of Newton and of Hooke in the 1670's. Boyle treated color like other qualities and sought for its origin purely in the structure of the colored body. In spite of his drawing attention to the "prismatical iris," as he called the spectrum, he seems to have thought of this in the same way as scientists considered the rainbow, to be discussed in terms of reflection and refraction. At least, he never speculated at all about the nature of ordinary light and what it is that makes it possible to produce colored rays from white light, seeming to regard this as but a special case of what interested him much more, the production of colored solutions, often from two colorless liquids.

That color was essentially the product of the alignment

and motion of the particles seemed to be confirmed by his successful investigation of the nature of whiteness and blackness, which was supported by numerous ingenious experiments: whiteness was clearly the result of the total reflection of light, blackness of the total absorption of light, and this explained why white clothes were cooler than black, rooms hung with black tapestry warmer than those hung with light colors, and so on. This was well done, and some of the experiments became classic; but it did not offer much that was useful in explaining other colors, though in trying to do so Boyle described many interesting experiments, from which much could be learned.

The mechanical explanation of light was set about with many difficulties. To the Peripatetic philosophers, light had always been a form, like heat; just as heat lingered for a while after a body was withdrawn from contact with fire, so light lingered after the sun had sunk below the horizon. In reaction, the new learning favored the corpuscular theory of light, which seemed the most mechanical because the most different from the Peripatetic explanation; the Cartesian explanation, that light was the result of pressure in the ether, though fundamentally mechanical, seemed less so because it did not involve any specifically luminiferous particles. Boyle was not dogmatic on the subject, but he did regard light and fire as essentially related; as with Newton later, this involved a slight ambiguity in the description of exactly what happened when a body was heated hot enough to shine. But Boyle thought that light from the sun was similar to or identical with light from the fire, and as he remarked, "fire, which is the hottest body we know, consists of parts so vehemently agitated, that they perpetually and swiftly fly abroad in swarms." That light and fire are really the same is the basis for the experiments contained in that curious work, *New Experiments to Make Fire and Flame Stable and*

Ponderable: he had intended to test the corporeal nature of light, but the English sun defeating him, he resigned himself to proving the corpuscular nature of fire instead. This is the aim of the treatise, as the title indicates; it is concerned with the corporeal and chemical nature of fire, not with any theory of combustion. Similarly, the sequel to these experiments is contained in a treatise entitled *A Discovery of the Perviousness of Glass to the Ponderable Parts of Flame.* And Boyle was satisfied that he had indeed proved what he set out to show, that fire was corporeal because it combined with metals and minerals when they were heated either in air or in closed vessels, though the corpuscles were exceedingly minute.

These experiments have always been difficult for historians. Boyle's experimental technique was excellent; he was carefully quantitative, and he was equally careful to consider all aspects of the experiments. And yet he failed to understand the role of the air in combustion. But it is only when one approaches this work with poor historical perspective that one is confused. If one looks at the past only with a view to the present, then one cannot but tend to regard these experiments as dealing with combustion; and in this perspective Boyle is a failure because he did not anticipate Lavoisier's discovery of the role of air in combustion. This is bad history not only because it ignores the hundred years of work on pneumatic chemistry and on chemical analysis that lay between these experiments, made before 1673, and those of Lavoisier a century later; it also ignores Boyle's professed intention. He failed to notice the role of the air because he was not interested in combustion or calcination *per se,* nor in trying to show (what he already knew) that all metals gain weight when heated. He wanted to understand why they gained weight; he believed that it was eminently reasonable to assume that fire was a chemically active substance (more reasonable than to assume that air was chemically involved) and so he devised experiments to prove this. It is true that he found that if he heated metals in closed vessels, these burst; but he thought that they exploded because of the expansion of the air when heated. Consequently, he heated the vessels slightly before sealing, so as to drive out some of the excess air; naturally when he broke the seal, the air rushed in to take the place of what had, earlier, been driven out. Curiously, Boyle's own good technique was partly responsible for his missing the possible role of the air, though it is doubtful if, had he known of it, he could have assumed anything more than had been assumed earlier by Jean Rey, namely, that the air mixed physically with the metal to produce the calx.[8] Boyle was too good a chemist not to expect a chemical reaction necessary to produce such a marked change; hence fire, not air, must be involved. Boyle was not the first person to succumb to the errors he was most apt to denounce, in this case a priori reasoning. In his defense it can be said only that he thought he had good empirical justification for a corpuscular explanation of a form or quality.

There was, in fact, nothing, according to Boyle's view, that the corpuscular philosophy could not illuminate, make plain, or explicate. This was its great glory, that it did so much without being dogmatic, and with the aid of experiment. Whatever had been occult before became rational and reasonable when understood in the light of the corpuscular philosophy. Boyle wrote a whole essay on specific medicines (those presumed to be valuable for some one specific disease) to show that, when interpreted corpuscularly, this supposedly occult medical concept was in fact acceptable mechanism. In the same way, as a part of his Essay on Gems (1672), he offered a corpuscular, mechanical theory of the medical virtue of amulets—even solids give off effluvia, very small, fine particles; and why should not a jewel hung about the person give off effluvia which could penetrate the skin and so work beneficially to restore the health and avert disease? The very excess of his rationalism could permit Boyle to accept the near occult, if it could be interpreted mechanically. So much that was useful did, in fact, come out of his extensive use of the corpuscular, mechanical philosophy that it is not surprising that while he disliked the idea that it might be a complete system, he yet thought that it was the true key to an understanding of nature, since it was at once theoretical and experimental.

[IV]

Chemistry

IT SHOULD by now be apparent that it is impossible to separate Boyle's theoretical work in natural philosophy from his experimental work in chemistry. Indeed, one of his important flashes of inspiration was the recognition that chemical experiment is highly suitable for illustrating and confirming the mechanical philosophy in its explanation of the properties of bodies. By putting this vision to work, Boyle conferred enormous benefits upon the mechanical philosophy, and upon chemistry. It was not easy to convince natural philosophers that chemistry was genuinely useful, nor others that this was the best use of chemistry. In the latter regard there is the rather touching letter (Part Two, Section III, no. 15) to an unnamed friend, in which Boyle defends his use of chemical experiments to advance natural philosophy rather than to advance medicine or alchemical art. In contrast to this is the passage in which he remarks that many of his friends found it strange and disturbing that a man who could make contributions to pure natural philosophy should waste his time on chemistry.

As Boyle's dilemma indicates, chemistry in the middle of the seventeenth century was in a peculiar position, for neither natural philosophers nor chemists thought of it as a part of the new learning. Chemists, in general, were either mystics or artisans, or both; they were not philosophers. At best, chemistry was a useful art, useful to medicine on the one hand and to the technology of metals, glass, dyes, and so forth on the other. This usually meant

81

that practical chemistry was rule of thumb empiricism; the scientists of the Royal Society who interested themselves in the history of trades noted this, but were unable to influence the conservative practitioners of the various chemical crafts. Equally, much chemistry, especially that of the textbooks, was iatrochemistry, that is, medical chemistry, almost totally concerned with the preparation of drugs, the new chemical remedies which created such a controversy in the medical profession in the sixteenth century, but which were in such great popular demand in the seventeenth century that the profession had to change its attitude and encourage their use.

Increased use of chemical drugs meant that apothecaries and pharmacists had to learn how to compound them; hence, especially in France, there was a new development in the demand for popular vernacular lectures on chemistry, lectures which the professor usually turned into a textbook.[1] These textbooks provided the source for most elementary instruction in chemistry, and were much alike throughout the century—indeed, it took nearly a century, at this time, before a textbook was regarded as obsolete. They begin with a short introductory section on theoretical chemistry, a discussion mainly limited to explaining the meaning of the word, indicating the scope of the art of chemistry itself, presenting the author's chosen theory of matter, and describing the necessary furnishings of a chemical laboratory. This very brief section—a mere bow in the direction of theoretical knowledge and learning—is followed by the bulk of the book dealing with strictly practical rules for the preparation of drugs, usually derived variously from the mineral, animal, and vegetable kingdoms. A textbook's value was judged by the ease of following the directions, and the number of new preparations, invented by the author, which it contained. One useful by-product of the teaching and textbook tradition was that it tended to eliminate the secrecy formerly maintained by chemists about their discoveries—a rather slow process, as seen for example by the fact that the German chemist, J. R. Glauber (1604–70), who did not lecture, kept the method of preparation of his new salt (sodium sulphate) as obscure as was consistent with boasting of its discovery.

As the century progressed, the textbook writers, all Spagyrists (followers of Paracelsus) at the beginning of the century, became followers of the influential Belgian mystical chemist, J. B. van Helmont (1580?–1644).[2] The Spagyrists may be distinguished by their acceptance of the *tria prima*, salt, sulphur, and mercury, as the three elements of which all matter is composed, and by their firm conviction that chemistry existed to serve medicine. Helmontian chemists were somewhat different. Their theory of elements varied a good deal; few of them believed, with Helmont, that all substances were made of water, but they tended to lay stress on the importance of either water or phlegm as an element. What distinguishes them as Helmontians is that they accepted and even exaggerated Helmont's view of chemistry as a theoretical body of knowledge, a science in fact. Helmont ardently believed that chemistry was more than art or craft, but his view of science was a mystic one, and he never considered the possibility that chemistry might be akin to the new learning. He thought it rather akin to medical science; so for him iatrochemistry was not an art in the service of medicine, but a science nearer to what we now call physiology, that is, the theoretical science dealing with the functioning of the human body.

The key to chemical reactions lay in the understanding of the mechanisms of living matter; for chemistry in Helmont's view did not deal with inanimate nature, like natural philosophy, but with animate nature. This is the nineteenth century approach stood on its head, and leads to such anomalies as the acid-alkali theory of matter. He observed empirically (mainly by taste) that the secretions of the body concerned in digestion—gastric juice, bile, pancreatic juice—were either acid or alkaline; from this (and presumably from the massive indigestibility of the seventeenth-century diet) he concluded that digestion was an acid-alkaline neutralization accompanied by effervescence. Not content with this, he concluded further that all chemical reactions outside the body were also acid-alkaline reactions, and his followers added that all substances were either acids or alkalies. This whole chain of reasoning depended on the presupposition that chemistry was primarily a science dealing with living processes. Many of the Helmontians, like the rational textbook writers who lectured in Paris (Lefebvre or Glaser)[3] adapted this into defining chemistry as the key to arts and crafts and all knowledge.

So too, the most influential of all textbook writers, Nicolas Lemery,[4] was a Helmontian in his belief in the scope and knowledge of chemistry, which, he thought, lets us understand not only all natural processes, like rain, mineralogy, nutrition, and growth, but even assists us to understand the order which God observed in the creation of the universe. This is mystic enough; yet Lemery's approach is otherwise eminently rational, and he had even absorbed some of the mechanical views of Descartes and of Boyle. Whatever the conviction about the nature of chemistry which was held in theory, in practice it was still either wild mysticism or the practical preparation of chemical remedies.

The first person to try to make chemistry truly a part of natural philosophy was Boyle. It is clear that his early interest in chemistry was medical and practical. As an eager member of Hartlib's Comenian group he was anxious to apply chemistry to the relief of man's estate; this obviously meant the preparation of new remedies, an occupation to which his own ill health added urgency. His first attempts at chemistry filled him with extraordinary delight, as his letters to his sister indicate, and he found it difficult to interest himself in anything else. The striking thing is, however, that even in his bewitchment he did not neglect the rationality with which his temperament and education had endowed him. He read Helmont avidly, and discussed his ideas with Hartlib's chemical friends, all of whom were ardent and rather mystic Helmontians. But he did not forget that he had already read Galileo, Bacon, and Descartes, and he did not desert natural philosophy because he had become addicted to chemistry. Rather, he tried to combine the two, and to transmute Helmont's notion of chemistry as a mystic science into his own concept of chemistry as a rational science.

Chemistry, it seemed to Boyle, came as near to dealing directly with the fundamental structure of matter as anything could do, and therefore chemistry must be an integral part of the corpuscular philosophy. Chemistry, however, should not be just a handmaid to the corpuscular philosophy, as it had once been a handmaid to medicine; it was and must be a science in its own right, dealt with as a part of the new experimental philosophy of the new learning. This was Boyle's real contribution to the development of chemistry: that he did successfully deal with chemical experiment and theory as a part of natural philosophy, and that by precept and example he persuaded others to do the same.

To make chemistry genuinely a part of natural philosophy meant that theory and experiment must be combined and balanced just as was being done in experimental physics at the time, and meant as well that chemical theory must be rational, nonoccult, mechanical, and experimentally grounded. It also meant, paradoxically, that chemistry must become less directly useful, for usefulness in chemistry meant too close an adherence to practical processes, and not enough attention to experiments which would demand and lead to theoretical explanations of chemical behavior and composition. Boyle realized that what was needed was a genuine body of philosophical chemistry, as he called it; he had hopes of one day being able to present such a complete theoretical chemistry. But just as was the case with the mechanical philosophy, he never wrote the great treatise he had early planned, and instead presented, in individual and mainly experimental essays, fragments of the great work he envisaged but could not bring to fruition (Part Two, Section III, no. 15).

Rather easier to perceive than the chemical theory Boyle somewhat tentatively developed was his attack on the erroneousness of the prevailing theories. It was not just because of their belief in elements and principles that Boyle attacked the "chymists" and Spagyrists; it was rather for the occult, inaccurate, and obscurantist character of their thought. He felt that the doctrine of elements and principles was physically erroneous, because there were in fact no such things, as reason and experiment amply proved. It was also chemically erroneous, because it led to a state of thought that was highly prejudicial to chemical progress and real chemical understanding. Because we still use the term "elements," and because salts at least are still a valid chemical class, it is tempting to assume that chemists meant something closer to the chemical facts as known today than was actually the case. When they spoke of salt or salts they did include sea-salt, and most of the substances we now class as salts; but they also included acids, alkalies, and many substances that we would no longer regard as salts. And this was their best— in the sense of clearest—taxonomic class. Sulphurs were more complex: sulphide ores were sulphurs, so were many substances known to contain the mineral brimstone, so were substances whose principal characteristics were those attributed to the element sulphur: oiliness or inflammability, for example. Similarly with mercuries: these were amalgams, substances made with mercury as reagent, and, even more obscurely, entities like the supposed "mercury of antimony" reputed to be made from antimony but having the properties of mercury. So oils were any substance that had as a prime characteristic the property of oiliness, and this included such diverse substances as organic vegetable oils and viscous liquids like oil of vitriol (concentrated sulphuric acid). Metals were, under this system, obviously complex substances since they shared the properties of more than one element—and indeed if there were only three to five elements, most substances which we should now call elements were bound to be considered complex.

The difficulty was not entirely resolved by eliminating elements, for what was needed was further understanding of chemical composition and chemical classification. Boyle began with the initial advantage of rejecting elements, so that he could no longer classify substances as sulphurs or mercuries or phlegms. Further, the scepticism about elements led to a healthy scepticism about the composition of substances, and so he looked for, and ultimately found, ways of determining composition in terms of relatively stable and well-known chemical entities.

His greatest success lay in his experimental differentiation of acid, alkali, and neutral substances, which was a by-product of his antichemical bias. Some chemists had partially replaced the theory of elements with an acid-alkali theory, derived, as indicated above, from Helmont's work on digestion; this assumed that all chemical substances were either acids or alkalies, and so that all reactions were acid-alkali neutralizations. A substance was acid if it reacted with alkalies, and vice versa, though most simple acids and alkalies were well enough known. Boyle was able to develop tests to show whether a solution—and hence a substance dissolved in water—was acid, alkali, or neutral (Part Two, Section III, no. 16). This, which is described in the *Experiments and Considerations touching Colours,* and more generally in "Reflections Upon the Hypothesis of Alcali and Acidum" (in the *Mechanical Origin and Production of Qualities)* was at one and the same time an attack on the erroneous theories of the chemists, a triumphant vindication of his own experimental-philosophical method, and a useful and true classification to replace the erroneous system he was attacking. It consisted in the use of chemical indicators which showed characteristic color changes in the presence of acids or alkalies, and which did not change color in the presence of neutral solutions. Further, again by characteristic color changes of a chemical reagent (in this case mercuric chloride), Boyle differentiated between volatile animal alkalies and fixed vegetable alkalies—ammonia, and either potassium or sodium carbonate. Besides this, Boyle showed that the volatile animal alkalies (ammonia), known by a variety of names according to origin—hartshorn, spirit of urine, spirit of sal ammoniac, spirit of soot —were all one substance; and that the fixed vegetable alkalies (potassium carbonate)—potash, salt of tartar, lixiviate salt—were all the same.

Much of Boyle's experimental work was, in fact, devoted to clearing up the confusions left from previous chemical theory, and trying to understand what exactly might be the chemical entities with which he was dealing. There was no other class of substances for which he could be quite so definitive as he was for acids and alkalies, but he did his best to be clear and exact and to base his distinctions upon chemical tests. His success varied; he was clear about the differences and similarities between copper and iron vitriol (sulphate), though he sometimes called any salt of a metal and a mineral acid a vitriol. But he could detect individual constituents of compounds in a surprising number of cases. Copper, for example, could be detected by the color it gave to certain menstruums—green to strong acids and flame, blue to ammoniacal solutions—and he showed that some substances previously thought to contain copper, like Helmont's *ens veneris*, did not; whereas his own newly discovered resin of copper (cuprous chloride) was certainly a copper compound. Silver could be detected by its solubility—it dissolved in aqua fortis, but not in aqua regia—and certain characteristic reactions, like the formation of luna cornea (silver chloride) with spirit of salt (hydrochloric acid). (Boyle noticed its property of blackening with time; he thought this was caused by the action of the air, and seems not to have suspected the role of light.) He noted that many chemists thought that silver would produce a blue-green color in strong acid solutions; this, he was able to show, was an error, for it occurred only with silver contaminated with copper, as so much silver was. This in turn led him to comment on the need for purity in substances which are to be used for tests or in reactions; as he pointed out, the chemicals bought from apothecaries were by no means pure enough to suit the chemist, who ought to purify them by distillation, filtration, crystallization, and so on. Many salts, as Boyle noted, had distinctive and definite crystalline forms: hartshorn crystallized in parallelopipedons, saltpetre in prisms, sea salt in "imperfect cubes," sal ammoniac in "combs and feathers," rock alum in octahedrons, and so on. This could be used both for identification and, possibly, as some hint of the underlying corpuscular structure.

These are but samples of the tests and techniques which Boyle developed over the years and of which he made use for practical identification of compounds, for the investigation of new compounds, and for the determination of composition of common compounds. This gave him an enormous advantage over others. Many chemists, for example, worked on mineral waters, their composition and use; mineral waters were first widely used for therapeutic purposes in this period, and scientists were constantly asked for advice on their usefulness, and on their composition. Many rule of thumb techniques were invented; by far the best survey in this period is Boyle's *Short Memoirs for the Natural Experimental History of Mineral Waters* (1685) (Part Two, Section III, no. 16)—not a finished treatise but a mass of suggestive ideas for a complete investigation, which should make use of such physical tests as specific gravity, as well as all the chemical tests which Boyle knew or had devised.

An even better example of the effectiveness of Boyle's chemical tests, and indeed of his whole experimental technique, is his examination of phosphorus, which he usually preferred to call "noctiluca"; this is contained in the *Aerial Noctiluca*, published in 1680, and the *Icy Noctiluca*, published in 1681 (Part Two, Section III, no. 16). As his investigations of the aerial noctiluca were mainly concerned with investigating the necessity of air in the production of light, some selections from that work have been included in Part Two, Section IV, no. 23. Boyle was not the original discoverer of phosphorus, but he was the first to reveal its secrets. He heard of it from a German, Daniel Kraft, who showed some samples at Court and elsewhere of two shining substances, one liquid and one solid, about a year before Boyle first published on the subject. Kraft seems to have kept the secret of the preparation of this fascinating new chemical, only hinting at its method of preparation to the German chemist Kunckel, and to Boyle. (Kraft himself probably obtained the secret from another German, named Brand.) Boyle learned only that it differed from other "phosphoruses" (shining substances) by being derived from "somewhat that belonged to the body of man"; by trial and error he obtained it from urine, distilling this in a strong fire and collecting the result under water to prevent its bursting into flame. He actually prepared it in two forms, the icy noctiluca, a white solid (occasionally mixed with red phosphorus) and a liquid form, the aerial noctiluca, which would not shine unless in contact with air. The investigation of solid phosphorus is particularly thorough and brilliant; in fact Boyle discovered almost all the properties known for the next 200 years. He overlooked nothing: besides superficial physical examination of the solid itself he examined the water in which the sample is kept; searched for solvents far and wide (his discovery that certain aromatic oils were solvents for phosphorus particularly pleased him, because it made the examination of phosphorus more pleasant); found various ways in which its luminescent properties may be exhibited, including its ability to shine at very low concentrations (a fascinating example of the quantitative approach in chemistry); studied its inflammability; examined for acidity the liquid created when phosphorus was left in the air to run *per deliquium;* and so on.

These are true physico-chemical experiments and show many aspects of Boyle's experimental technique. One can see here how he devised his experiments, how he carried them out, what practical and theoretical use he made of his knowledge, and how well he could deal with small quantities. One can find here too some indication of his relations with his laboratory assistants, and of the influence on his presentation of the constant interest his work aroused among the curious laymen who laid claim to a virtuoso interest in science. These are ingenious, amusing, important, and perceptive experiments; the results are ample justification of Boyle's own carefully devised chemical method.

The sanity of Boyle's approach as contrasted with the hazy occult spirit of the ordinary chemist is patently illustrated in the work on phosphorus. Not so evident is the changed point of view that this implied. For when he stopped thinking in terms of elements and principles, and thought instead in terms of simple, stable, identifiable chemical entities, Boyle was in a fair way to revolutionize chemistry. It had not, for example, been of much use to try to understand the course of a chemical reaction—one could say only that the sulphureous or the mercurious or the earthy part of one substance was joined to another, and the use, either practical or theoretical, of this kind of discussion was negligible. Chemists had talked before of the sulphureous part of copper vitriol, for example; but it was unclear, even to themselves, what they really meant. When Boyle talked about the sulphureous part of copper vitriol he meant the part containing the chemical substance sulphur, which he knew to be the part which came from oil of vitriol. So if he spoke of the mercurious part of mercury sublimate, he meant the part derived from mercury when the sublimate was prepared from common quicksilver and spirit of salt.

These are obvious examples; but they prepared the way for an understanding of more complex, less well-known substances in the same spirit. And this was a very necessary preliminary to further studies in chemical analysis and the study of chemical reactions. However much later chemists might still pay lip service to elements and principles, as indeed they did, this was lip service only, and they no longer tried, in general, to explain reactions in terms of elements and principles. To cease to think in terms of elements, and begin to think in terms of simple substances—this is a tremendous step on the road to clear chemical thinking. It did not, perhaps, require the corpuscular philosophy, but Boyle's use of the corpuscular philosophy helped because it explained what these simple substances were. They were the concretions and clusters of corpuscles that could persist unchanged through sublimation and chemical reactions, though not in themselves elementary; Boyle instanced the sublimation of sulphur and sal ammoniac, and the persistence of nitre through a long chain of reactions.

It is a great pity that Boyle never developed this point of view more systematically; yet he developed it in great enough detail so that his contemporaries understood what he was doing. Some rejected Boyle's point of view because they found it too clear-sighted, nonmystical, and physical; some few accepted it wholeheartedly and campaigned for its complete adoption; more compromised, accepting the spirit of Boyle's approach while denying that one must reject the theory of elements. It did not matter very much, in fact, whether one continued to believe in elements or not; what mattered was whether one fixed one's attention on elements or on simple substances. It was the latter point of view that increasingly won out; the more successful it was, the more chemistry advanced and became, as Boyle had insisted it should, a recognized part of natural philosophy.

[V]

Pneumatics

A T INFREQUENT but recurring intervals in the history of
science there are exciting moments when a question
long subject to pure speculation suddenly becomes acces-
sible to direct investigation. When this happens, a whole
new scientific subject is opened up to experimental research, and these experiments dramatically revise men's
theoretical concepts—usually not without natural and
conservative opposition. Such moments occurred with
more frequency in the seventeenth century than at most
other periods in history, and were usually the result of the
application of a new scientific instrument to old problems.
When Galileo turned his telescope on the heavens and
found that what had previously been observed was but a
fragment of the total possible visible universe, such a dramatic moment occurred in full measure. Equally dramatic
was the mid-seventeenth-century discovery of the vacuum,
for its connection with the mechanical philosophy, for the
possibility of investigation and proof of notable problems
of mechanics, and more especially for the creation of the
science of pneumatics.

There were several acts to this drama: first came the discovery that it was possible to create a vacuum, publicized
by the work of Torricelli, and then came the exploitation
of the vacuum, made possible by the work of Boyle. The
Torricellian experiment was so simple that it seemed peculiarly spectacular, consisting as it did merely of filling a
tube with liquid, and then inverting it in a basin of the

same liquid, when, if the tube were long enough, the liquid fell part way down the tube, leaving an empty space at the top of the tube. It was particularly wonderful when performed, as Torricelli did it, with mercury (it had earlier been performed with water), when the tube did not have to be much above thirty inches long. It was hard to decide which was the more surprising: the ease with which a vacuum was produced, or the extraordinary ability of air to support a column of mercury thirty inches long—for so Torricelli and most "modern" natural philosophers immediately and correctly explained the experiment. The Puy-de-Dôme experiment of 1648, devised by Pascal and performed by his brother-in-law, who measured the height of a column of mercury at the foot and the top of a steep mountain, confirmed Torricelli's interpretation. Ever since the Greeks, men had argued that what appeared "empty" space was in fact filled with air; but here was indeed empty space, space in which no air could possibly exist. Even those who denied that it was, in fact, the pressure of the atmosphere which held the mercury suspended, admitted that the air had been removed. Thoughtful philosophers saw in this a possibility of checking many long-held beliefs concerning the role of the air in the transmission of sound, the supporting of flame, and so on, but although Torricelli performed his experiment with tubes whose ends were of different sizes and shapes (to show that there was nothing about the space above the mercury itself which was responsible for the peculiar behavior of the mercury), there was no available means of making use of the vacuum so obtained to perform experiments. The experiment was useful to confirm various hypotheses of the mechanical philosophy, and it demonstrated a new state of matter, but the problem rested, temporarily, there, though the Torricellian experiment and the acceptance of its consequences had rapidly become one of the tenets of the new philosophy, as it was one of the subjects discussed in 1645 by the embryonic Royal Society.

Ten years' discussion produced many arguments pro and con: there were those who accepted the experiment and its conclusions wholeheartedly; those like Descartes who accepted the role of the air but denied that there was a vacuum, since absence of air did not mean absence of ether; and those who rejected the whole experiment and its conclusions as being basically erroneous and misguided. The next development came, in fact, from Boyle, acting on news of the invention of a new method for producing a vacuum. In 1657 Gaspar Schott, a Peripatetic writer on the minor aspects of mechanics, published his *Mechanica Hydraulico-Pneumatica*, in which he described the invention of the air pump by Otto von Guericke, mayor of Magdeburg. Schott described the air pump only to refute von Guericke's contention that he had created a vacuum. Boyle saw in the description an immediate incentive to construction of a pump to be used for the investigation of pneumatics. Guericke's pump was only a modified form of water pump; indeed, he had begun by trying to pump the water out of a wine cask, arguing that what would be left would be a vacuum, and had then seen that the air could be pumped out directly. It took two strong men to work his pump, which only slowly emptied a metal receiver. (The account of the Magdeburg hemisphere experiment, so often illustrated in modern textbooks, is not in Schott's book, but in von Guericke's own *New Magdeburg (as They are Called) Experiments on Empty Space*, published in 1672.) Boyle seems to have been the only man to notice the potential importance of this; at least he immediately and excitedly decided to have an improved pump of his own, one easier to work and with a glass receiver, so that there should be, as in the Torricellian experiment, a visible vacuum, but, unlike the Torricellian tube, one in which it would be easy to introduce objects for experimental purposes. He set two of his laboratory assistants, Greatorex, a chemist, and Robert Hooke, already noted for his mechanical ingenuity, to devising an air pump that should conform to his specifications. It was Hooke who succeeded in producing the air pump that Boyle immediately used in a long series of experiments, some of them with Hooke's assistance.

It has sometimes been said that Hooke should receive the major share of the credit of Boyle's pneumatic work, on the ground that Hooke later became famous for his physical experiments, whereas the bulk of Boyle's experiments were chemical, except for his pneumatic work. But Boyle was notoriously open and generous in his attribution of credit, while Hooke was notoriously very jealous of claiming credit for all he did; yet Hooke remained on good terms with Boyle and never asked for more credit than he publicly received—unlike his behavior in the controversy with Newton over the inverse-square law of universal gravitation. On the whole, one is tempted to suspect that perhaps it should be the other way around, and that Boyle should receive some credit for Hooke's early work on capillarity, which he began in Boyle's laboratory as a by-product of the work on pneumatics.

As soon as the pump was available, Boyle set to work to devise means of carrying out a vast series of experiments to test the known properties of air and to establish as clearly as possible its exact physical nature. These were clearly exciting days, and Boyle's laboratory was haunted by the other Oxford philosophers, Wren and Wallis in particular, who came to see the new experiments performed, to suggest experimental aids and to conjecture the theoretical implications of Boyle's work. There were so many possible experiments that it was impossible to be wholly systematic, but at the end of 1659, when Boyle found himself in the country with leisure to write up his results, he was fairly selective in presenting mainly (though not entirely) those indicated by the title of the published book, *New Experiments Physico-Mechanical, Touching the Spring of the Air and its Effects.* The success of the book was immediate; scientists who had not known of von Guericke's work, or had overlooked its possibilities, like Huygens, immediately constructed air pumps of their own, repeated Boyle's experiments, and tried to devise new experiments with the aid of what rapidly became known as the Boyleian vacuum. (It was after the publication of Boyle's work that the members of the Accademia del Cimento in Florence began constructing Torricellian tubes with large bulbs in which pneumatic experiments could be tried.) Not everyone, of course, accepted Boyle's work without question; his two most formidable opponents were the philosopher Thomas Hobbes and the Jesuit Franciscus Linus (Francis Hall), who later engaged Newton in controversy. Boyle answered them in *A Defence of the Doctrine Touching the Spring and Weight of the Air,* published in 1662 as an addition to the second edition of the *New Experiments,* with much new information. Some time after this he gave his air pump to the Royal Society, to be used at their meetings and to show to visitors. He had a new and different pump devised, in which the cylinder was immersed in water and the glass receiver was connected to the cylinder by a tube; the improvements were suggested by his own experience, and by that of Hooke and others. This is the pump described in *A Continuation of New Experiments Physico-Mechanical Touching the Spring and Weight of the Air and their Effects,* published in 1669 (he had published a few short papers on pneumatics in the intervening period); in these experiments his assistant was clearly not Hooke, who had left him to become Curator of the Royal

Society. More miscellaneous papers followed, and in 1682 there was the *Second Continuation,* especially concerned with the production of "air" from fruits and vegetables. For these experiments his chief assistant was Denis Papin, who had devised his own air pump (which Boyle found not so convenient as his own) and who actually wrote up the experiments, though he by no means performed them all.

Although Huygens, Papin, and many others copied Boyle, devised air pumps, repeated his experiments, and tried to invent fruitful experiments of their own, no one besides Boyle succeeded during the seventeenth century in making original contributions to pneumatics. This is an astonishing fact for, given the air pump, most of the experiments Boyle tried seem obvious and not too difficult of performance. But this is in fact an illusion. Boyle himself could not always make experiments succeed, either because he could not devise ways of illustrating the point he wanted to test or because even his technique was not sufficiently refined. No one else approached Boyle in ingenuity and technique. For this reason Boyle's pneumatic experiments are particularly instructive in demonstrating the inherent difficulties of the experimental approach in the seventeenth century, as well as in showing how superb his own technique really was. The precautions he took and the difficulties he noted are not just the minutiae of a careful man, they are essential to any attempt to repeat his experiments. He understood well enough the novelty of his technique and the importance of his subject. This led him on the one hand to very careful and detailed descriptions so that anyone—even a mere amateur like his nephew—could understand how to perform them; and on the other to an avoidance of theoretical discussion. He felt that description and explanation of the experiments themselves were enough; the place for discussing their conse-

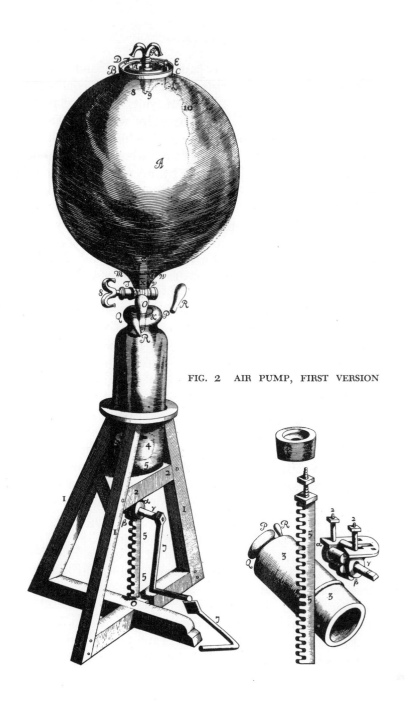

FIG. 2   AIR PUMP, FIRST VERSION

quences lay elsewhere, chiefly in treatises devoted to the mechanical philosophy. Hence, as will be seen from the selections below, if one wants Boyle's view of the composition of air, and of the cause of its elasticity, one looks to other treatises than those on the air pump, where Boyle finds it enough to explain how air behaves, without trying to explain why it behaves in these ways. His description of how air behaved was necessarily of a different order of certainty from his speculations on why it behaved so; for these, the curious were invited to read works devoted to that theoretical aspect of the mechanical philosophy—treatises which he composed in great number.

Boyle began the account of his experiments by giving an elaborate description of his first (and largest) air pump, but as very few modern readers will wish to build one of their own without, at least, some modification, perhaps a reproduction of the original plate showing the appearance of the machine will suffice. This shows clearly how aptly contrived it was to make full and easy utilization of the vacuum possible. Boyle's first experiment (or at least the one which he chose to describe first) is de-

FIG. 2   AIR PUMP, FIRST VERSION

A is the glass receiver, large enough to hold 30 "wine quarts," with its brass stopper K ground to fit a hole HI in the larger brass stopper FG which, in turn, fits the 4-inch ring DE of the cover BC. K has a small hole, 8, which can either be used to let in small amounts of air or to support a string, 8,9,10, to permit the suspension and moving of objects in the vacuum.

The receiver is connected to the brass pumping cylinder (14 inches long and 3 inches wide) through a stopcock N,S with valve R. Within the cylinder is the "sucker" 4,4,5,5; the upper part fits the cylinder loosely and is made to fit tightly by means of a piece of tanned leather; the lower part is a long, narrow piece of iron with a serrated edge which is made to retract by manipulating the handle 7.

The frame is of wood.

signed to demonstrate the "elater," or elasticity of the air from the behavior of bladders in a vacuum. From this he proceeded to confirm numerous previous conclusions about the behavior of air when rarefied or compressed, the elegance of his experimental proof being very much greater than any previously devisable. The most obviously important experiment to perform, as Boyle indicated, was a test of the Torricellian experiment (Part Two, Section IV, no. 17). If it could be performed *in vacuo,* obviously the prevailing explanation was wrong; if as the air was withdrawn the mercury fell, the air was obviously indeed the instrument which held the mercury up. This experiment he successfully performed, and it was clearly an exciting moment when the mercury duly fell with each stroke of the pump—though his comments show how difficult technically it actually was to perform this experiment satisfactorily under the conditions provided by the pump.

It was the behavior of the Torricellian barometer in his vacuum that suggested to Boyle that it ought to be possible to frame an hypothesis expressing the relation of the amount of air withdrawn to the actual height of the mercury, that is, a relation between the pressure of the air and the weight of mercury. This clearly would have some connection as well with the volume actually occupied by the air. Tongue in cheek, he remarked that he was not a good enough mathematician to calculate this; his real reason seems to have been the hope of interesting others. As he said, he had not time, leisure nor skill to calculate the hypothesis, "yet would we not discourage any from attempting" such an hypothesis. He changed his mind very soon in response to Linus' insistence that the air could never hold up such a tremendous weight as a thirty-inch column of mercury, so that there must be some "funiculi," little, invisible threads which actually attached the top of the mercury to the top of the Torricellian tube. Hence the experiment with the J-tube (Part Two, Section IV, no. 18) which established the accuracy of "the hypothesis, that supposes the pressures and expansions to be in reciprocal proportions," which is generally now known as Boyle's Law. It was published with work on rarefied (expanded) air—his own experiments being concerned with compressed air—from data supplied by Richard Towneley, inspired, as were Hooke and Lord Brouncker (President of the Royal Society) by Boyle's suggestion that such experiments were desirable. There is a curious desire among modern scholars to insist that Boyle's Law is wrongly named. Yet, especially in view of his careful assignment of credit where due, there seems no reason to deny him the credit for having originated both the initial idea and the hypothesis itself, as well as of devising the best and most ingenious experimental confirmation of the hypothesis. Even more curious is the French. habit of calling it Mariotte's Law. It is true that Mariotte in 1676 published some experiments which confirmed the validity of what he called a "law of nature"; yet he must have known of Boyle's work, both from the Latin editions of Boyle's book and from a report by Huygens, who read and discussed Boyle's work as fast as it appeared—in fact if he did not it is hardly to his credit.

It was not only the Torricellian experiment which could benefit from confirmation in the air pump; there were many others as well. For example, it was obviously possible to check Galileo's conclusions about the behavior of falling bodies, by finding out how their speed varied as the amount of air—and hence its resistance—was reduced. Boyle never performed the celebrated feather and guinea experiment, but he did make a very ingenious experiment about the fall of a light body first in air and then in vacuum, noting the difference in its fall in the two cases (Part

Two, Section IV, no. 20). He also, though less successfully, studied the behavior of pendulums in air and in
vacuum; his relative lack of success here is as good an indication as it would be possible to find of the inherent difficulties of devising and conducting pneumatic experiments.
That sound was conveyed by vibrations in the air was
known to Aristotle and repeatedly confirmed in succeeding centuries; but its proof was a more difficult matter.
Earlier works had tried to show that a bell rung *in vacuo*
produced no sound, but they failed lamentably when
working with the Torricellian vacuum because they could
never devise an experiment in which the vibration was not
conveyed to the outer air by the tube. Boyle's elaborate
precautions to prevent the transmission of vibrations to
the outer air explain his success where others failed; even
he found it a difficult experiment to carry through successfully, though one well worth achieving (Part Two,
Section IV, no. 21).

Though Boyle insisted that he had no intention of dealing with theoretical questions, he could not ignore the
tremendous dilemma of the nature of the vacuum left by
his air pump. Was this truly empty space—a real void?
If so, how was it that objects placed therein were visible?
Apparently light did traverse this space, as did magnetism;
presumably, then, it was not completely empty, merely
devoid of air. Was there some form of ether continually
present? The Cartesians thought that there was; but the
Cartesians denied the possibility of empty space, since for
them space and matter were synonymous. Boyle, like Newton later, though prepared to believe in a very fine and
subtle ether, found the Cartesian ether far too coarse and
solid for credibility. He could not but think that if the
Cartesian ether existed it ought to be possible to detect
it experimentally. For if it were, as was supposed, an elastic fluid made of very small, fine particles, it ought to

exert a sensible pressure when it filled the space made empty by withdrawing the air. Hence, he devised a number of experiments which, he thought, ought to detect the ether if any such ether were actually present in his receiver. His experiments were necessarily somewhat clumsy, and of course led to negative results. That he could not detect the ether was no proof to the Cartesians that it did not exist, though to skeptics like Boyle himself it must have seemed reasonably corroborative evidence on the negative side (Part Two, Section IV, no. 22).

The relation of air to fire was an obvious problem for investigation in the air pump, which Boyle was not slow to pursue. It was not easy: there was always the difficulty of securing a good vacuum, and some confusion arose because it was possible to produce sparks *in vacuo*—were these light or fire? Hence Boyle's caution in stating (what he genuinely believed) that air was an *absolute* necessity for flame; there were enough possible exceptions to raise doubts. Further investigation was called for, and Boyle pursued the problem off and on throughout his life (Part Two, Section IV, no. 23). Thus, in 1672 he published a series of *Tracts Touching the Relation between Flame and the Air,* an exhaustive review of the subject; and the discovery of the aerial noctiluca suggested to him a new source for the investigation of the role of the air in producing flame. He was somewhat handicapped in his investigations by the fact that his theory of calcination centered around fire, rather than around air, and he thus missed a chance to instance yet one more example of the special importance of air—a thing he did not often do. Similar to the problem of the relation of flame to the air was that of respiration (Part Two, Section IV, no. 24). Many a bird, mouse, and kitten was sacrificed to show the effect of depriving a living creature of air, and to ascertain whether it was the absence of air or the presence of "ful-

ginous steams" breathed out by the creature (similar in
Boyle's mind to the smoke of a candle, for respiration and
combustion were associated long before Lavoisier) which
in the end killed it—many people had maintained that it
was suffocation, rather than lack of air, which was the
cause of death. Boyle rightly concluded that it was lack
of air, though he did not try to determine what the physiological role of the air might be.

The physical properties of air were very thoroughly investigated by Boyle, and its physical nature very satisfactorily determined by his experiments. His attempts at
establishing a chemical theory of air were less happy.
Necessarily so, for on the one hand, he had no such instrument as the air pump to assist him in his chemical investigations, and on the other hand, he thought of air as a
unique form of matter. He did, to be sure, reject the concept of air as an element; but this only made him more
sure than he otherwise might have been that air was
essentially nonchemical. In this he did not differ from his
contemporaries, none of whom thought of air as capable
of combining chemically with substances in the same way
as liquids and solids might do. This is perhaps ironic when
one considers the number of chemical reactions in which
Boyle thought the air played a role: he knew that a solution of copper in ammonia would not turn blue except in
the presence of air; that the aerial noctiluca shone only
in air; that copper and hydrochloric acid turned green
only in air; that many salts and liquids responded to the
moisture in the air; in fact, he was so sure that air played
an important role that he ascribed the blackening of silver
chloride to the action of air. But it is doubtful if he thought
that pure air played any chemical role in these cases. And
for this he had, he thought, ample experimental justification. In respiration, in combustion, in chemical experiments, however much one appeared to use up air and

"weaken its spring," yet the air that remained was still elastic, and permanently so. Air that would not support life or flame was a highly elastic fluid still. What more natural, then, than to assume that air was composed of two parts: a permanently elastic part, which was a special kind of matter, unreactive and inert; and a reactive part, probably not elastic, and hence essentially not air? For there were clearly many foreign bodies mixed with air, and it was easier to assume that it was they which were the active part rather than to assume that air, so very different in its physical behavior from any other kind of matter, should behave chemically in an ordinary way (Part Two, Section IV, no. 25).

This notion was all the easier to accept in the absence of any clear idea of the cause of the elasticity of the air. There were many theories, which Boyle often quoted, wryly confessing that he could not entirely accept any of them. His most complete discussion is in the *General History of the Air,* posthumously published in 1691; this was a collection of notes compiled over the years, dealing with various problems of the chemical nature of air and its role in the universe, as well as the physical variations associated with meteorological phenomena. (The philosopher John Locke supplied much of the meteorological data from records he kept during his years at Oxford.) The cause of elasticity was a complex problem, even for solids. Boyle inclined to associate it with compression of the particles; thus, when iron or silver became elastic on hammering, this was clearly because the particles were realigned by the motion imparted by the hammer—a very satisfactorily mechanical explanation. With air it was more difficult to decide; was its elasticity to be explained by the shape of the corpuscles? He described many quaintly ingenious theories of their possible shape, and seems to have felt this a perfectly mechanical kind of explanation. On the other hand, it was possible that the springiness came from the motion of the air particles: "The elastical power of the . . . air may be as well increased by the agitation of the aerial particles (whether only moving them more swiftly and scattering them or also extending or stretching them out, I determine not),"[1] and this received some partial confirmation from the fact that heat increased the springiness of the air, and heat was the result of the motion of the particles. In the end he left the problem unresolved, as too difficult to determine without further experiments; and these he did not live to make.

That air was a mixture appeared to Boyle to admit of no dispute. As he remarked, air is "a confused aggregate of effluviums from such differing bodies, that, though all agree in constituting, by their minuteness and various motions, one great mass of fluid matter, yet perhaps there is scarce a more heterogeneous body in the world." There was good experimental evidence for the complexity of air. There was certainly a great mass of water particles, which accounted for the deliquescence of salts; there were salt particles, as witness the rusting of metals and the corrosion of many substances in air; and there were corpuscles of light, magnetism, and electricity as well. To Boyle, these were solid particles carried in air just as solid particles may be carried in a liquid solution; and after all, air was an elastic *fluid* and might be expected to behave like one. It did not occur to him that solid particles could behave like an elastic fluid; in fact he thought he had good evidence that they did not, since water particles which appeared to behave like air in fact were readily condensed back into water. Air alone was permanently elastic, though perhaps some exception should be made for factitious airs like that generated by pouring strong acids on iron filings (hydrogen) and that from fruit and vegetables. And so air was unique and a permanent substance which could not be changed or altered by any means known to him.

The belief in the heterogeneous nature of air was common to those, like Sendivogius, Kenelm Digby, Hooke, and John Mayow, who believed that something from the air entered into a body on calcination or combustion.[2] They did not believe that this something was a fraction of the air; it was rather a different substance which was universally found in air, as water particles were. It had something, they tended to think, in common with the role of the air in creating saltpetre in barnyards, and for that reason, as well as for the explosive quality of saltpetre, they called this something variously a "universal nitre" and "nitro-aerial particles." There is no real similarity between this theory and the oxygen theory of Lavoisier. It was besides, as Boyle pointed out, totally unconfirmed by experiment; as he slyly remarked, if there is indeed such a salt in the air it ought to be detectable, and he suggested a number of tests to prove or disprove its existence. That the proponents of this theory never tried to prove or disprove it by such tests he thought a very good reason for assuming it to be wrong, for it was founded on no empirical evidence. Perhaps it was partly because he distrusted what he thought of as the flights of fancy of the nitro-aerial supporters that he refused to assign any very important role to air in calcination, though he was otherwise so ready to magnify the importance of air.

Boyle could not resolve the chemical nature of the air, nor elucidate the differences between atmospheric air and factitious air. This was left to later generations of chemists. Boyle was, however, the first real pneumatic chemist, and it was his experiments on air, both physical and chemical, that served as the point of departure for all the important work on air and gases which was to make eighteenth-century chemistry so remarkable.

[VI]

Conclusion

BOYLE DIED just as Newtonian physics was beginning its ascendancy, and the success of the Newtonian synthesis somewhat obscured Boyle's influence upon science and thought. How many readers of Locke's *Essay on Human Understanding*, published three years after Newton's *Principia* and directly associated with Newtonian philosophy, have realized that the "Newtonian" echoes were, in fact, derived from Boyle? Newton himself drew much from Boyle, whose work he studied extensively. For this reason Boyle's work could be, and often was, treated as a branch of Newton's, as if the two were strictly contemporary; thus many eighteenth-century treatises on Newtonian philosophy used Boyle's experiments, pneumatical and chemical, as a supplement to Newton's optics and mechanics.

Newton was so much the greater scientist that Boyle's share in promoting theoretical physics has often been overlooked. Nevertheless, the eighteenth century certainly read Boyle extensively; and because a demand for his books existed, various collected works, culminating in Birch's two great editions, were made available in fairly large quantity. Perhaps they were read more for the experiments with which they were filled to overflowing than for the theory they contained. But that was partly because the theory Boyle advanced was now so familiar as to be of seemingly negligible originality. Yet theory and experiment were so thoroughly mingled that neither stood quite alone; we should not be misled by the attitude of the generations close to Boyle, for with historical perspective it is abundantly clear that in fact Boyle had an enormous influence on the theoretical aspects of science.

In physics, Boyle's major theoretical contributions were the spreading of the corpuscular philosophy and the advocacy of empiricism. The eighteenth-century editions of the *Encyclopaedia Britannica* were perhaps being excessively nationalistic when they called Boyle the restorer of the mechanical philosophy—the French *Encyclopédie* had more justice when it assigned this role, for similarly nationalistic reasons, to Descartes—but there is no doubt that Boyle's own brand of mechanical philosophy was of extreme importance in making mechanism acceptable. His corpuscular philosophy was reasonable, useful, rational, empirical, and unattached to any "system"; though its individual explanations might be replaced, its spirit remained, and most scientists followed Boyle in banishing "occult forces" once and for all from natural philosophy. The reasonable but divinely created "world machine," product of a rational God, was Boyle's concept before it was Newton's and much "physico-theology," as the Newtonian exponents of natural religion came to name it, derives from Boyle's very early approach. So also, emphasis on an almost Baconian empiricism made Boyle's works seem like an extension of Newton's, especially after the middle of the century, when French scientists came to admire English empiricism. Instead of the attitude of the seventeenth century, when Cartesian scientists like Huygens and rational philosophers like Leibniz had deplored the waste of time involved in trying to prove by experiment what could be understood only by reason, even theoretical physicists in the eighteenth century approved Boyle's empiricism while deploring what to them was the limited nature of his endeavor. That most Baconian of all scientific manifestoes, the preface to the *Encyclopédie*, written by the great mathematical physicist D'Alembert, gave Boyle a high place in the scientific hierarchy because, before Newton, he exemplified so much of what was to be the Newtonian spirit. As he became a purely historical figure in physics, Boyle's theoretical achievements were once again thoroughly appreciated.

Similarly with theoretical chemistry. Not all Boyle's detailed chemical ideas were accepted—the four Aristotelian elements reappeared in chemistry, though as agents rather than as principles—but Boyle's concepts of the proper spirit and subject matter of chemistry were universally accepted, to the great advantage of the science. The minor English chemist Richard Watson was quite correct when, in his *Chemical Essays* (Cambridge, 1781) he remarked, "Mr. Boyle, by his various writings and experiments, greatly contributed to the introducing into England, a taste for rational chemistry."[1] It was not only in England that, under Boyle's influence, alchemy and iatrochemistry were transmuted into natural philosophy: through Homberg, who had worked in Boyle's laboratory, and through others who had been influenced by his books, French chemistry came to accept Boyle's ideas and so became "philosophical" (theoretical and rational) chemistry. An eighteenth-century French historian of science correctly assessed this influence when he wrote, "He taught chemists to talk of their science in an intelligible manner, to unite it to physics or at least to regard it as related to physics."[2]

Besides this, Boyle taught chemists to think primarily in terms of real chemical entities rather than in terms of elements or principles; to think, that is, in terms of detectable and specific substances rather than vague concepts. Thus, chemists increasingly discarded the Paracelsan "Salt" in favor of specific salts, like sea-salt, alum, blue vitriol, potash; the principle "phlegm" was replaced by specific watery fluids like water itself, weak acids, alcohol, or ether; "oils" were differentiated into different kinds, and so on. This made chemical analysis take an entirely new turn. Previously, all analyses had, as a necessary consequence from the definition of "element," merely detected the varying proportions of each element that the analyst expected to find, since all elements were supposedly present in all substances. Now elements were ignored in laboratory analysis (to be kept, if at all, in mental analysis only), to be replaced by simple substances, real entities, chemically differentiated and therefore chemically detectable. Hence, eighteenth-century analysis differed entirely from that of the seventeenth century. In fact, eighteenth-century analytical chemistry is one of the glories of the age, and enormously advanced true chemical knowledge. Boyle was not, as the nineteenth century liked to say, "the father of modern chemistry"— no one man was that—but he was a great and influential preceptor who infused chemistry with an exceedingly fruitful and rewarding attitude and method of attack.

Whatever assessment might be made of Boyle's contribution to theoretical science, his experimental work continued to be of very great importance and is undoubtedly the chief reason for the continued and genuine popularity of his writings. For his experiments were extraordinarily well conceived and executed, and they were in many of the areas most thoroughly studied by the generations which immediately succeeded him. His work in pneumatics was kept fresh in the minds of all scientists by the association of the air pump with his name: for in common parlance it was the "Boyleian vacuum" that was produced in the pump, just as it was "Boyle's Law" of the elastic nature of air. His experiments on physical qualities—color, heat, magnetism, electricity, and so on—were widely cited, for his accounts of his own experiments were considered eminently trustworthy, and few could better them. Above all, his chemical experiments were quoted and requoted. His tests for acids and alkalies were adopted; his methods of preparation were used; his details of analysis were considered authoritative. As late as the 1770's the great French chemist Lavoisier, a supremely independent scientist, found it uncomfortable to disagree with Boyle's conclusions, even though Boyle had, in fact, suggested the possibility of amending these conclusions through further experiment. Writing of the calcination of tin in closed vessels, where his experiments disagreed with Boyle's conclusions, he remarked cautiously, "Such important experiments made by a physicist like Boyle naturally tended to put me on my guard against my own belief, however well demonstrated that was in my own eyes."[4] Most of Lavoisier's experimental works—on the combustion of diamonds, on the proof that water was not changed into earth, on artificial airs, on calcination, on respiration—contain tributes to Boyle's vast experimental skill and the brilliance with which he saw so many of the key problems that needed solution. In Boyle's day there was only pneumatics, there was as yet no pneumatic chemistry; nevertheless, his experiments had to be reckoned with nearly a century after they were made, and both the problems he posed and the results he had obtained were suggestive of the proper approach, even though his conclusions were here often erroneous.

It is not often that a scientist's books are read for the sake of their experimental discoveries after the lapse of a century, and it is the highest possible tribute to Boyle that his were so read. In summary, one can hardly better the appraisal of the Scotch mathematician Colin Maclaurin, who wrote, in his semipopular *Account of Sir Isaac Newton's Philosophical Discoveries:*

> As Lord Bacon's plan comprehended the whole compass of nature, so the variety of enquiries prosecuted by Mr. *Boyle,* with great care and attention, is very surprizing, and perhaps

not to be parallel'd. Hydrostatics, tho' a most useful branch of mechanical philosophy, had been but ill understood, till he established its principles, and illustrated its paradoxes, by a number of plain experiments, in a satisfactory manner. The doctrine of the air afforded him an ample field; and in all his researches, he shewed a genius happily turned for experimental philosophy, with a perfect candour, and a regular condescension in examining with patience, and refuting without ostentation, the errors which philosophers had been led into from their prejudices, and the many artful subterfuges by which they strove to support them.[5]

PART TWO
Selections

Note: *The following selections are taken from Thomas Birch,* The Works of the Honourable Robert Boyle *(London, 1744) and from the Boyle Papers in the Library of the Royal Society of London. It is suggested that the reader refer to the appropriate sections of Part One for a more detailed discussion of the topics presented here.*

1. In Defense of Experimental Essays

In the following extract from *Certain Physiological Essays* (written in 1657, published in 1661), Boyle is at his most empirical. This is a philosophy of science dealing only with one aspect, the philosophy of experiment. From this, one could almost conclude that Boyle cared nothing for theory, but this would be incorrect. One can readily detect here Boyle's wide reading in contemporary theoretical writers, as well as his desire to emphasize the independence of his own opinion. Very characteristic is his insistence that scientific polemic should be conducted in both a gentlemanly and a Christian spirit. "Physiology" means natural philosophy, the study of nature. Theoretically, at least, these essays were intended for the education of his nephew (here called Pyrophilus), Lady Ranelagh's son.

I must freely acknowledge, Pyrophilus, that it has long seemed to me none of the least impediments of the real advancement of true natural philosophy, that men have been so forward to write systems of it, and have thought themselves obliged either to be altogether silent, or not to write less than an entire body of physiology; for, from hence seem to have ensued not a few inconveniences.

And first, when men, by having diligently studied either chymistry, anatomy, botanics, or some other particular part of physiology, or perhaps by having only read authors on those subjects, have thought themselves thereby qualified to publish compleat systems of natural philosophy, they have found themselves, by the nature of their undertaking, and the laws of method, engaged to write of several other things than those, wherein they had made themselves proficients; and thereby have been reduced, either idly to repeat what has been already, though perhaps but impertinently enough, written by others on the same subjects; or else to say any thing on them rather than nothing, lest they should appear not to have said something to every part of the theme, which they had taken upon themselves to write of.

In the next place, the specious and promising titles and comprehensive method of these systems have been often found to persuade unwary readers, that all the parts of natural philosophy have been already sufficiently explicated; and, that consequently it were needless for them to put themselves to trouble and charges in making further inquiries into nature, since others having already sufficiently made it their business to investigate and explicate physiological truths, our business needs now be no more than to learn what they have taught, and thankfully to acquiesce in it.

Nor has the systematical way of writing been prejudicial only to the proficiency of some readers, but also to the reputation of some writers of systematical books. For it not unfrequently happens, that when a writer, to vent some few peculiar notions or discoveries of his own, presumes to write a whole body of philosophy, what is truly his own, though excellent in its kind, is either lost in the crowd of the things he has borrowed from others, and so comes to be over-looked, or at least not sufficiently taken notice of, by the reader; or else the unwelcome, and yet in such composures scarce evitable, repetition of many things, that others had, I know not how often, written before, occasions the laying aside of the whole book, as a rhapsody of trite and vulgar notions, scarce worth the perusing. And by this means the author often loses the reputation of his peculiar notions, as well as the reader the benefit of them; and that, which would have made an excellent and substantial essay, passes but for a dull and empty book.

But the worst inconvenience of all is yet to be mentioned, and that is, That whilst this vanity of thinking men obliged to write either systems or nothing is in request, many excellent notions or experiments are, by sober and modest men, suppressed; because such persons being forbidden by their judgment and integrity to teach more than they understand, or assert more than they can prove, are likewise forbidden by custom to publish their thoughts and observations, unless they were numerous enough to swell into a system. And indeed it may be doubted, whether the systematical writers have not kept the world from much more useful composures than they have presented it with. For there are very few men, if any at all, in the world, that are enriched with a competent stock of experiments and observations to make out clearly and solidly, I say not all the phaenomena of nature, but all those, that belong to chymistry, anatomy, or any such considerable subordinate doctrine of physiology. And those very men, that are diligent and judicious enough to study prosperously any of those parts of physiology, are obliged to spend so much time in the accurate prosecution of that, and are wont to be thereby made so wary, and so thoroughly acquainted with the difficulty of physiological investigations, that they will least of all men be forward to write systems.

And what I say . . . of the inconveniences, that have hitherto been observed to flow from men's forwardness to write entire bodies of philosophy, may be, in its degree, applied to the practice of those, that pretend to give us complete accounts of chymistry, or almost (I say almost) any other considerable and comprehensive part of natural philosophy: though I deny not, that in such attempts, which are much less difficult than the former, some men have done mankind considerable service, though they have not fully performed what the titles of their writings seem to promise. Nor am I so rigid as to be unwilling, that, from time to time, some very knowing writer should publish a system of physiology, or any part of it, according to the best authors and observations of that time: for such a work may be useful, partly, for the instructing of youth in schools and academies; and partly, that men may have from time to time, an inventory of what hath been already discovered; whereby the needless labour of seeking after known things may be prevented, and the progress of mankind, as to knowledge, might the better appear. But then it is to be wished, that such writings were not published but by very intelligent persons, nor till some considerable improvement have been made in knowledge since the last work of that nature. Nor would I be thought to disallow such writings of very learned men, as though they may bear very general titles, yet are not published by their authors as complete bodies or systems of physiology, but rather as general principles (almost like the hypotheses of astronomers) to assist men to explicate the already known phaenomena of nature. For of such kind of writings, if their authors be (as for the most part they are) subtle and inquisitive men, there may be very good use, not so much by their gratifying the intellect with the plausible account of some of nature's mysteries; as because on the one side their writers, to make good their new opinions, must either bring new experiments and observations, or else must consider those, that are known already, after a new manner, and thereby make us take notice of something in them unheeded before; and on the other side, the curiosity of readers, whether they like or disapprove the hypothesis proposed, is wont to be thereby excited to make trial of several things, which seeming to be consequences of this new doctrine, may, by their proving agreeable or repugnant to experiment, either establish or overthrow it.

And that you may know . . . what kind of writings I mean, I shall name to you the learned Gassendus his little *Syntagma* of Epicurus's philosophy, and that most ingenious gentleman Monsieur Descartes his principles of philosophy. . . .[1]

And truly, . . . if men could be persuaded to mind more the advancement of natural philosophy than that of their own reputations, it were not, methinks, very uneasy to make them sensible, that one of the considerablest services, that they could do mankind, were to set themselves diligently and industriously to make experiments and collect observations, without being over-forward to establish principles and axioms, believing it uneasy to erect such theories, as are capable to explicate all the phaenomena of nature, before they have been able to take notice of the tenth part of those phaenomena, that are to be explicated. Not that I at all disallow the use of reasoning upon experiments, or the endeavouring to discern as early as we can the confederations, and differences, and tendencies of things: for such an absolute suspension of the exercise of reasoning were exceeding troublesome, if not impossible, And, as in that rule of arithmetic, which is commonly called *regula falsi*, by proceeding upon a conjecturally supposed number, as if it were that, which we inquire after, we are wont to come to the knowledge of the true number sought for; so in physiology it is sometimes conducive to the discovery of truth, to permit the understanding to make an hypothesis, in order to the explication of this or that difficulty, that by examining how far the phaenomena are, or are not, capable of being solved by that hypothesis, the understanding may, even by its own errors, be instructed. For it has been truly observed by a great philosopher, that truth does more easily emerge out of error than confusion. That then, that I wish for, as to systems, is this, that men, in the first place, would forbear to establish any theory, till they have consulted with (though not a fully competent number of experiments, such as may afford them all the phaenomena to be explicated by that theory, yet) a considerable number of experiments, in proportion to the comprehensiveness of the theory to be erected on them. And, in the next place, I would have such kind of superstructures looked upon only as temporary ones; which though they may be preferred before any others, as being the least imperfect, or, if you please, the best in their kind that we yet have, yet are they not entirely to be acquiesced in, as absolutely perfect, or uncapable of improving alterations. . . .

The next thing . . . of which I am to give you an account, is, why I have in the ensuing essays delivered many experiments and observations, which may seem slight and easy, and some of them obvious also, or else perhaps mentioned by others already. To satisfy you about this, I must inform you, that many of the particulars, which we are now considering, were in my design collected in order to a continuation of the Lord Verulam's [Bacon's] *Sylva Sylvarum*, or natural history. And that my intended centuries might resemble his, to which they were to be annexed, it was requisite, that such kind of experiments and observations, as we have newly been speaking of, should make up a considerable part of them. And indeed it were to be wished, that such inquisitive persons, as cannot be at the charge, or have not the opportunity, of making new experiments, would busy themselves, as they have opportunity, in industriously collecting, and carefully setting down the phaenomena to be met with without the assistance of new experiments, especially such particulars, as

seem either to be of moment in order to the hinting or confirmation of some considerable truth, or to the detection of
some applauded error, or else to have been, though obvious
enough, yet little taken notice of. For I am confident, that
very much may be done towards the improvement of philosophy by a due consideration of, and reflexion on, the
obvious phaenomena of nature, and those things, which
are almost in every body's power to know, if he pleases
but seriously to heed them; and I make account, that
attention alone might quickly furnish us with one half of
the history of nature, as well as industry is requisite, by
new experiments to enrich us with the other. And therefore I confess I think myself beholden to him, that first
makes me take notice of what I might easily have known,
but heeded not before: it not seldom happening, that we
are prejudiced by, though we do not complain of that
ignorance, from which we might relieve ourselves, if we
did but diligently turn our eyes to the observations, wherewith even neighbouring and familiar objects would, if duly
consulted, present us. . . . And the second reason, why I
have often made use of seemingly slight experiments, is,
because such are more easily and cheaply tried, and they
being alleged for the most part to prove some assertion,
or credit some admonition, I thought their easiness or ob-
viousness fitter to recommend them, than depreciate them;
and I judged it somewhat unkind, or at least indiscreet, to
refer you most commonly for proof of what I delivered,
to such tedious, such difficult, or such intricate processes,
as either you can scarce well make, unless you be already,
what I desire my experiments should help to make you,
a skilful chymist; or else are as difficult to be well judged,
as the truth they should discover is to be discerned. . . .

Perhaps you will wonder . . . that in almost every one
of the following essays I should speak so doubtingly, and
use so often, *perhaps, it seems, it is not improbable,* and

such other expressions, as argue a diffidence of the truth of the opinions I incline to, and that I should be so shy of laying down principles, and sometimes of so much as venturing at explications. But I must freely confess to you, . . . that having met with many things, of which I could give myself no one probable cause, and some things, of which several causes may be assigned so differing, as not to agree in any thing, unless in their being all of them probable enough; I have often found such difficulties in searching into the cause and manner of things, and I am so sensible of my own disability to surmount those difficulties, that I dare speak confidently and positively of very few things, except of matters of fact. And when I venture to deliver any thing, by way of opinion, I should, if it were not for mere shame, speak yet more diffidently than I have been wont to do. It is not, that I at all condemn the practice of those inquisitive wits, that take upon them to explicate to us even the abstrusest phaenomena of nature; for I am so far from censuring them, that I admire them, when their endeavours succeed, and applaud them even where they do but fairly attempt. But I think it is fit for a man to know his own abilities and weaknesses, and not to think himself obliged to imitate all that he thinks fit to praise. . . . But I am content, provided experimental learning be really promoted, to contribute even in the least plausible way to the advancement of it; and had rather not only be an under-builder, but even dig . . . for materials towards so useful a structure, as a solid body of natural philosophy, than not to do something towards the erection of it. Nor have my thoughts been altogether idle and wanting to themselves, in framing notions and attempting to devise hypotheses, which might avoid the deficiencies observed in other men's theories and explications: but I have hitherto, though not always, yet not unfrequently, found, that what pleased me for a while, as fairly comporting with the observations, on which such notions were grounded, was soon after disgraced by some further or new experiment, which at the time of the framing of those notions was unknown to me, or not consulted with. And indeed I have the less envied many (for I say not all) of those writers, who have taken upon them to deliver the causes of things, and explicate the mysteries of nature, since I have had opportunity to observe, how many of their doctrines, after having been for a while applauded, and even admired, have afterwards been confuted by the discovery of some new phaenomenon in nature, which was either unknown to such writers, or not sufficiently considered by them. . . .

There are two very distinct ends, that men may propound to themselves in studying natural philosophy. For some men care only to know nature, others desire to command her; or, to express it otherwise, some there are, who desire but to please themselves by the discovery of the causes of the known phaenomena; and others would be able to produce new ones, and bring nature to be serviceable to their particular ends, whether of health, or riches, or sensual delight. Now as I shall not deny, but that the atomical, the Cartesian, or some such principles, are likely to afford the most of satisfaction to those speculative wits, that aim but at the knowledge of causes; so I think, that the other sort of men may very delightfully and successfully prosecute their ends, by collecting and making variety of experiments and observations; since thereby learning the qualities and properties of those particular bodies they désire to make use of, and observing the power that divers chymical operations, and other ways of handling matter, have of altering such bodies, and varying their effects upon one another, they may, by the help of attention and industry, be able to do many things, some of them very strange, and more of them very useful in human life. When a gunner or a soldier employs gunpowder, it is not necessary, that he should consider, or so much as know, of what, and of how many ingredients (much less what kind of atoms) it is made, and the proportion and manner, wherein they are mingled; but the notice experience gives him, of the power of that admirable concrete, as it is made up and brought to his hands, suffices to enable him to perform things with it, that nothing but their being common and unheeded can keep from being admired. The physician, that has observed the medicinal virtues of treacle, without knowing so much as the names, much less the nature of each of the sixty and odd ingredients, whereof it is compounded, may cure . . . patients with it. And though it must not be denied, that it is an advantage as well as a satisfaction, to know in general, how the qualities of things are deducible from the primitive affections of the smallest parts of matter; yet whether we know that or no, if we know the qualities of this or that body they compose, and how it is disposed to work upon other bodies, or be brought on by them, we may, without ascending to the top in the series of causes, perform things of great moment; and such, as without the diligent examination of particular bodies, would, I fear, never have been found out *a priori*, even by the most profound contemplators. We see that the artificers, that never dreamed of the Epicurian philosophy, have accommodated mankind with a multitude of useful inventions. And Paracelsus, who (besides that he seems none of the most piercing and speculative wits) sure had little recourse to atomical notions, if he ever so much as heard of them, was able to perform some things, that were truly admirable, besides those he vainly boasted of. . . . But we need not go far to find a noble example to our present purpose, since we see, that the bare making of trials with the loadstone, and irons touched by it, though the experimenters were ignorant (as some fear we yet are) of the true and first causes of magnetical phaenomena, have produced inventions of greater use to mankind, than were ever made by *Leucippus,* or *Epicurus,*[2] or *Aristotle,* or *Telesius,* or *Campanella,*[3] or perhaps any of the speculative devisers of new hypotheses; whose contemplations aiming for the most part but at the solving, not the increasing or applying, of the phaenomena of nature, it is no wonder they have been more ingenious than fruitful, and have hitherto more delighted than otherwise benefited mankind: I say hitherto, because though experience warrants me so to speak now, yet I am not unwilling to think, that hereafter, and perhaps in no long time, when physiological theories shall be better established, and built upon a more competent number of particulars, the deductions, that may be made from them, may free them from all imputation of barrenness. . . .

I have purposely, in the ensuing essays, refrained from swelling my discourses with solemn and elaborate confutations of other men's opinions, unless it be in some very few cases, where I judged, that they might prove great impediments to the advancement of experimental learning; and even such opinions I have been wary of meddling with, unless I supposed I could bring experimental objections against them. For it is none of my design to engage myself with, or against, any one sect of Naturalists, but barely to invite you to embrace or refuse opinions, as they are consonant to experiments, or clear reasons deduced thence, or at. least analogous thereunto; without thinking it yet seasonable to contend very earnestly for those other opinions, which seem not yet determinable by such experiments or reasons. . . .

But when at any time . . . I have been induced to oppose others, as I have not denied myself the freedom, that is requisite unto loyalty to truth; so I have endeavoured to use that moderation, and civility, that is due to the persons

of deserving men. And therefore you shall find me not
only in one essay oppose an author, whom in another I
applaud; but sometimes you may find me commending a
writer in the very same page, perhaps, where I am endeavouring to disprove his opinions: for I love to speak of
persons with civility, though of things with freedom. Nor
do I think it reasonable, either that a man's reputation
should protect his errors, or that the truth should fare the
worse for his sake, that delivers it. And as for the (very
much too common) practice of many, who write, as if they
thought railing at a man's person, or wrangling about his
words, necessary to the confutation of his opinions; besides that I think such a quarrelsome and injurious way
of writing does very much misbecome both a philosopher
and a Christian, methinks it is as unwise, as it is provoking.
For if I civilly endeavour to reason a man out of his opinions, I make myself but one work to do, namely, to convince his understanding; but if, in a bitter or exasperating
way I oppose his errors, I increase the difficulties I would
surmount, and have as well his affections against me as his
judgment: and it is very uneasy to make a proselyte of
him, that is not only a dissenter from us, but an enemy
to us. . . . But . . . when I speak of dealing respectfully
with those I dissent from, I would be understood of such,
as have well deserved of experimental learning, or at least
been candid and sober inquirers after truth. For, as I
think, that it would much discourage any prudent person
from venturing to communicate what he thinks he knows
to the world, to find, that an error proceeding from human
weakness, or the darkness and abstrusity of things, seldom
escapes being detected without being made matter of dis-
grace or reproach to the author: so, on the other side,
when vain writers, to get themselves a name, have presumed to intrude upon the credulous world such things,
under the notion of experimental truths, or even great

mysteries, as neither themselves ever took the pains to make trial of, nor received from any credible persons that professed themselves to have tried them; in such cases, I see not how we are obliged to treat writers, that took no pains to keep themselves from mistaking or deceiving, nay, that cared not how they abuse us to win themselves a name, with the same respect, that we owe to those, who, though they have missed of the truth, believed they had found it, and both intended to deliver it, and took some (though not prosperous) pains, that they might convey nothing else to us. [*Works*, I, 300–313]

2. The Aim of Scientific Books

This, from *Experiments and Considerations touching Colours* (1664), represents Boyle's desire to be the herald of science, rather than the natural philosopher who developed a system. But though he does not care for systems, and is ardently experimental, he insists on searching for the true theoretical basis of things.

The professed design of this treatise is to deliver things rather historical than dogmatical, and consequently if I have added divers new speculative considerations and hints, which perhaps may afford no despicable assistance towards the framing of a solid and comprehensive hypothesis, I have done at least as much as I promised, or as the nature of my undertaking exacted. . . . I do not pretend to present my reader with a complete fabric, or so much as a model; but only to bring in materials proper for the building. . . .

To be short, those I reason with, do concerning blackness what the chymists are wont also to do concerning other qualities, namely, to content themselves to tell us, in what ingredient of a mixt body, the quality inquired after does reside, instead of explicating the nature of it, which (to borrow a comparison from their own laboratories) is much as if in an inquiry after the cause of salivation,[4] they should think it enough to tell us, that the several kinds of precipitates of gold and mercury, as likewise of quicksilver and silver (for I know they make and use of such precipitates also) do salivate upon the account of the mercury, which though disguised abounds in them; whereas the difficulty is as much to know upon what account mercury itself, rather than other bodies, has that power of working by salivation. Which I say not, as though it were not something (and too often the most we can arrive at) to discover in which of the ingredients of a compounded body the quality, whose nature is sought, resides; but because, though this discovery itself may pass for something, and is oftentimes more than what is taught us about the same subjects in the schools, yet we ought not to think it enough, when more clear and particular accounts are to be had. [*Works*, I, 662–63, 724]

3. The Requisites of a Good Hypothesis

The following are two versions of the only coherent part of a projected treatise on philosophy of science, to which Boyle frequently referred in his printed works, but which he never completed for publication. Though neither version indicates it, the form in which it was to be cast was that of a dialogue between a group of friends. Here we apparently have a projected outline; it is tempting to think that the doggerel verse version is the ingenious mnemonic of an amanuensis.

The Requisites of a *Good* Hypothesis are:
1. That it be Intelligible.
2. That it neither Assume nor suppose anything Impossible, Unintelligible, absurd, or demonstrably False.
3. That it be Consistent with it self.
4. That it be fit and sufficient to Explicate the Phaenomena, especially the chief.
5. That it be, at least consistent, with the rest of the Phaenomena it particularly relate to; and do not contradict any other known Phaenomena of Nature, or manifest Physical Truth.

The Qualityes & Conditions of an *Excellent* Hypothesis are
1. That it be not Precarious, but have sufficient Grounds in the Nature of the Thing itself, or at least be well recommended by some Auxiliary Proofs.
2. That it be the *simplest* of all the Good ones we are able to frame, at least containing nothing that is superfluous or Impertinent.

3. That it be the *only* Hypothesis that can Explicate the Phaenomena; or at least, that dos explicate them so well.
4. That it enable a skilful Naturalist to foretell future Phaenomena by their Congruity or Incongruity to it; and especially the events of such Experiments as are aptly devis'd to examine it, as Things that ought or ought not, to be consequent to it.

    1. To frame a good Hypothesis, one must see
       First, that it clearly Intelligible be.
    2. Next that it nought assume, or do suppose
       That flatly dos any known Truth oppose.
       Or else requires that we should believe
       What can't be don, or what we can't conceive.
    3. Thirdly, that with itself it do consist
       So that no one part, th'other do resist.
    4. Fourthly, Fit and sufficient it should be,
       T'explain all the Phaenomena that we
       Upon good grounds, may unto it refer;
       Or those at least, that do the chief appear.
    5. Fifthly, the Framer carefully must see
       That with the Rest it do at least agree,
       And contradict no known Phaenomena
       Of th'Universe, or any Natural Law.
    6. Sixthly, An Hypothesis to be Excellent,
       Must not beg a praecarious Assent;
       But be built on Foundations Competent.
    7. Next of all Good, the simplest it must be;
       At least from all that is superfluous, free.
    8. Eightly, It should the only be, that may
       The given Phaenomena & so wel display.
    9. Ninthly, It should enable us to foreshow
       Th'Events that will, from wel made Tryals flow.

[Royal Society Boyle Papers, Vols. xxxviii and xxxvi]

4. Natural Religion

The following selections are a fair, though brief, sample of Boyle's theological work. The first is the most extreme defense of theology against natural philosophy which he ever conceived; this preface to *The Excellency of Theology* was published in 1674, though written in 1665, and clearly refers to comments by men of science rather than by the general public. It amply indicates Boyle's own estimate of his current scientific standing. The second selection is taken from Tome I of *The Usefulness of Experimental Natural Philosophy*, published in 1663; the bulk of it was written as early as 1647–49, and is the tract on the theological use of natural philosophy from which chemistry seduced his interest (cf. Section III, selection 14). The third selection from the work of the same title (published in 1685/6) supplements this with a clear statement of his views on God as a clock-maker. The fourth selection from the same work (published in 1688), shows Boyle, that devout Baconian, in rebellion against a too strict adherence to Bacon's demand that final causes be banished from natural philosophy.

The Excellency of Theology, compared with Natural Philosophy (as both are Objects of Men's Study)

Preface

I am not so little acquainted with the temper of this age, and of the persons, that are likeliest to be perusers of the following tract, as not to foresee it to be probable enough, that some will ask, for what reason a discourse of this nature was written at all, and that others will be displeased, that it has been written by me.

Those, that would know, by what inducements my pen was engaged on this subject, may be in great part informed by the epistle itself, in divers places whereof, as especially about the beginning, and at the close, the motives, that invited me to put pen to paper, are sufficiently expressed. And though several of those things are peculiarly applied, and (if I may so speak) appropriated to the person the letter is addressed to; yet that under-valuation, I would dissuade him from, of the study of things sacred, is not his fault alone, but is grown so rife among many (otherwise ingenious) persons, especially studiers of physicks, that I wish the ensuing discourse were much less seasonable than I fear it is.

But I doubt, that some readers, who would think a discourse of this nature needless or useless, may yet not be pleased at its being written by one, whom they imagine the acceptance his endeavours have met with, ought to oblige to spend his whole time in cultivating that natural philosophy, which in this letter he would persuade to quit the precedency, they think it may well challenge, before all other sorts of learning.

I am not unsensible of the favourable reception, that the philosophical papers, I have hitherto ventured abroad, have had the happiness to receive from the curious: but I hope, they will not be displeased, if I represent, that I am no lecturer, or professor of physicks, nor have ever engaged myself, by any promise made to the publick, to confine myself never to write of any other subject; nor is it reasonable, that what I did, or may write, to gratify other men's curiosity, should deprive me of mine own liberty, and confine me to one subject; especially, since there are divers persons, for whom I have a great esteem and kindness, who think they have as much right to solicit me for composures of the nature of this, that they will now have to go abroad, as the virtuosi have to exact of me physiological pieces. And though I be not ignorant, that, in particular, the following discourse, which seems to depreciate the study of nature, may, at first sight, appear somewhat improper for a person, that has purposely written to show the excellence and usefulness of it; yet I confess, that upon a more attentive consideration of the matter, I cannot reject, no, nor resist their reasons, who are of a quite differing judgement.

And 1. My condition, and my being a secular person (as they speak) are looked upon as circumstances, that may advantage an author, that is to write upon such a subject as I have handled. I need not tell you, that as to religious books in general, it has been observed, that those penned by lay-men, and especially gentlemen, have (*caeteris paribus*) been better entertained, and more effectual, than those of ecclesiastics. And indeed it is no great wonder, that exhortations to piety, and dissuasions from vice, and from the lusts and vanities of the world, should be the more prevalent for being pressed by those, who have, and yet decline, the opportunities to enjoy plentifully themselves the pleasures they dissuade others from. And (to come yet closer to our present purpose) though I will not venture to say with an excellent divine, that whatever comes out of the pulpit, does with many pass but for the foolishness of preaching; yet it cannot well be denied, but that if all other circumstances be equal, he is the fittest to commend divinity, whose profession it is not; and that it will somewhat add to the reputation of almost any study, and consequently to that of things divine, that it is praised and preferred by those, whose condition and course of life exempting them from being of any particular calling in the commonwealth of learning, frees them from the usual temptations to partiality to this or that sort of study, which others may be engaged to magnify, because it is their trade or their interest, or because it is expected from them; whereas these gentlemen are obliged to commend it, only because they really love and value it.

But there is another thing, that seems to make it yet more fit, that a treatise on such a subject should be penned by the author of this: for professed divines are supposed to be busied about studies, that even, by their being of an higher, are confessed to be of another nature, than those, that treat of things corporal. And since it may be observed, that there is scarce any sort of learned men, that is more apt to undervalue those, that are versed only in other parts of knowledge, than many of our modern naturalists, (who are conscious of the excellency of the science they cultivate) it is much to be feared, that what would be said of the pre-eminence of divinity above physiology, by preachers (in whom the study of the latter is thought either but a preparatory thing, or an excursion) would be looked upon as the decision of an incompetent, as well as interested judge; and their undervaluations of the advantages of the study of creatures would be (as their depreciating the enjoyment of the creatures too often is) thought to proceed but from their not having had sufficient opportunities to relish the pleasures of them. But these prejudices will not lie against a person, who has made the investigation of nature somewhat more than a parergon, and having, by a not lazy, nor short enquiry, manifested, how much he loves and can relish the delight it affords, has had the good fortune to make some discoveries in it, and the honour to have them publicly, and but too complimentally, taken notice of by the virtuosi. And it may not be impertinent to add, that those, who make natural philosophy their mistress, will probably, be the less offended to find her in this tract represented, if not as a handmaid to divinity, yet as a lady of a lower rank; because the inferiority of the study of nature is maintained by a person, who, even whilst he asserts it, continues, if not a passionate, an assiduous courter of nature: so that as far as his example can reach, it may show, that as on the one side a man need not be acquainted with, or unfit to relish the lessons taught us in the book of the creatures, to think them less excellent than those, that may be learned in the book of the scriptures; so on the other side, the preference of this last book is very consistent with an high esteem and an assiduous study of the first. [*Works*, IV, 2–3]

Of the Usefulness of Experimental Natural Philosophy
Part i: Of its Usefulness in reference to the Mind of Man

The natural philosophy, wont to be taught in schools, being little other than a system of the opinions of Aristotle, and some few other writers, is not, I confess, . . . very difficult to be learned; as being attainable by the perusal of a few of the more current authors. But . . . that experimental philosophy, which you will find treated of in the following Essays, is a study, if duly prosecuted, so difficult, so chargeable, and so toilsome, that I think it requisite before I propose any particular subjects to your enquiries, to possess you with a just value of true and solid physiology; and to convince you, that by endeavouring to addict you to it, I invite you not to mispend your time or trouble on a science unable to merit and requite it. In order . . . to the giving you this satisfaction, give me leave to mind you, that it was a saying of Pythagoras, worthy of so celebrated a philosopher, that there are two things, which most enoble man, and make him resemble the gods:

to know the truth, and *to do good.* For . . . that diviner part of man, the soul, which alone is capable of wearing the glorious image of its author, being endowed with two chief faculties, the understanding and the will; the former is blest and perfectionated by knowledge, and the latter's loveliest and most improving property is goodness. A due reflection upon this excellent sentence of him, to whom philosophers owe that modest name, should, methinks, . . . very much endear to us the study of natural philosophy. For there is no human science, that does more to gratify and enrich the understanding with variety of choice and acceptable truths; nor scarce any, that does more enable a willing mind to exercise a goodness beneficial to others.

To manifest these truths more distinctly, . . . and yet without exceeding that brevity, my avocations and the bounds of an essay exact of me, I shall, among the numerous advantages accruing to men from the study of the book of nature, content myself to instance only in a couple, that relate more properly to the improving of men's understandings, and to mention a few of those many, by which it encreases their power.

The two chief advantages, which a real acquaintance with nature brings to our minds, are, first, by instructing our understandings, and gratifying our curiosities; and next, by exciting and cherishing our devotion. . . .

The next advantage . . . that we mentioned the knowledge of nature to bring to the minds of men, is, that therein it excites and cherishes devotion; which when I say, . . . I forget not, that there are several divines (and some of them eminent ones) that out of a holy jealousy (as they think) for religion, labour to deter men from addicting themselves to serious and thorough inquiries into nature, as from a study unsafe for a Christian, and likely to end in atheism, by making it possible for men (that I may propose to you their objection as much to its advantage as I can) to give themselves such an account of all the wonders of nature, by the single knowledge of second causes, as may bring them to disbelieve the necessity of a first. And certainly, . . . if this apprehension were well grounded, I should think the threatened evil so considerable, that instead of inviting you to the study of natural philosophy, I should very earnestly labour to dissuade you from it. For I, that had much rather have men not philosophers than not Christians, should be better content to see you ignore the mysteries of nature, than deny the author of it. But though the zeal of their intentions keep me from harbouring any unfavourable opinion of the persons of these men, yet the prejudice that might redound from their doctrine (if generally received) both to the glory of God from the creatures, and to the empire of man over them, forbids me to leave their opinion unanswered; though I am sorry, that the necessity of vindicating the study I recommend to you from so heinous a crime as they have accused it of, will compel me to theologize in a philosophical discourse: which that I may do, with as much brevity as the weight and exigency of my subject will permit, I shall content myself only in the explication of my own thoughts, to hint to you the grounds of answering what is alledged against them. . . .

Now if you should put me upon telling you . . . what those attributes of God are, which I so often mention to be visibly displayed in the fabrick of the world, I can readily answer you, that though many of God's attributes are legible in his creatures, yet those, that are most conspicuous there, are his power, his wisdom, and his goodness, in which the world, as well as the Bible, though in a differing, and in some points a darker way, is designed to instruct us; which, that you may not think to be affirmed gratis, we must insist a while on each of the three.

And first, how boundless a power, or rather what an

almightiness is eminently displayed in God's making
out of nothing all things, and without materials or instruments constructing this immense fabrick of the world,
whose vastness is such, that even what may be proved of
it, can scarcely be conceived, and after a mathematical
demonstration its greatness is distrusted! which yet is, I
confess, a wonder less to be admired, than the power expressed by God in so immense a work, which nevertheless
some modern philosophers (whose opinions I find some
cabalists to countenance) suppose to be not the only production of God's omnipotence. . . .

The next attribute of God, that shines forth in his creatures, is his wisdom; which to an intelligent considerer
appears very manifestly expressed in the world, whether
you contemplate it as an aggregate or system of all natural
bodies, or consider the creatures it is made up of, both in
their particular and distinct natures, and in relation to
each other, and the universe they constitute. In some of
these the wisdom of God is so conspicuous, and written
in such large characters, that it is legible even to a vulgar
reader: but in many others the lineaments and traces of
it are so delicate and slender, or so wrapt up and covered
with corporeity, that it requires an attentive and intelligent peruser. So numberless a multitude, and so great a
variety of birds, beasts, fishes, reptiles, herbs, shrubs, trees,
stones, metals, minerals, stars, &c. and every one of them
plentifully furnished and endowed with all the qualifications requisite to the attainment of the respective ends of
its creation, are productions of a wisdom too limitless not
to be peculiar to God: to insist on any one of them in particular (besides that it would too much swell this discourse) might appear injurious to the rest; which do all
of them deserve that extensive exclamation of the Psalmist, "How manifold are thy works, O Lord; in wisdom hast
thou made them all." And therefore I shall content myself

to observe in general, that, as highly as some naturalists are pleased to value their own knowledge, it can at best attain but to understand and applaud, not emulate the productions of God. For as a novice, when the curiousest watch the rarest artist can make, is taken in pieces and set before him, may easily enough discern the workman-ship and contrivance of it to be excellent; but had he not been shown it, could never have of himself devised so skilful and rare a piece of work; so, for instance, an anato-mist, though when by many and dextrous dissections of human bodies, and by the help of mechanical principles and rules (without a competent skill wherein, a man can scarce be an accomplished and philosophical anatomist) he has learned the structure, use and harmony of the parts of the body, he is able to discern that matchless engine to be admirably contrived, in order to the exercise of all the motions and functions, whereto it was designed: and yet this artist, had he never contemplated a human body, could never have imagined or devised an engine of no greater bulk, any thing near so fitted to perform all the variety of actions we daily see performed either in or by a human body. Thus the circular motion of the blood, and structure of the valves of the heart and veins (the con-sideration whereof, as he himself told me, first hinted the circulation to our famous Harvey) though now modern experiments have for the main (the modus not seeming yet so fully explicated) convinced us of them, we acknowl-edge them to be very expedient, and can admire God's wisdom in contriving them: yet those many learned anat-omists, that have for many succeeding ages preceded both Dr. Harvey and Columbus, Cesalpinus, Padre Paulo, and Mr. Warner[5] (for each of these four last are supposed by some to have had some notion of the circulation) by all their diligent contemplation of human bodies, never dreamed (for aught appears) of so advantageous an use

of the valves of the heart, nor that nimble circular motion
of the blood, of which our modern circulators think they
discern such excellent use, not to say, necessity. . . .

And in a word, there is a multitude of problems, especially such as belong to the use of the parts of the human
body, and to the causes and cures of the diseases incident
thereunto, in whose explication those, we write of,* content themselves to tell us, that nature does such and such
a thing, because it was fit for her so to do; but they endeavour not to make intelligible to us, what they mean
by this nature, and how mere, and consequently brute,
bodies can act according to laws, and for determinate
ends, without any knowledge either of the one or of the
other. Let them therefore, until they have made out their
hypothesis more intelligibly, either cease to ascribe to
irrational creatures such actions, as in men are apparently
the productions of reason and choice, and sometimes even
of industry and virtue; or else let them with us acknowledge, that such actions of creatures in themselves irrational are performed under the superintendence and
guidance of a wise and intelligent author of things. But
that you may not mistake me . . . it will be requisite for
me, to acquaint you, in two or three words, with some of
my present thoughts concerning this subject: that there
are some actions so peculiar to man, upon the account of
his intellect and will, that they cannot be satisfactorily
explicated after the manner of the actings of mere corporeal agents, I am very much inclined to believe. And
whether or no there may be some actions of some other
animals, which cannot well be mechanically explicated, I
have not here leisure or opportunity to examine. But for
(most of) the other phaenomena of nature, methinks we
may, without absurdity, conceive, that God, of whom in

* those, that would exclude the Deity from intermeddling with Matter.
[Author's note]

the scripture it is affirmed, "That all his works are known
to him from the beginning," having resolved, before the
creation, to make such a world as this of ours, did divide
(at least if he did not create it incoherent) that matter,
which he had provided, into an innumerable multitude
of very variously figured corpuscles, and both connected
those particles into such textures or particular bodies, and
placed them in such situations, and put them into such
motions, that by assistance of his ordinary preserving
concourse, the phaenomena, which he intended should
appear in the universe, must as orderly follow, and be
exhibited by the bodies necessarily acting according to
those impressions or laws, though they understand them
not at all, as if each of those creatures had a design of
self-preservation, and were furnished with knowledge and
industry to prosecute it; and as if there were diffused
through the universe an intelligent being, watchful over
the publick good of it, and careful to administer all things
wisely for the good of the particular parts of it, but so far
forth as is consistent with the good of the whole, and the
preservation of the primitive and catholick laws established by the supreme cause; as in the . . . clock of Strasbourg, the several pieces making up that curious engine
are so framed and adapted, and are put into such a motion,
that though the numerous wheels, and other parts of it,
move several ways, and that without any thing either of
knowledge or design; yet each performs its part in order
to the various end, for which it was contrived, as regularly and uniformly as if it knew and were concerned
to do its duty. And the various motions of the wheels and
other parts concur to exhibit the phaenomena designed
by the artificer in the engine, as exactly as if they were
animated by a common principle, which makes them
knowingly conspire to do so, and might, to a rude Indian,
seem to be more intelligent than Conradus Dasypodius"

himself, that published a description of it; wherein he tells the world, that he contrived it, who could not tell the hours, and measure time so accurately as his clock. . . . When I see in a curious clock, how orderly every wheel and other parts perform its own motions, and with what seeming unanimity they conspire to show the hour, and accomplish the other designs of the artificer; I do not imagine, that any of the wheels, &c. or the engine it self is endowed with reason, but commend that of the workman, who framed it so artificially. So when I contemplate the actions of those several creatures, that make up the world, I do not conclude the inanimate pieces, at least, that it is made up of, or the vast engine it self, to act with reason or design, but admire and praise the most wise Author, who by his admirable contrivance can so regularly produce effects, to which so great a number of successive and conspiring causes are required. . . .

In the third place then I consider, that whether or no it be true, which our antagonists suggest, that there are some things in nature, which tempt philosophers more than they do the vulgar, to doubt or deny a God; yet certainly there are divers things in nature, that do much conduce to the evincing of a Deity, which naturalists either alone discern, or at least discern them better than other men. For besides the abstruse properties of particular bodies, not discovered by any but those, that make particular inquiries into those bodies, there are many things in nature, which to a superficial observer seem to have no relation to one another; whereas to a knowing naturalist, that is able to discern their secret correspondencies and alliances, these things, which seem to be altogether irrelative each to other, appear so proportionate and so harmonious both betwixt themselves, and in reference to the universe they are parts of, that they represent to him a very differing and incomparably better prospect

than to another man: as he, that looks upon a picture
made up of scattered and deformed pieces, beholding
them united into one face by a cylindrical looking glass
aptly placed, discerns the skill of the artist, that drew it,
better than he, that looks only on the single parts of that
picture, or upon the whole picture, without the uniting
cylinder. . . .

In the fourth place, I consider, that the universal experience of all ages manifests, that the contemplation of the
world has been much more prevalent to make those, that
have addicted themselves to it, believers, than deniers of
a Deity. For it is very apparent, that the old philosophers,
for the most part, acknowledged a God; and as evident
it is, by their want of revelation, by many passages in their
writings, and by divers others things not now to be insisted on, that the consideration of the works of nature
was the chief thing, that induced them to acknowledge a
divine author of them. . . .

In the fifth place . . . I consider, that when the divines
we are answering, suppose physiology likely to render a
man an atheist, they do it (as hath above been noted already) upon this ground, that natural philosophy may
enable him to explicate both the regular phaenomena, and
the aberrations of nature, without having recourse to a
first cause or God. But though this supposal were as great
a truth, as we have endeavoured to make it a mistake, yet
I see not, why a studier of physiology, though ever so
great a proficient in it, may not rationally be an utter
enemy to atheism. For the contemplation of the creatures
is but one of the ways of coming to be convinced, that
there is a God; and therefore, though religion were unable
to make use of the argument drawn from the works of
nature, to prove the existence of a Deity, yet has she other
arguments enough besides, to keep any considerate and
impartial man from growing an atheist. . . .

In the sixth and last place, I will here add (on this occasion) that an insight into physiological principles may very much assist a man to answer the objections of atheists against the being of a Deity, and the exceptions they make to the arguments brought to prove, that there is one. For though it has long been the custom of such men, to talk, as if themselves, and those of their mind, were not alone the best, but almost the only naturalists; and to perplex others with pretending, that, whereas it is not conceivable, how there can be a God; all things are by the principles of the atomical philosophy, made clear and facile; Though this, I say, have long been used among the opposers of a Deity, yet he, that, not regarding their confidence, shall attentively consider the very first principles of things, may plainly enough discern, that of the arguments, wherewith natural philosophy has furnished atheists, those, that are indeed considerable, are far fewer than one would readily think; and that the difficulty of conceiving the eternity, self-existence, and some other attributes of God (though that afford them their grand objection) proceeds not so much from any absurdity belonging to the notion of a Deity, as such; as from the difficulty, which our dim human intellects find to conceive the nature of those first things (whatever we suppose them) which, to be the causes of all others, must be themselves without cause: for he, that shall attentively consider, what the atomists themselves may be compelled to allow, concerning the eternity of matter, the origin of local motion (which plainly belongs not to the nature of body) the infinity or boundlessness of space, the divisibleness or non-divisibility of each corporeal substance into infinite material parts, may clearly perceive, that the atomist, by denying, that there is a God, cannot free his understanding from such puzzling difficulties, as he pretends to be the reasons of his denial: for instead of one God, he must confess an infinite number of atoms to be eternal, self-existent, immortal, self-moving, and must make suppositions, incumbered with difficulties enough to him, that has competently accustomed his thoughts to leave second causes, beneath them, and contemplate those causes, that have none. . . . [*Works*, II, 5–6, 15, 20–22, 38–40, 49–50,55, 58, 59]

A Free Inquiry into the Vulgarly Received Notion of Nature

It seems to detract from the honour of the great author and governor of the world, that men should ascribe most of the admirable things, that are to be met with in it, not to him but to a certain nature, which themselves do not well know what to make of. It is true, that many confess, that this nature is a thing of his establishing, and subordinate to him: but, though many confess it, when they are asked, whether they do or no? yet, besides that many seldom or never lifted up their eyes to any higher cause, he, that takes notice of their way of ascribing things to nature, may easily discern, that, whatever their words sometimes be, the agency of God is little taken notice of in their thoughts: and however, it does not a little darken the excellency of the divine management of things, that, when a strange thing is to be accounted for, men so often have recourse to nature, and think she must extraordinarily interpose to bring such things about; whereas it much more tends to the illustration of God's wisdom, to have so framed things at first, that there can seldom or never need any extraordinary interposition of his power. And, as it more recommends the skill of an engineer to contrive an elaborate engine so, as that there should need nothing to reach his ends in it but the contrivance of parts devoid of understanding, than if it were necessary, that ever and anon a discreet servant should be employed to concur notably to the operations of this or that part, or to hinder the engine from being out of order; so it more sets off the wisdom of God in the fabric of the universe, that he can make so vast a machine perform all those many things, which he designed it should, by the mere contrivance of brute matter managed by certain laws of local motion and upheld by his ordinary and general concourse, than if he employed from time to time an intelligent overseer, such as nature is fancied to be, to regulate, assist, and control the motions of the parts. . . .

And here give me leave to prevent an objection, that some may make, as if to deny the received notion of nature, a man must also deny providence, of which nature is the grand instrument. For, in the first place, my opinion hinders me not at all from acknowledging God to be the author of the universe, and the continual preserver and upholder of it; which is much more than the Peripatetick hypothesis, which . . . makes the world eternal, will allow its embracers to admit:[7] and those things, which the school philosophers ascribe to the agency of nature interposing according to emergencies, I ascribe to the wisdom of God in the first fabric of the universe, which he so admirably contrived, that, if he but continue his ordinary and general concourse, there will be no necessity of extraordinary interpositions, which may reduce him to seem, as it were, to play after-games; all those exigencies, upon whose account philosophers and physicians seem to have devised what they call nature, being foreseen and provided for in the first fabric of the world; so that mere matter, so ordered, shall, in such and such conjuctures of circumstances, do all, that philosophers ascribe on such occasions to their almost omniscient nature, without any knowledge of what it does, or acting otherwise than according to the catholic laws of motion. And methinks the difference betwixt their opinion of God's agency in the world, and that, which I would propose, may be somewhat adumbrated by saying, that they seem to imagine the world to be after the nature of a puppet, whose contrivance indeed may be very artificial, but yet is such, that almost every particular motion the artificer is fain (by drawing sometimes one wire or string, sometimes another) to guide and oftentimes overrule the actions of the engine; whereas, according to us, it is like a rare clock, such as may be that at Strasbourg, where all things are so skilfully contrived, that the engine being once set a-moving, all things proceed, according to the artificer's first design, and the motions of the little statues, that at such hours performs these or those things, do not require, like those of puppets, the peculiar interposing of the artificer, or any intelligent agent employed by him, but perform their functions upon particular occasions, by virtue of the general and primitive contrivance of the whole engine. . . . And when I consider, how many things, that seem anomalies to us, do frequently enough happen in the world, I think it is more consonant to the respect we owe to divine providence, to conceive, that as God is a most free, as well as a most wise agent, and may in many things have ends unknown to us, he very well foresaw, and thought fit, that such seeming anomalies should come to pass, since he made them (as is evident in the eclipses of the sun and moon) the genuine consequences of the order he was pleased to settle in the world; by whose laws the grand agents in the universe were impowered and determined to act, according to the respective natures he had given them, and the course of things was allowed to run on, though that would infer the happenings of seeming anomalies, and things really repugnant to the good or welfare of divers particular portions of the universe: this, I say, I think to be a notion more respectful to divine providence, than to imagine, as we commonly do, that God has appointed an intelligent and powerful Being, called nature, to be, as his viceregent, continually watchful for the good of the universe in general, and of the particular bodies, that compose it. . . . [*Works*, V, 162–64]

A Disquisition about the Final Causes
of Natural Things
The Conclusion

The result of what has been hitherto discoursed, upon the four questions proposed at the beginning of this small treatise, amounts in short to this:

That all consideration of final causes is not to be banished from natural philosophy; but that it is rather allowable, and in some cases commendable, to observe and argue from the manifest uses of things, that the author of nature pre-ordained those ends and uses.

That the sun, moon and other celestial bodies, excellently declare the power and wisdom, and consequently the glory of God; and were some of them, among other purposes, made to be serviceable to man.

That from the supposed ends of inanimate bodies, whether celestial or sublunary, it is very unsafe to draw arguments to prove the particular nature of those bodies, or the true system of the universe.

That as to animals, and the more perfect sorts of vegetables, it is warrantable, not presumptuous, to say, that such and such parts were pre-ordained to such and such uses, relating to the welfare of the animal (or plant) itself, or to the species it belongs to: but that such arguments may easily deceive, if those, that frame them, are not very cautious, and careful to avoid mistaking, among the various ends, that nature may have in the contrivance of an animal's body, and the various ways, which she may successfully take to compass the same ends. And,

That, however, a naturalist, who would deserve that name, must not let the search or knowledge of final causes make him neglect the industrious indagation of efficients. [*Works*, V, 444]

5. On the Practical Uses of Natural Philosophy

The second volume of *The Usefulness of Experimental Natural Philosophy* was published in 1671, eight years after the first volume, and, as the preface indicates, some half-dozen years after its completion. It contained a discussion of the usefulness of mathematics, as well as several long essays (from which the following are drawn) on the practical uses of science. The "Preamble" contains a brief, but characteristic, account of Boyle's reasons for writing in such a discursive style as he affected, and for including a plethora of experiments.

Some Considerations Touching the Usefulness of Experimental Natural Philosophy. The Second Tome.

The Preamble

. . . If it be demanded, why this latter part did not more closely follow the former, I have this to answer; that the papers it consisted of, chanced to be so unfortunately disposed of, during the late publick confusions,ˢ that for a great while I was not the master of them, and in the mean while was, sometimes upon one occasion, and sometimes upon another, engaged to venture abroad the *History of Colours,* the *History of Cold,* . . . *Hydrostatical Paradoxes,* and the *Origin of Forms and Qualities;* the publication of which treatises, besides that of some anonymous

papers, as it took up much of the time I had to spare for
the press; so it may, I suppose, keep it from being thought
strange, that I did not trouble myself and others with this
book also. And indeed, this having been (as the scope and
divers passages of it sufficiently intimate) one of the first
I wrote to the gentleman I call Pyrophilus, I had occasion,
whilst it was out of the way, to make use of so many of
the experiments and observations, that belonged to it, that
fearing I had thereby too much robbed, and disfigured it,
to leave it any way fit for publick view, I had the greater
temptation to neglect the looking after it.

But if it be further demanded, why then, since it was
not ready to come out more early, I did not condemn it
not to come out at all? I have two things to return by way
of answer.

The first is, that some eminent virtuosi, to whom I owe
a peculiar respect, were pleased to challenge the edition
of this tome, as if I had made myself a debtor to the publick for the second part of this work, by having suffered
what I wrote to a private friend to be divulged in the
first. Especially since the publick had given that so very
favourable an entertainment; as besides other things, the
early reprinting of it manifested.

The other part of my answer, and that, which made the
former consideration prevalent, is, that I was overcome,
either by the reasons, or by the authority, of those ingenious persons, that were pleased to think, that this work
would not prove unserviceable to mankind, to whose good,
both as a man and Christian, I have been long ambitious
to contribute, as well upon the account of the great Author
and divine Redeemer of men, as that of common nature,
whereof all men partake. What the utilities of this work
were conceived to be, the reader will find disclosed at the
end of this preface. To which I will therefore refer him for
an account of them; and now only take notice, that as to

one of the scruples I had against the publication, namely, that I had plundered this present treatise of divers particulars, wherewith I had accommodated some of my other writings; I could not well reject this answer, that in so many years as had passed since the writing of this book, I had not been so negligent a commercer with the works of nature and art, as not to be able to make some amends for what I had taken away, and easily substitute other experiments and observations, to supply the vacancies left by those I had transferred to other discourses.

And as to another of my scruples, about venturing abroad this tome, namely, that it must come forth so late, if it should come forth at all, it was answered, that it could scarce come forth more seasonably to recommend the whole design of the Royal Society, whose generous aims being to promote the knowledge of nature, and make it useful to human life. This treatise may procure them some number of assistants, in a work, whose vastness and difficulty will need very many, if men's curiosity and industry can by this treatise (or any other to the like purpose) be well excited by a conviction of the real and wide disparity betwixt true natural philosophy, and that of the Peripatetick schools; and that in cultivating the former, they will not meet with a field, that will afford them nothing, but (the wonted production of the latter) the thorns and thistles, acute indeed, but useless, and oftentimes troublesome, subtilties; but, that they may expect a soil, that may by a due culture be brought to afford them both curious flowers to gratify curiosity, and delight their senses, and excellent fruits, and other substantial productions, to answer the necessities, and furnish the accommodations of human life.

And I will not deny, that I have had the fortune to be looked upon, as not the unfittest person in the world to offer something in this kind; for those, that are mere

scholars, though never so learned and critical, are not wont
to be acquainted enough with nature and trades, to be
able to suggest those instances, that are the most proper
to manifest that, which men are convinced of. The mere
chymists, besides that their curiosity is wont to be too
much confined to let them be fittest for such a work, have
the ill fortune to be distrusted by the generality of men,
not credulous, which is a great unhappiness in this case,
because, that though their experiments were never so true
(as divers of them are) yet skill in their art being requisite
to make them, men's diffidence of the proposers, joined
with the difficulty of examining the things, will not allow
them, either to believe what is proposed, or to try it. And
as for the new philosophers (as they call them) though,
if they were to write but for philosophical readers, I know
several of them, that would questionless do it rarely well;
yet the generality of those readers, to whom we would
give good impressions of the study of nature, being such
as will probably be more wrought upon by the variety of
examples, and easy experiments, than by the deepest notions, and the neatest hypotheses, such a treatise for the
kind, as that which follows, containing many practices of
artifices and such particulars, that are either of easy trial,
or immediate use, may perhaps by that variety gratify,
and persuade a greater number of differing sorts of
readers, than a far more learned and elaborate piece, and
might be welcomer to more intelligent and philosophical
perusers. . . .

To shun needless controversies, I am somewhat shy of
naming this or that person, as the first proposer or inventor
of an experiment, which, especially if the person or things
be not considerable, is often difficult enough to discover:
witness the contests, that have been, and yet continue,
about the first inventors of common weather-glasses, the
ascension of water in slender pipes, the glass drops that

fly in pieces, the measuring of time by a pendulum, and, which is more strange, the art of printing itself. If it be asked, why I did not forebear to make use of some practices of tradesmen, and other known, and perhaps seemingly trivial, experiments; these things may be replied.

1. That since on divers occasions it was requisite, that my discourse should tend rather to convince, than barely to inform my reader, it was proper, that I should employ at least some instances, whose truth was generally enough known, or easy to be known, by making enquiry among artificers, even by such as out of laziness, or want of skill, or accommodation, cannot conveniently make themselves trials.

2. But yet I have taken care, that these should not be the only, nor yet the most numerous instances, I make use of; it being in this tome, as well as in my other physiological writings, my main business, to take all just occasions, to contribute as much, as without indiscretion I can, to the history of nature and arts.

3. As to the practices and observations of tradesmen, the two considerations already alledged may both of them be extended to the giving of an account of the mention I make of them. Of the truth of divers of the experiments I alledge of theirs, one may be easily satisfied, by inquiring of artificers about it; and the particular, or more circumstantial accounts I give of some of their experiments, I was induced to set down by my desire to contribute toward an experimental history. For I have found by long and unwelcome experience, that very few tradesmen will, and can give a man a clear and full account of their own practices; partly out of envy, partly out of want of skill to deliver a relation intelligibly enough, and partly (to which I may add chiefly) because they omit generally, to express either at all, or at least clearly, some important

circumstance, which because long use hath made very
familiar to them, they presume also to be known to others:
and yet the omission of such circumstances doth often
render the accounts they give of such practices, so dark
and so defective, that, if their experiments be any thing
intricate or difficult (for if they be simple and easy, they
are not so liable to produce mistakes) I seldom think
myself sure of their truth, and that I sufficiently comprehend them, till I have either tried them at home, or caused
the artificers to make them in my presence. . . .

But I here must give the reader notice, that as mechanical arts for the most part advance from time to time
towards perfection; so the practices of artificers may vary
in differing times, as well as in differing places, as I have
often had occasion to observe. And therefore I would
neither have him condemn other writers or relators, for
delivering accounts of the experiments of craftsmen differing from those I have given; nor condemn me, for having
contented myself to set down such practices faithfully, as
I learned them from the best artificers (especially those
of London) I had opportunity to converse with. . . .

I shall now represent, that though some little inconvenience may happen to some tradesmen by the disclosing
some of their experiments to practical naturalists, yet, that
may be more than compensated, partly, by what may be
contributed to the perfecting of such experiments themselves, and, partly by the diffused knowledge and sagacity
of philosophers, and by those new inventions, which may
probably be expected from such persons, especially if they
be furnished with variety of hints from the practices already in use. For these inventions of ingenious heads do,
when once grown into request, set many mechanical hands
a-work, and supply tradesmen with new means of getting
a livelihood, or even enriching themselves. As to the disci-

pline subordinated to the pure mathematicks, this is very evident; for those speculative sciences have (though not immediately) produced their trades, that make quadrants, sectors, astrolabes, globes, maps, lutes, phials, organs, and other geometrical, astronomical, geographical, and musical instruments; and, not to instance those many trades that subsist by making such things as mechanicians, proceeding upon geometrical propositions, have been the authors of; we know, that whether the excellent Galileo was, or was not, the first finder out of telescopes, yet he improved them so much, and by his discoveries in the heavens did so recommend their usefulness to the curious, that many artificers in divers parts of Europe have thought fit to take up the trade of making prospective glasses. And since his death, several others have had profitable work laid out for them, by the newer directions of some English gentlemen, deeply skilled in dioptricks, and happy at mechanical contrivances; insomuch, that now we have several shops, that furnish not only our own virtuosi, but those of foreign countries, with excellent microscopes and telescopes, of which latter sort I lately bought one (but I confess the only one, that the maker of it, or any man, that I hear of, hath perfected of that bigness) which is of threescore foot in length, and which the ingenious artist that made it, Mr. Reeves,[9] prized constantly at no less than an hundred pounds English money. I know not, whether or no I should add, that possibly some particular experiments of mine have not been hitherto unprofitable to several tradesmen. But this I may safely affirm, that a great deal of money hath been gained by tradesmen, both in England and elsewhere, upon the account of the scarlet dye, invented in our time by Cornelius Drebbel, who was not bred a dyer, nor other tradesman.[10] And, what we daily see the shops of clockmakers and watchmakers more and more furnished with those useful instruments, pendulum

clocks, as they are now called, which, but very few
years ago, were brought into request by that most ingenious gentleman, who discovered the new planet about
Saturn. . . .[11]

Of this following book, such as it is, it was suggested,
that the uses would not prove despicable, in regard, that
beside . . . the improvement of minds of men, and (especially) the assisting them to understand the works of God,
and thereby engage them to admire, praise, and thank him
for them: besides these (I say) there may be other uses
of the following tome, which, to avoid increasing a prolixity that I fear is already too great, I shall rather name
than discourse of, contenting myself briefly to intimate,
that it was conceived, the peculiar uses of the present
tome might be such as these.

1. It may afford materials for the history of nature,
which, that it may the more plentifully do, I have purposely, on several occasions, added a greater number of
instances, than were absolutely necessary, for the making
out of what I intended to declare or prove.

2. It may afford some instructions, advices, and hints
to promote the practical or operative part of natural philosophy in divers particulars, wherein men have been
either not able, or not solicitous to assist the curious.

3. It may enable gentlemen and scholars to converse
with tradesmen, and benefit themselves (and perhaps the
tradesmen too) by that conversation; or, at least, it will
qualify them to ask questions of men that converse with
things; and sometimes to exchange experiments with them.

4. It may serve to beget a confederacy, and an union
between parts of learning, whose possessors have hitherto
kept their respective skills strangers to one another; and
by that means may bring great variety of observations and
experiments of differing kinds into the notice of one man,

or of the same persons; which how advantageous it may prove towards the increase of knowledge, our illustrious Verulam [Bacon] has somewhat taught us.

5. It may contribute to the rescuing natural philosophy from that unhappy imputation of barrenness, which it has so long lain under, and which has been, and still is, so prejudicial to it. And to effect this rescue, it will in some measure enable those, that desire it, to employ these practical arguments, that are proper to convince many, that are not to be convinced by any other sort of proofs.

6. And which is the main of all, it may serve by positive considerations, and directions, to rouse up the generality of those that are in any way inquisitive, and both loudly excite, and somewhat assist, the curiosity of mankind; from which alone may be expected a greater progress in useful learning, and consequently greater advantages to men, than in the present state of human affairs will be easily imagined. [*Works*, III, 394–401]

That the Goods of Mankind may be much Increased by the Naturalist's Insight into Trades

And first, it seems to me to be none of the least prejudices, that either the haughtiness and negligence, which most men naturally are prone to, or, that wherewith they have been infected by the superciliousness and laziness, too frequent in schools, have done to the progress of natural philosophy, and the true interest of mankind, that learned and ingenious men have been kept such strangers to the shops and practices of tradesmen. For there are divers considerations that persuade me, that an inspection into these may not a little conduce, both to the increase of the naturalist's knowledge, and to the melioration of those mechanical arts.

1. And I consider, in the first place, that the phaenomena afforded by trades, are (most of them) a part of the history of nature, and therefore may both challenge the naturalist's curiosity, and to add to his knowledge. Nor will it suffice to justify learned men in the neglect and contempt of this part of natural history, that the men, from whom it must be learned, are illiterate mechanicks, and the things that are exhibited are works of art, and not of nature. For the first part of the apology is indeed childish, and too unworthy of a philosopher, to be worthy of a solemn answer. And as for the latter part, I desire that you would consider, what we elsewhere expressly discourse against, the unreasonable difference that the generality of learned men have seemed to fancy betwixt all natural things and factitious ones. For besides, that many of those productions that are called artificial, do differ from those that are confessedly natural, not in essence, but in efficients; there are very many things made by tradesmen, wherein nature appears manifestly to do the main parts of the work: as in malting, brewing, baking, making of raisins, currants, and other dried fruits; as also hydromel, vinegar, lime, &c. and the tradesman does but bring visible bodies together after a gross manner, and then leaves them to act one upon another, according to their respective natures; as in making of green or coarse glass, the artificer puts together sand and ashes, and the colliquation and union is performed by the action of the fire upon each body, and by as natural a way, as the same fire, when it resolves wood into ashes, and smoke unites volatile salt, oil, earth, and phlegm into soot; and scarce any man will think, that when a pear is grafted upon a white thorn, the fruit it bears is not a natural one, though it be produced by a coalition of two bodies of distant natures put together by the industry of man, and would not

have been produced without the manual and artificial operation of the gardener.

2. But many of the phaenomena of trades are not only parts of the history of nature, but some of them may be reckoned among its more noble and useful parts. For they show us nature in motion, and that too, when she is (as it were) put out of her course, by the strength or skill of man, which I have formerly noted to be the most instructive condition, wherein we can behold her. And as it is manifest that these observations tend directly to practice, so, if I mistake not, they may afford a great deal of light to divers theories, especially by affording instances, wherein we see by what means things may be effected by art, and consequently by nature, that work mechanically.

3. The phaenomena afforded by trades are therefore the fitter to be translated into the history of nature by philosophers, because they, whose profession it is to manage those things, being generally but shopkeepers, and their servants being for the most part but apprentices and boys, they neither of them know themselves how to describe in writing their own practices, and record the accidents they meet with; so that either learned men must observe and register these things, or we must, to the no small prejudice of philosophy, suffer the history of nature to want so considerable an accession, as the shops and workhouses of craftsmen might afford it; which accession would be much the more copious, if the experiment of trades were made by a naturalist, who would doubtless manage them, as to make them far more instructive, and better fitted for the design of a natural history, than the same experiment would be, if they were related but by an illiterate tradesman, though never so honest. [*Works*, III, 442–43]

6. On Hydrostatics

This is the work which Pepys found "of infinite delight," proving Boyle's success in making a mathematical science comprehensible to the layman. Its occasion was Boyle's interest in Pascal's *Treatise on the Aequilibrium of Liquors;* he read a critique of Pascal's method to the Royal Society in 1664.[12] It is primarily a defense of the experimental as against the mathematical tradition, which Boyle traces from Archimedes, *On Things Floating in Liquids,* through Marino Ghetaldi (1566–1627), *Promotus Archimedes, or on the Comparison of Weight and Magnitude of Various Bodies* (published in 1603, with special emphasis on the specific gravity of metals); Simon Stevin (1548–1620), whose hydrostatical work *The Elements of the Art of Weighing* appeared (in Flemish) in 1586, and within twenty years in French and Latin;[13] and Galileo, whose *Discourse on All Things that Float on Water* appeared in 1612. Boyle had clearly mastered the mathematical literature before he turned his ingenuity to devising experimental proofs of the more interesting and startling hydrostatical problems.

Hydrostatical Paradoxes
Made Out by New Experiments, for the Most Part
Physical and Easy

The Hydrostaticks is a part of philosophy, which, I confess, I look upon as one of the ingeniousest doctrines, that belong to it; theorems and problems of this art being most of them pure and handsome productions of reason, duly exercised on attentively considering subjects, and making in them such discoveries as are not only pleasing, but divers of them surprising, and such as would make one at first wonder, by what kind of ratiocination men came to attain the knowledge of such unobvious truths. Nor are the delightfulness and the subtility of the Hydrostaticks the only things, for which we may commend them: for there are many, as well of the more familiar, as of the more abstruse phaenomena of nature, that will never be thoroughly understood, nor clearly explicated by those, that are strangers to the Hydrostaticks; upon whose principles depend, besides many other things, the explications of most of the physico-mechanical experiments, we have ventured to present the publick, and the decision of those many controversies, which they and the phaenomena of the Torricellian experiment have occasioned among the modern inquirers into nature.

But the use of this art is not alone speculative, but practical, since not only the propositions it teaches, may be of great importance to navigation, and to those that inquire into the magnitudes and gravities of bodies, as also to them that deal in salt-works; but . . . the Hydrostaticks may be made divers ways serviceable to the chymists themselves. . . .

But that, which invited me to write something of this part of philosophy, is, not only that I think it considerable, but that, notwithstanding its being so, I find it but very little, and not very happily cultivated. For, being not looked upon as a discipline purely mathematical, the generality of mathematicians have not in their writings so much as taken notice of it, much less improved it. And since the admirable Archimedes, who, in his little tract *De Insidentibus Humido*, has left us three or four very excellent propositions, (but proved by no very easy dem-

onstrations) among divers others, that have more of geometrical subtility than usefulness; those mathematicians,
that (like Marinus Ghetaldus, Stevinus, and Galileo) have
added any thing considerable to the Hydrostaticks, have
been (that I know of) very few; and those too have been
wont to handle them rather as geometricians, than as philosophers, and without referring them to the explication
of the phaenomena of nature. And as for the Peripateticks
and other school-philosophers, though on some occasions,
as when they tell us, that water weighs not in water, nor
air in air, they deliver assertions about matters belonging
to the Hydrostaticks; (which term, in this treatise, I often
take in a large sense, because most of the things delivered
about the weight of bodies, may, by easy variations, be
made applicable to other fluids) yet they are so far from
having illustrated, or improved them, that they have but
broached, or credited, divers of the most erroneous conceits, that are entertained about them. So that, there being
but few treatises written about the Hydrostaticks, and
those commonly bound up among other mathematical
works, and so written, as to require mathematical readers,
this useful part of philosophy has been scarce known any
farther, than by name, to the generality even of those
learned men, that have been inquisitive into the other
parts of it, and are deservedly reckoned among the ingenious cultivators of the modern philosophy. But this is not
all; for some eminent men, that have of late years treated
of matters hydrostatical, having been prepossessed with
some erroneous opinions of the Peripatetick school, and
finding it difficult to consult experience about the truth of
their conclusions, have interwoven divers erroneous doctrines among the sounder propositions, which they either
borrowed from Archimedes, and other circumspect mathematicians, or devised themselves; and these mistakes being
delivered in a mathematical dress, and mingled with prop-

ositions demonstrably true, the reputation of such learned men (from which I am far from desiring to detract) and the unqualifiedness of most readers to examine mathematical things, has procured so general an entertainment for those errors, that now the Hydrostaticks is grown a part of learning, which it is not only difficult to attain, but dangerous to study.

Wherefore, though neither the occasion and design of this treatise exacted, nor my want of skill and leisure qualified me to write either a body, or elements of Hydrostaticks; yet I hoped I might do something, both towards the illustrating, and towards the rescue of so valuable a discipline, by publishing the ensuing tract; where I endeavour to disprove the received errors, by establishing the paradoxes contrary to them, and to make the truths the better understood and received, partly by a way of explicating them unemployed in hydrostatical books, and partly by confirming the things I deliver, by physical and sensible experiments. And over and above this, the more to recommend Hydrostaticks themselves to the reader, I have, besides the paradoxes opposed to the errors I would disprove, taken occasion by the same way to make out some of the usefullest of those hydrostatical truths, that are wont to seem strange to beginners.

If it be here demanded, why I have made some of my explications so prolix, and have on several occasions inculcated some things; I answer, That those, who are not used to read mathematical books, are wont to be so indisposed to apprehend things, that must be explicated by schemes; and I have found the generality of learned men, and even of those new philosophers, that are not skilled in mathematics, so much more unacquainted, than I had before imagined, both with the principles and theorems of Hydrostaticks, and with the ways of explicating and proving them, that I feared, that neither the paradoxes themselves, that I maintain, nor the hypotheses about the weight and pressure of the air, upon which little less than my whole pneumatical book depends, would be thoroughly understood without such a clear explication of some hydrostatical theorems, as, to a person not versed in mathematical writings, could scarce be satisfactorily delivered in few words. And therefore, though I do not doubt, that those, who are good at the most compendious ways of demonstrating, will think, I might in divers places have spared many words without injury to my proofs; and though I am myself of the same mind I expect to find them of; yet I confess, that it was out of choice, that I declined that close and concise way of writing, that in other cases I am wont most to esteem. For writing now not to credit myself, but to instruct others, I had rather geometricians should not commend the shortness of my proofs, than that those other readers, whom I chiefly designed to gratify, should not thoroughly apprehend the meaning of them.

But this is not all, for which I am to excuse myself to mathematical readers. For some of them, I fear, will not like, that I should offer for proofs such physical experiments, as do not always demonstrate the things, they would evince, with a mathematical certainty and accurateness; and much less will they approve, that I should annex such experiments to confirm the explications, as if suppositions and schemes, well reasoned on, were not sufficient to convince any rational man about matters hydrostatical.

In answer to this, I must represent, that in physical enquiries it is often sufficient, that our determinations should come very near the matter, though they fall short of a mathematical exactness. And I choose rather to presume upon the equity of the reader, than to trouble him and myself with tedious circumlocutions, to avoid the possibility of being misunderstood, or of needing his candour. And we see, that even mathematicians are wont, without finding any inconvenience thereby, to suppose all perpendicular lines, made by pendulous bodies, to be parallel to one another: though indeed they are not; since, being produced, they would meet at the centre of the earth. And to presume, that the surface of every calm water, in a vessel, is parallel to the horizon, and consequently a plane; though, in strictness, themselves think it the portion of a sphere; and though also I have usually observed it to be higher, where it is almost contiguous to the sides of the vessel, than it is in other places. . . .

And as for my confirmation of hydrostatical propositions by physical experiments, if some readers dislike that way, I make no doubt, but that the most will not only approve it, but thank me for it. For though, in pure mathematics, he, that can demonstrate well, may be sure of the truth of a conclusion, without consulting experience about it; yet because demonstrations are wont to be built upon suppositions or postulates; and some things, though not in arithmetic or geometry, yet in physical matters, are wont to be taken for granted, about which men are liable to slip into mistakes; even when we doubt not of the ratiocination, we may doubt of the conclusion, because we may of the truth of some of the things it supposes. And this consideration, if there were no other, will, I hope, excuse me to mathematicians, for venturing to confute some reasonings, that are given out for mathematical demonstrations. For I suppose it will be considered, that those, whose presumed demonstrations I examine, though they were some of them professors of mathematics, yet did not write merely as mathematicians, but partly as naturalists; . . . and therefore . . . it cannot but be a satisfaction to a wary man to consult sense about those things, that fall under the cognisance of it, and to examine by experiences, whether men have not been mistaken in their hypotheses and reasonings; and therefore the learned Stevinus himself (the chief of the modern writers of Hydrostaticks) thought fit, after the end of his *Hydrostatical Elements,* to add in an appendix some pragmatical examples, (as he calls them) that is, mechanical experiments, (how cogent I now enquire not) to confirm the truth of his tenth proposition, to which he had, not far from the beginning of his book, annexed what he thinks a mathematical demonstration. And, about the very subjects we are now upon, the following paradoxes will discover so many mistakes of eminent writers, that pretend to have mathematically demonstrated what they teach, that it cannot but make wary naturalists (and it is chiefly to gratify such, that I publish this) be somewhat diffident of conclusions, whose proofs they do not well understand. And it cannot but, to such, be of great satisfaction to find the things, that are taught them, verified by the visible testimony of nature herself. The importance of this subject, and the frequent occasion I have to make use of this kind of apology, will, I hope, procure me the reader's pardon, if I have insisted somewhat long upon it. [*Works,* II, 739–42]

7. A Letter on his Method of Work

This letter, as internal evidence shows, was written in 1665 to Henry Oldenburg, Secretary of the Royal Society. Doubtless Boyle had, at this time, fled to the country to avoid the plague which was raging in Oxford as well as in London during the winter of 1665–66. Boyle allowed Oldenburg to publish several of his works, which was equivalent to giving him the profits from their sale, a dignified form of bounty. Oldenburg was also the compiler of the *Philosophical Transactions,* begun as a private venture; the *"Phil. Trans."* soon, however, became the official journal of the Royal Society. Mr. Davis was the printer of the *Hydrostatical Paradoxes,* published in 1666. Mr. Reeves and his telescopes are referred to in selection 5 above (p. 161); Campani was a well-known Italian optical maker. Longacre (near Covent Garden in London) was a center for instrument makers. Auzoit (properly Auzout) was an astronomer and a member of the French Academy of Science. Rob: Murry is Sir Robert Moray, a courtier and one of the Royalist founders of the Royal Society. Dr. Beale was one of the original members of the Hartlib group; he wrote on cider apples, and was deeply interested in Boyle's works on physics. "Our worthy President" is Lord Brouncker, mathematician and President of the Royal Society. This letter, which has not been published previously, is interesting both as an example of scientific correspondence, showing how seventeenth-century scientists kept abreast of one another's work, and for the light it sheds on Boyle's own method of work.

Stanton[14] Dec 9th [1665]

Sr

Calling at Oxford the day before yesterday I met with a Letter of yours for which this Paper is to returne you Thanks. I wonder Mr Davis had not when your Letter was written sent you the Hydrostaticall sheets his Promise having engagd him to doe it a good while before, but though my relyance on It was the only thing that kept me from sending you them myselfe; yet 'tis not the only promise he has faild in; since he undertooke to bring before such a time precisely, the four pound that remaind due for the 1st Transactions he printed, which if he had done, (& I suspected not the contrary till I was out of Towne) you might have received it some days sooner then now I fear you will, but perhaps he will be brought to make you some amends by paying in together with 4 pound what is due for the Transactions this weeke which I have not yet seene, but am told that they amount but to a sheete & a halfe. As for what you mention of Campani's glasses Mr Reeves chancing when I was yesterday at Oxford to dine with mee I acquainted him with it, who assurd mee that his glasses will performe soe much if not more then the seeing of a man foure Leagues off. And when I demanded whether he sayd upon coniecture only or upon particular Tryall, (which latter, in case he had made it, I desird him to be informd of circumstantially,) he told mee that from his house he could plainly see upon the steeple of Harrow on the Hill, not only the shape of the Windows & the differing colours of the stones of the steeple (which is 10 or 12 miles distant from Long aker) but the weathercock itselfe, which is an obiect farr lesse then the Body of a man. If there were any Virtuoso abroad that would bye his 60 foot glasse I find that provided the price were conceald he would be brought to abate near halfe of that which he hath hitherto stood upon. He talkes likewise of makeing some very large Concave glasses for burning, in which Designe I have not discouragd him. Monsr Auzoits French Paper I delivered to Sr Rob: Murry at Oxford to show to some of our Mathematicall Freinds & was not aware that it was brought home to my Lodging, but the last time I made a step over to Oxford I brought it thence, and now inclose it you, though halfe ashamd that it is soe much the worse for the wearing in mens Pockets. I am not here so neere a Hermite but that there din'd with mee today Dr Wallis & Dr Melancthon,[15] the former of whome I hear is upon some worke (as he loves not to be idle) which when I have an Opportunity, which I wanted to day, I purpose to inquire after. I now live in a Village soe perfectly disfurnished of all that is requisite for an Experimenter that t'would make you smile to see what shifts I am put to for a few Magneticall Tryalls, which are the only ones I here can allow myselfe for a Diversion. You would doe more then smile if I should tell you that the frost & snow that the last winter gave mee soe much imployment have this winter afforded mee only recreation, & that the chiefe Expts I try in hard weather are whether my stone-bow will carry true: & instead of persueing Nature I follow the birds with a Gun on my shoulder to the commons & the woods. But this puts mee in mind of leaving to your Consideration whether you will in yor next Transactions take occasion to intimate, that having by the hardships to which my Tryalls about cold exposd mee the last Winter, incurrd those Inconveniencys in point of health that deterr mee from repeating the like attempts this winter, especially being in a place disfurnished of all accomodations for the makeing of nice Expts; I doe not intend to meddle this season with the prosecution of the History of Cold hopeing that some of the curious that are better befreinded with health and opportunys will repayr my necessitated Omissions.

I have met with some rough copys of my notes about some subiects of which possibly ev'n some small elucidations will not be unwellcome. I did not will know what was become of those Papers, & some of them I have not yet, that I remember, read over this 5 or 7 years, the cheife heads are about sensation in generall, about the pores of greater & figures of smaller Bodys; & about occult Qualitys. The ordering of these & some other papers that I found with them will take up a good part of that leisure time that is not challenged by a small Booke of Devotion upon an unusuall Subiect which he was a good while since engagd to write that has roome in this Paper to write noe more then that he is

Sr yr Very Affect. Freind &c.
Ro: Boyle

The Company stayd soe late with mee, that I had not time to compare the Note you did me the favor to send mee with the Passages in the history of Cold it referrs to. But I intend to doe it before the next time I write to you. I presume you have ere this receivd the Hydrostaticall sheets from Mr Davis, who will hence forward send them more immediately to you then by directing them to Mr Thompson. Dr. Beale write [sic] mee word that he has sent you some observations of his about the Aire which are to be imparted to mee

When you send the French paper to our worthy President, pray obleige ·me to accompany it with my most humble service to his Lp. [Royal Society MS. B 1, no. 100]

8. An Assessment of Aristotelianism

The first selection below is an uncompleted preface to an un-determined work, a manuscript fragment in Boyle's own hand-writing. It is interesting for its biographical information as well as being an example of how and why an intelligent young scientist of the mid-seventeenth century came to reject Aris-totelian doctrines. The praise for Aristotle as against the scorn for his followers is characteristic of the times. It is similar in tone to the second selection, which is the Preface to the *Origin of Forms and Qualities*, published in 1666, Boyle's first printed work devoted to the general theory of the corpuscular philosophy. It is actually a series of essays dealing with various problems in the acceptance of this philosophy. The "little physico-chemical tract about the different parts and redinte-gration of nitre" to which he here refers is one of the *Physiological Essays* (published in 1661). As Boyle indicates, the *Origin of Forms and Qualities* was intended to gain converts to the mechanical philosophy; his own version, the corpuscular philosophy, had already been very successful in this respect, in large part because it was founded upon and supported by chemical and physical experiments.

Introductory Preface

Which the Reader is earnestly requested to Peruse in
order to the receiving an Accompt of the ensuing Worke

Having ever since I first addicted my Time & Thoughts
to the more serious parts of Learning, found my selfe by
a secret but strong Propensity, inclin'd to the Study of

Naturall Philosophy; the first course I tooke to satisfy my
Curiosity, was to instruct my selfe in the Aristotelian Doctrine, as that whose Principles I found generally acquiesc'd
in by the Universitys & Schools, & by numbers of celebrated Writers, celebrated for little lesse, then Oraculous.
But I had scarce well acquainted my selfe with the Peripatetick Theory, before I was strongly tempted to doubt
it's Solidity. For the commands of my Parents engaging
me to visit divers forreigne Countrys, I could not but in
my Travells, meet with many things capable to make me
distrust the Doctrine wherewith I had freshly been im-
bu'd. For first I found Aristotle's Principles much more
strongly asserted than prov'd by his Admirers & by not
inconsiderable arguments oppos'd not only by the Chymists in generall & great store of Moderne Physitians, but
[by many] acute & fam'd Philosop[hers] . . . & the sect
of the new Cope[rnicans such as Tele]sius, Campanella
(& his Ingenious Epitomist Comenius), Ba[con, Ga]sen-
dus, Descartes & his sect to name no more. In the next
place I observ'd many things in my Travells which were
wholly unintelligible from Aristotles Theory which being
grounded but upon a few obvious & not thoroughly exam-
in'd appearances of things is much too narrow & slight to
reach either all or the more abstruse effects of Nature &
lastly I found the same Theory alltogether barren as to
useful productions & that with the assistance of it I could
doe noe more then I could have done when I was a
stranger to it. And tho I deny not that wee owe divers
usefull discoveryes & Inventions to the Embracers of the
Doctrine wee mention, yet I find not but that they [them]-
selves ow'd them not to Aristotles principles but to some
luckynes or sagacity of their owne genius or to some other
notions or Experiments which they might have acquir'd tho
they had never heard of Aristotles writings, wherefore tho
I much reverenced the rare abilityes of that Great Philos-

opher who what he would have done had his vast reason had experiments to worke upon wee may guesse by his excellent Treatises concerning Animalls yet finding so many things in nature either not intelligible from his principles or not consistent with them I could not acquiesce in 'um being encourag'd to decline them by that sober sentence of. . . . [Royal Society Boyle Papers, Vol. xxxviii]

The Author's Proemial Discourse to the Reader

As it is the part of a mineralist, both to discover new mines, and to work those that are already discovered, by separating and melting the ores to reduce them into perfect metal; so I esteem, that it becomes a naturalist, not only to advise hypotheses and experiments, but to examine and improve those that are already found out. Upon this consideration (among other motives) I was invited to make the following attempt, whose productions coming to be exposed to other eyes, than those for which they were first written, it will be requisite to give the public some account of the occasion, the scope, and some circumstances. And this I shall do the more fully, because the reasons I am to render of my way of writing, in reference to the Peripatetic philosophy, must contain intimations, which, perhaps, will not be useless to some sorts of readers (especially gentlemen) and, by being applied to most of those other parts of my writings that relate to the school-philosophy, may do them good service, and save both my readers and me some trouble of repetitions.

Having four or five years ago published a little physico-chemical tract about the different parts and redintegration of nitre, I found as well by other signs, as by the early solicitations of the stationer for a new edition, that I had no cause to complain of the reception that had been given

it: but I observed too, that the discourse, consisting chiefly
of reflexions that were occasionally made upon the phaenomena of a single experiment, was more available to confirm those in the corpuscularian philosophy, that had
already somewhat inquired into it, than to acquaint those
with the principles and notions of it, who were utter strangers to it; and, as to many readers, was fitter to excite a
curiosity for that philosophy, than to give an introduction
thereunto. Upon this occasion it came into my mind, that
about the time when I writ that essay about saltpetre
(which was divers years before it was published) I had
also some thoughts of a history of qualities, and that having in loose sheets set down divers observations and experiments proper for such a design, I had also drawn up a
discourse; which was so contrived, that though some parts
of it were written in such a manner, as that they may serve
for expository notes upon some particular passages of the
essay; yet those parts with the rest might serve for a general preface to the history of qualities, in case I should
ever have conveniency, as well as inclination, to make the
prosecuting of it my business; and in the mean time might
present . . . some kind of introduction to the principles
of the mechanical philosophy, by expounding, as far as my
thoughts and experiments would enable me to do, in few
words, what, according to the corpuscularian notions, may
be thought of the nature and origin of qualities and forms;
the knowledge of which either makes or supposes the most
fundamental and useful part of natural philosophy. And
to invite me to make use of these considerations and trials
about qualities and forms, it opportunely happened, that
though I could not find many of the notes written about
particular qualities (my loose papers having been, during
the late confusions, much scattered by the many removes
I had then occasion to make); yet when last winter, being
urged to publish my *History of Cold* (which soon after

came forth)[16] I rummaged among my loose papers, I found, that the several notes of mine, that he had met with under various heads, but yet all concerning the origin of forms and qualities, together with the preface . . . (though written at distant times and places) had two or three years before, by the care of an industrious person, with whom I left them, been fairly copied out together (which circumstance I mention, that the reader may not wonder to find the following book not written uniformly in one continued tenor) excepting some experiments, which having been of my own making, it was not dificult for me to perfect, either out of my notes and memory, or (where I doubted their sufficiency) by repeated trials. So that if the urgency, wherewith divers ingenious men pressed the publication of my new experiments about cold, and my unwillingness to protract it, till the frosty season, that was fittest to examine and prove them, were all past, had not prevailed with me to let those observations be made public the last winter, they might have been accompanied with the present essay of the "Origin of Qualities and Forms," which have been premised to what I have written touching any of the particular qualities, since it contains experiments and considerations fit to be preliminary to them all. . . .

And indeed the doctrines of forms and qualities, and generation, and corruption, and alteration, are wont to be treated of by scholastical philosophers in so obscure, so perplexed, and so unsatisfactory a way, and their discourses upon these subjects do consist so much more of logical and metaphysical notions and niceties than of physical observations and reasonings, that it is very difficult for any reader of but an ordinary capacity to understand what they mean, and no less difficult for any intelligent and unprejudiced reader to acquiesce in what they teach: which is oftentimes so precarious and so contradictious to itself, that most readers (without always excepting such as are learned and ingenious) frighted by the darkness and difficulties wherewith these subjects have been surrounded, do not so much as look after or read over these general and controverted matters, about which the schools make so much noise; but despairing to find any satisfaction in the study of them, betake themselves immediately to that part of physics that treats of particular bodies. So that to these it will not be unacceptable to have any intelligible notions offered them of these things, which, as they are wont to be proposed, are not wont to be understood: though yet the subjects themselves, if I mistake not, may be justly reckoned not only amongst the noblest and most important, but (in case they be duly proposed) amongst the usefulest and most delightful speculations that belong to physics.

I consider too that among those that are inclined to that philosophy, which I find I have been much imitated in calling Corpuscularian, there are many ingenious persons, especially among the nobility and gentry, who having been first drawn to like this new way of philosophy by the sight of some experiments, which for their novelty or prettiness they were much pleased with, or for their strangeness they admired, have afterwards delighted themselves to make or see variety of experiments, without having ever had the opportunity to be instructed in the rudiments or fundamental notions of that philosophy whose pleasing or amazing productions have enamoured them of it. . . . It is not impossible, but that such readers . . . will not be sorry to meet with a treatise, wherein though my chief and proper business be the giving some account of the nature and origin of forms and qualities; yet, by reason of the connexion and dependance betwixt these and divers of the other principal things that belong to the general part of physics, I have been obliged to touch upon so many other important points, that this tract may in some sort exhibit a scheme of, or serve for an introduction into the elements of the Corpuscularian philosophy. . . .

If it be said, that I have left divers things unmentioned, which are wont to be largely treated of by the Aristotelians, and particularly have omitted the discussion of several questions, about which they are wont very solemnly and eagerly to contend; I readily acknowledge it to be true: but I answer further, that to do otherwise than I have done were not agreeable to the nature of my design . . . and that though most readers will not take notice of it, yet such as are conversant in that sort of authors will, I presume, easily find that I have not left them unconsulted, but have had the curiosity to resort to several both of the more and of the less recent scholastical writers about physics, and so some of the best metaphysicians to boot, that I might the better inform myself, both what their opinions are, and upon what arguments they are grounded. But as I found those inquiries far more troublesome than useful, so I doubt not, that my omissions will not much displease that sort of readers, for whose sake chiefly it is that these papers are permitted to be made public. . . . And there being many doctrines, to which number this we are speaking of seems to belong, wherein the same innate light or other arguments, that discover the truth, do likewise sufficiently show the erroneousness of dissenting opinions; I hope it may suffice to propose and establish the notions that are to be embraced, without solicitously disproving what cannot be true, if these be so. And indeed there are many opinions and arguments of good repute in the schools, which do so entirely rely upon the authority of Aristotle, or some of his more celebrated followers, that where that authority is not acknowledged, to fall upon a solemn confutation of what has been so precariously advanced, were not only unnecessary, but indiscreet, even in a discourse not confined to the brevity challenged by the nature of this of ours. And there are very many questions and controversies, which, though hotly and clamorously contended about, and indeed pertinent and fit enough to be debated in their philosophy, do yet so much suppose the truth of several of their tenets, which the new philosophers reject; or are grounded upon technical terms or forms of speaking, that suppose the truth of such opinions; or are expressions, whereof we neither do nor need make any use; that to have inserted such debates into such a discourse as mine, would have been not only tedious, but impertinent. As (for instance) those grand disputes, whether the four elements are endowed with distinct substantial forms, or have only their proper qualities instead of them? and whether they remain in the mixed bodies, according to their forms, or according to their qualities? And whether the former or the latter of those be or be not refracted? These, I say, and divers other controversies about the four elements and their manner of mistion, are quite out of doors in their philosophy, that acknowledge neither, that there are four elements, nor that cold, heat, dryness, and moisture are, in the peripatetic sense, first qualities, or that there are any such things as substantial forms *in rerum natura*. . . .

By which nevertheless I would not be understood to censure or decry the whole Peripatetick philosophy, much less to despise Aristotle himself; whose own writings give me sometimes cause a little to wonder, to find some absurdities so consistently fathered upon him by his scholastic interpreters. For I look upon Aristotle as one (though but as one amongst many) of those famed ancients, whose learning about Alexander's time ennobled Greece; and I readily allow him most of the praises due to great wits, excepting those which belong to clear-headed naturalists. And I here declare once for all, that, where in . . . any of my writings, I do indefinitely depreciate Aristotle's doctrine, I would be understood to speak of his physics, or rather of the speculative part of them (for his historical writings concerning animals I much esteem) nor do I say that even these may not have their use among scholars, and even in universities, if they be retained and studied with due cautions and limitations. . . .

But whether we have treated of the nature and origin of forms and qualities in a more comprehensive way than others; whether we have by new and fit similitudes and examples and other means rendered it more intelligible than they have done; whether we have added any considerable number of notions and arguments, towards the compleating and confirming of the proposed hypothesis; whether we have with reason dismissed arguments unfit to be relied on; and whether we have proposed some notions and arguments so warily as to keep them from being liable to exceptions or evasions, whereto they were obnoxious as others have proposed them; whether (I say) we have done all or any of these in the first or speculative part of this treatise, we willingly leave the reader to judge. But in the second or historical part of it perhaps he will be invited to grant that we have done that part of physics we have been treating of some little service; since by the lovers of real learning it was very much wished that the doctrines of the new philosophy (as it is called) were backed by particular experiments; the want of which I have endeavoured to supply, by annexing some whose nature and novelty, I am made to believe, will render them as well acceptable as instructive. . . .

And though some virtuosi, more conversant perhaps with things than books, presuming the decay of the Peripatetic philosophy to be everywhere as great as it is among them in England, may think a doctrine which they look on as expiring, need not have been so solicitously confuted;

yet those that know how deep rooting this philosophy has taken (both elsewhere, and particularly) in those academies where it has flourished for many ages, and in some of which it is, exclusively to the mechanical philosophy, watered and fenced by their statutes or their superiors: and he that also knows how much more easy some (more subtile than candid) wits find it plausibly to defend an error, than ingenuously to confess it, will not wonder that I should think that a doctrine so advantaged, though it be too erroneous to be feared, is yet too considerable to be despised. And not to question whether several of those that most contemn the favorers of the Peripatetic hypothesis, as the later discoveries have reduced them to reform it, be not the least provided to answer their arguments . . . there are divers of our adversaries (misled only by education and morally harmless prejudices) who do so much deserve a better cause, than that which needs all their subtilty, without being worthy of it, that I shall think more pains than I have taken usefully bestowed, if my arguments and experiments prove so happy as to undeceive persons whose parts, too unluckily confined to narrow and fruitless notions, would render them illustrious champions for the truths they are able so subtily to oppose; and who might questionless perform considerable things, if they employed as much dexterity to expound the mysteries of nature, as the riddles of the schoolmen, and laid out their wit and industry to surmount the obscurity of her works, instead of that of Aristotle's. . . . [*Works*, III, 3–10]

9. The Corpuscular Philosophy

The following is the complete text of *The Excellency and Grounds of the Corpuscular or Mechanical Philosophy,* published in 1674. There is no indication of the person for whom it was written. It is one of the most complete and succinct statements of Boyle's reasons for rejecting either chemical, hypostatical principles, or Aristotelian elements with their associated forms and qualities in favor of the tenets of the mechanical philosophy. The scorn for such terms as "Archeus, Astral Beings, Blas" shows Boyle's assessment of the mystical doctrines of the famous chemist J. B. van Helmont (1577–1644), much of whose work in chemistry, however, he admired. Spagyrists are followers of Paracelsus (c. 1493–1541), the mystical iatrochemist and alchemist, and here especially those who maintain that all matter is made of the *tria prima:* salt, sulphur, and mercury. Daniel Sennert (1572–1637), of whom Boyle usually spoke with great respect for his learning, was a German medical chemist whose most famous work was an attempt to reconcile Paracelsan chemistry with Galenic and Aristotelian doctrine; he also espoused an atomic theory in which, however, Peripatetic "forms" played a vital role.

OF THE

EXCELLENCY AND GROUNDS

OF THE

CORPUSCULAR OR MECHANICAL PHILOSOPHY

The importance of the question, you propose, would oblige me to refer you to "the dialogue about a good hypothesis," and some other papers of that kind, where you

may find my thoughts about the advantages of the mechanical hypothesis somewhat amply set down, and discoursed of. But, since your desires confine me to deliver
in few words, not what I believe resolvedly, but what I
think may be probably said for the preference of the pre-
eminence of the corpuscular philosophy above Aristotle's,
or that of the chymists, you must be content to receive
from me, without any preamble, or exact method, or ample
discourses, or any other thing, that may cost many words,
a succinct mention of some of the chief advantages of the
hypothesis we incline to. And I the rather comply, on this
occasion, with your curiosity, because I have often observed you to be alarmed and disquieted, when you hear
of any book, that pretends to uphold, or repair the decay-
ing philosophy of the schools, or some bold chymist that
arrogates to those of his sect the title of philosophers, and
pretends to build wholly upon experience, to which he
would have all other naturalists thought strangers. That
therefore you may not be so tempted to despond, by the
confidence or reputation of those writers, that do some of
them applaud, and others censure, what, I fear, they do not
understand, (as when the Peripateticks cry up substantial forms, and the chymists, mechanical explications) of
nature's phaenomena, I will propose some considerations,
that, I hope, will not only keep you kind to the philosophy
you have embraced, but perhaps, (by some considerations,
which you have not yet met with,) make you think it
probable, that the new attempts you hear of from time to
time, will not overthrow the corpuscularian philosophy,
but either be foiled by it, or found reconcilable to it.

But when I speak of the corpuscular or mechanical philosophy, I am far from meaning with the Epicureans, that
atoms, meeting together by chance in an infinite vacuum,
are able of themselves to produce the world, and all its
phaenomena; nor with some modern philosophers, that,

supposing God to have put into the whole mass of matter such an invariable quantity of motion, he needed do no more to make the world, the material parts being able by their own unguided motions, to cast themselves into such a system (as we call by that name): But I plead only for such a philosophy, as reaches but to things purely corporeal, and distinguishing between the first original of things, and the subsequent course of nature, teaches, concerning the former, not only that God gave motion to matter, but that in the beginning he so guided the various motions of the parts of it, as to contrive them into the world he designed they should compose, (furnished with the seminal principles and structures, or models of living creatures,) and established those rules of motion, and that order amongst things corporeal, which we are wont to call the laws of nature. And having told this as to the former, it may be allowed as to the latter to teach, that the universe being once framed by God, and the laws of motion being settled and all upheld by his incessant concourse and general providence, the phaenomena of the world thus constituted are physically produced by the mechanical affections of the parts of matter, and what they operate upon one another according to mechanical laws. And now having shown what kind of corpuscular philosophy it is, that I speak of, I proceed to the particulars, that I thought the most proper to recommend it.

I. The first thing, that I shall mention to this purpose, is the intelligibleness or clearness of mechanical principles and explications. I need not tell you, that among the Peripateticks, the disputes are many and intricate about matter, privation, substantial forms, and their eduction, &c. And the chymists are sufficiently puzzled, (as I have elsewere shown,) to give such definitions and accounts of their hypostatical principles, as are reconcileable to one another, and even to some obvious phaenomena. And much more dark and intricate are their doctrines about the Archeus, Astral Beings, Gas, Blas, and other odd notions, which perhaps have in part occasioned the darkness and ambiguity of their expressions, that could not be very clear, when their conceptions were far from being so. And if the principles of the Aristotelians and Spagyrists are thus obscure, it is not to be expected, the explications, that are made by the help only of such principles should be clear. And indeed many of them are either so general and slight, or otherwise so unsatisfactory, that granting their principles, it is very hard to understand or admit their applications of them to particular phaenomena. And even in some of the more ingenious and subtle of the Peripatetick discourses upon their superficial and narrow theories, methinks, the authors have better played the part of painters than philosophers, and have only had the skill, like drawers of landskips, to make men fancy they see castles and towns, and other structures, that appear solid and magnificent, and to reach to a large extent, when the whole piece is superficial, and made up of colours and art, and comprised within a frame perhaps scarce a yard long. But to come now to the corpuscular philosophy, men do so easily understand one another's meaning, when they talk of local motion, rest, bigness, shape, order, situation, and contexture of material substances; and these principles do afford such clear accounts of those things, that are rightly deduced from them only, that even those Peripateticks or chymists, that maintain other principles, acquiesce in the explications made by these, when they can be had, and seek not any further, though perhaps the effect be so admirable, as would make it pass for that of a hidden form, or occult quality. Those very Aristotelians, that believe the celestial bodies to be moved by intelligences, have no recourse to any peculiar agency of theirs to account for eclipses. And we laugh at those East-Indians, that to this day go out in multitudes, with some instruments, that may relieve the distressed luminary, whose loss of light they fancy to proceed from some fainting fit, out of which it must be roused. For no intelligent man, whether chymist or Peripatetic, flies to his peculiar principles, after he is informed, that the moon is eclipsed by the interposition of the earth betwixt her and it, and the sun by that of the moon betwixt him and the earth. And when we see the image of a man cast into the air by a concave spherical looking-glass, though most men are amazed at it, and some suspect it to be no less than an effect of witchcraft, yet he, that is skilled enough in catoptrics, will, without consulting Aristotle, or Paracelsus, or flying to hypostatical principles and substantial forms, be satisfied that the phaenomenon is produced by the beams of light reflected, and thereby made convergent according to optical, and consequently mathematical laws.

But I must not now repeat what I elsewhere say, to show, that the corpuscular principles have been declined by philosophers of different sects, not because they think not our explications clear, if not much more so, than their own; but because they imagine, that the applications of them can be made but to few things, and consequently are insufficient.

II. In the next place I observe, that there cannot be fewer principles than the two grand ones of mechanical philosophy, matter and motion. For, matter alone, unless it be moved, is altogether unactive; and whilst all the parts of the body continue in one state without any motion at all, that body will not exercise any action, nor suffer any alteration itself, though it may perhaps modify the action of other bodies, that move against it.

III. Nor can we conceive any principles more primary, than matter and motion. For, either both of them were

immediately created by God, or, (to add that for their
sakes, that would have matter to be unproduced,) if matter be eternal, motion must either be produced by some
immaterial supernatural agent, or it must immediately flow
by way of emanation from the nature of the matter it
appertains to.

IV. Neither can there be any physical principles more
simple than matter and motion; neither of them being
resoluble into any things, whereof it may be truly, or so
much as tolerably said to be compounded.

V. The next thing I shall name to recommend the corpuscular principle, is their great comprehensiveness. I consider then, that the genuine and necessary effect of the
sufficiently strong motion of one part of matter against
another, is, either to drive it on in its entire bulk, or else
to break or divide it into particles of determinate motion,
figure, size, posture, rest, order or texture. The two first
of these, for instance, are each of them capable of numerous varieties. For the figure of a portion of matter may
either be one of the five regular figures treated of by
geometricians, or some determinate species of solid figures,
as that of a cone, cylinder &c. or irregular, though not
perhaps anonymous, as the grains of sand, hoops, feathers,
branches, forks, files &c. And as the figure, so the motion
of one of these particles may be exceedingly diversified,
not only by the determination to this or that part of the
world, but by several other things, as particularly by the
almost infinitely varying degrees of celerity, by the manner
of its progression with, or without rotation, and other modifying circumstances; and more yet, by the line, wherein
it moves, as (besides straight) circular, eliptical, parabol-
ical, hyperbolical, spiral, and I know not how many others.
For as later geometricians have shown, that those crooked
lines may be compounded of several motions, (that is,

traced by a body, whose motion is mixed of, and results from, two or more simpler motions,) so how many more curves may, or rather may not be made by new compositions and decompositions of motion, is no easy task to determine.

Now, since a single particle of matter, by virtue of two only of the mechanical affections, that belong to it, be diversifiable so many ways; how vast a number of variations may we suppose capable of being produced by the compositions and decompositions of myriads of single invisible corpuscles, that may be contained and contexed in one small body, and each of them be embued with more than two or three of the fertile catholick principles above-mentioned? Especially since the aggregate of those corpuscles may be farther diversified by the texture resulting from their convention into a body, which, as so made up, has its own bigness, and shape, and pores, (perhaps very many and various) and has also many capacities of acting and suffering upon the score of the place it holds among other bodies in a world constituted as ours is: so that, when I consider the almost innumerable diversifications, that compositions and decompositions may make of a small number, not perhaps exceeding twenty of distinct things, I am apt to look upon those, who think the mechanical principles may serve indeed to give an account of the phaenomena of this or that particular part of natural philosophy, as staticks, hydrostaticks, the theory of the planetary motions, &c. but can never be applied to all the phaenomena of things corporeal; I am apt, I say, to look upon those, otherwise learned men, as I would do upon him, that should affirm, that by putting together the letters of the alphabet, one may indeed make up all the words to be found in one book, as in Euclid, or Virgil; or in one language, as Latin, or English; but that they can by no means suffice to supply words to all the books of a great library, much less to all the languages in the world.

And whereas there is another sort of philosophers, that, observing the great efficacy of the bigness, and shape, and situation, and motion, and connexion in engines, are willing to allow, that those mechanical principles may have a great stroke in the operations of bodies of a sensible bulk, and manifest mechanism, and therefore may be usefully employed in accounting for the effects and phaenomena of such bodies, who yet will not admit, that these principles can be applied to the hidden transactions, that pass among the minute particles of bodies; and therefore think it necessary to refer these to what they call nature, substantial forms, real qualities, and the like unmechanical principles and agents.

But this is not necessary; for both the mechanical affections of matter are to be found, and the laws of motion take place, not only in the great masses, and the middle sized lumps, but in the smallest fragments of matter; and a lesser portion of it being as well a body as a greater, must, as necessarily as it, have its determinate bulk and figure: and he, that looks upon sand in a good microscope, will easily perceive, that each minute grain of it has as well its own size and shape, as a rock or mountain. And when we let fall a great stone and a pebble from the top of a high building, we find not, but that the latter as well as the former moves conformably to the laws of acceleration in heavy bodies descending. And the rules of motion are observed, not only in cannon bullets, but in small shot; and the one strikes down a bird according to the same laws, that the other batters down a wall. And though nature (or rather its divine author) be wont to work with much finer materials, and employ more curious contrivances than art, (whence the structure even of the rarest

watch is incomparably inferior to that of a human body;)
yet an artist himself, according to the quantity of the
matter he employs, the exigency of the design he under-
takes, and the bigness and shape of the instruments he
makes use of, is able to make pieces of work of the same
nature or kind of extremely differing bulk, where yet the
like, though not equal art and contrivance, and oftentimes
motion too, may be observed: as a smith, who with a
hammer, and other large instruments, can, out of masses
of iron, forge great bars or wedges, and make those strong
and heavy chains, that were employed to load malefac-
tors, and even to secure streets and gates, may, with lesser
instruments, make smaller nails and filings, almost as minute as dust; and may yet, with finer tools, make links of
a strange slenderness and lightness, insomuch, that good
authors tell us of a chain of divers links, that was fastened
to a flea, and could be moved by it; and if I misremember
not, I saw something like this, besides other instances, that
I beheld with pleasure, of the littleness, that art can give
to such pieces of work, as are usually made of a considerable bigness. And therefore to say, that though in natural
bodies, whose bulk is manifest and their structure visible,
the mechanical principles may be usefully admitted, that
are not to be extended to such portions of matter, whose
parts and texture are invisible; may perhaps look to some,
as if a man should allow, that the laws of mechanism may
take place in a town clock, but cannot in a pocket watch;
or, (to give you an instance, mixed of natural and artificial,) as if, because the terraqueous globe is a vast magnetical body of seven or eight thousand miles in diameter,
one should affirm, that magnetical laws are not to be expected to be of force in a spherical piece of loadstone, that
is not perhaps an inch long: and yet experience shows us,
that notwithstanding the inestimable disproportion betwixt these two globes, the terrella, as well as the earth,

hath its poles, aequator, and meridians, and in divers other magnetical properties, emulates the terrestrial globe.

They, that, to solve the phaenomena of nature, have recourse to agents, which, though they involve no self-repugnancy in their very notions, as many of the judicious think substantial forms and real qualities to do, yet are such, that we conceive not, how they operate to bring effects to pass: these, I say, when they tell us of such indeterminate agents, as the soul of the world, the universal spirit, the plastic power, and the like; though they may in certain cases tell us some things, yet they tell us nothing, that will satisfy the curiosity of an inquisitive person, who seeks not so much to know, what is the general agent, that produces a phaenomenon, as, by what means, and after what manner, the phaenomenon is produced. The famous Sennertus, and some other learned physicians, tell us of diseases, which proceed from incantation; but sure it is but a slight account, that a sober physician, that comes to visit a patient reported to be bewitched, receives of the strange symptoms he meets with, and would have an account of, if he be coldly answered, that it is a witch, or the devil, that produces them; and he will never sit down with so short an account, if he can by any means reduce those extravagant symptoms to any more known and stated diseases, as epilepsies, convulsions, hysterial fits, &c. and, if he cannot, he will confess his knowledge of this distemper to come far short of what might be expected and attained in other diseases, wherein he thinks himself bound to search into the nature of the morbific matter, and will not be satisfied, till he can, probably at least, deduce from that, and the structure of an human body, and other concurring physical causes, the phaenomena of the malady. And it would be but little satisfaction to one, that desires to understand the causes of what occurs to observation in a watch, and how it comes to point at, and strike the hours, to be told, that it was such a watch-maker that so contrived it; or to him, that would know the true cause of an echo, to be answered, that it is a man, a vault, or a wood, that makes it.

And now at length I come to consider that, which I observe the most to alienate other sects from the mechanical philosophy; namely, that they think it pretends to have principles so universal and so mathematical, that no other physical hypothesis can comport with it, or be tolerated by it.

But this I look upon as an easy, indeed, but an important mistake; because by this very thing, that the mechanical principles are so universal, and therefore applicable to so many things, they are rather fitted to include, than necessitated to exclude, any other hypothesis, that is founded in nature, as far as it is so. And such hypotheses, if prudently considered by a skilful and moderate person, who is rather disposed to unite sects than multiply them, will be found, as far as they have truth in them, to be either legitimately (though perhaps not immediately) deducible from the mechanical principles, or fairly reconcileable to them. For, such hypotheses will probably attempt to account for the phaenomena of nature, either by the help of a determinate number of material ingredients, such as the *tria prima* of the chymists, by participation whereof other bodies obtain their qualities; or else by introducing some general agents, as the Platonic soul of the world, or the universal spirit, asserted by some spagyrists; or by both these ways together.

Now, to dispatch first those, that I named in the second place, I consider, that the chief thing, that inquisitive naturalists should look after in the explicating of difficult phaenomena, is not so much what the agent is or does, as, what changes are made in the patient, to bring it to exhibit the phaenomena, that are proposed; and by what means, and after what manner, those changes are effected. So that the mechanical philosopher being satisfied, that one part of matter can act upon another but by virtue of local motion, or the effects and consequences of local motion, he considers, that as if the proposed agent be not intelligible and physical, it can never physically explain the phaenomena; so, if it be intelligible and physical, it will be reducible to matter, and some or other of those only catholick affections of matter, already often mentioned. And the indefinite divisibility of matter, the wonderful efficacy of motion, and the almost infinite variety of coalitions and structures, that may be made of minute and insensible corpuscles, being duly weighed, I see not, why a philosopher should think it impossible, to make out, by their help, the mechanical possibility of any corporeal agent, how subtle, or diffused, or active soever it be, that can be solidly proved to be really existent in nature, by what name soever it be called or disguised. And though the Cartesians be mechanical philosophers, yet, according to them, their *Materia Subtilis*,[17] which the very name declares to be a corporeal substance, is, for aught I know, little (if it be at all) less diffused through the universe, or less active in it than the universal spirit of some spagyrists, not to say, the *Anima Mundi* of the Platonists.[18] But this upon the by; after which I proceed, and shall venture to add, that whatever be the physical agent, whether, it be inanimate or living, purely corporeal, or united to an intellectual substance, the above-mentioned changes, that are wrought in the body, that is made to exhibit the phaenomena, may be effected by the same or the like means, or after the same or the like manner; as for instance, if corn be reduced to meal, the materials and shape of the millstones, and their peculiar motion and adaptation, will be much of the same kind; and (though they should not, yet) to be sure the grains of corn will suffer a various contrition and comminution in their passage to the form of meal; whether the corn be ground by a water-mill or a windmill, or a horse mill, or a hand-mill; that is, by a mill, whose stones are turned by inanimate, by brute, or by rational agents. And, if an angel himself should work a real change in the nature of a body, it is scarce conceivable to us men, how he could do it without the assistance of local motion; since, if nothing were displaced, or otherwise moved than before, (the like happening also to all external bodies to which it related) it is hardly conceivable, how it should be in itself other, than just what it was before.

But to come now to the other sort of hypothesis formerly mentioned; if the chymists, or others, that would deduce a complete natural philosophy from salt, sulphur, and mercury, or any other set number of ingredients of things, would well consider, what they undertake, they might easily discover, that the material parts of bodies, as such, can reach but to a small part of the phaenomena of nature, whilst these ingredients are considered but as quiescent things, and therefore they would find themselves necessitated to suppose them to be active; and that things purely corporeal cannot be but by means of local motion, and the effects, that may result from that, accompanying variously shaped, sized, and aggregated parts of matter: so that the chymist and other materialists, if I may so call them, must (as indeed they are wont to do) leave the greatest part of the phaenomena of the universe unexplicated by the help of the ingredients (be they fewer or more than three) of bodies, without taking in the mechanical, and more comprehensive affections of matter, especially local motion. I willingly grant, that salt, sulphur, and mercury, or some substances analogous to them, are to be obtained by the action of the fire, from a very great many dissipable bodies here below; nor would I deny, that in explicating divers of the phaenomena of such bodies, it may be of use to a skilful naturalist to know and consider, that this or that ingredient, as sulphur, for instance, does abound in the body proposed, whence it may be probably argued, that the qualities, that usually accompany that principle, when predominant, may be also, upon its score, found in the body, that so plentifully partakes of it. But not to mention, what I have elsewhere shown, that there are many phaenomena, to whose explication this knowledge will contribute very little or nothing at all; I shall only here observe, that, though chymical explications be sometimes the most obvious and ready, yet they are not the most fundamental and satisfactory: for, the chemical ingredient itself, whether sulphur or any other, must owe its nature and other qualities to the union of insensible particles in a convenient size, shape, motion or rest, and contexture; all which are but mechanical affections of convening corpuscles. And this may be illustrated by what happens in artificial fire-works. For, though in most of those many differing sorts that are made, either for the use of war, or for recreation, gunpowder be a main ingredient, and divers of the phaenomena may be derived from the greater or lesser measure, wherein the compositions partake of it; yet, besides that there may be fire-works made without gunpowder, (as appears by those made of old by the Greeks and Romans,) gunpowder itself owes its aptness to be fired and exploded to the mechanical contexture of more simple portions of matter, nitre, charcoal, and sulphur; and sulphur itself, though it be by many chemists mistaken for an hypostatical principle, owes its inflammability to the convention of yet more simple and primary corpuscles; since chymists confess, that it has an inflammable ingredient, and experience shows, that it very much abounds with an acid and uninflammable salt, and is not quite devoid of terrestreity. I know it may be here alledged, that the productions of chemical analyses are simple bodies, and upon that account irresoluble. But, that divers substances, which chymists are pleased to call the salts, or sulphurs, or mercuries of the bodies, that afforded them, are not simple and homogeneous, has elsewhere been sufficiently proved; nor is their not being easily dissipable, or resoluble, a clear proof of their not being made up of more primitive portions of matter. For, compounded, and even decompounded bodies, may be as difficultly resoluble, as most of those, that chymists obtain by what they call their analysis by the fire; witness common green glass, which is far more durable and irresoluble than many of those, that pass for hypostatical substances. And we see, that some enamels will be several times even vitrified in the fire, without losing their nature, or oftentimes so much as their colour; and yet enamel is manifestly, not only a compounded, but a decompounded body, consisting of salt and powder of pebbles or sand, and calcined tin, and, if the enamel be not white, usually of some tinging metal or mineral. But how indestructible soever the chymical principles be supposed, divers of the operations ascribed to them will never be well made out, without the help of local motion, (and that diversified too;) without which, we can little better give an account of the phaenomena of many bodies, by knowing what ingredients compose them, than we can explain the operations of a watch, by knowing of how many, and of what metals the balance, the wheels, the chain, and other parts are made; or than we can derive the operations of a wind-mill from the bare knowledge, that it is made up of wood, and stone, and canvas, and iron. And here let me add, that it would not at all overthrow the Corpuscularian Hypothesis, though either by more exquisite purifications, or by some other operations, than the usual analysis of the fire, it should be made appear, that the material principles, or elements of

mixed bodies, should not be the *tria prima* of the vulgar
chymists, but either substances of another nature, or else
fewer, or more in number; as would be, if that were true,
which some spagyrists affirm, (but I could never find,)
that from all sorts of mixed bodies, five, and but five,
differing similar substances can be separated: or, as if it
were true, that the Helmontians had such a resolving menstruum as the Alkahest of their master;[19] by which he
affirms, that he could reduce stones into salt of the same
weight with the mineral, and bring both that salt, and all
other kind of mixed and tangible bodies, into insipid
water. For, whatever be the number or qualities of the
chymical principles, if they be really existent in nature,
it may very possibly be shown, that they may be made
up of insensible corpuscles of determinate bulks and
shapes; and by the various coalitions and contextures of
such corpuscles, not only three or five, but many more
material ingredients, may be composed or made to result.
But, though the Alkahestical reductions newly mentioned
should be admitted, yet the mechanical principles might
well be accommodated even to them. For the solidity,
taste, &c. of salt, may be fairly accounted for, by the stiff-
ness, sharpness, and other mechanical affections of the
minute particles, whereof salts consist; and if, by a farther
action of the alkahest, the salt, or any other solid body,
be reduced into insipid water, this also may be explicated
by the same principles, supposing a farther comminution
of the parts, and such an attrition, as wears off the edges
and points, that enabled them to strike briskly the organ
of taste: for, as to fluidity and firmness, those mainly depend upon two of our grand principles, motion and rest.
And I have elsewhere shown, by several proofs, that the
agitation of rest, and the looser contact, or closer cohae-
sion, of the particles, is able to make the same portion of
matter, at one time a firm, and at another time a fluid

body. So that, though the further sagacity and industry of chymists (which I would by no means discourage) should be able to obtain from mixed bodies homogeneous substances, differing in number, or nature, or both, from their vulgar salt, sulphur, and mercury; yet the corpuscular philosophy is so general and fertile, as to be fairly reconcilable to such a discovery; and also so useful, that these new material principles will, as well as the old *tria prima*, stand in need of the more catholick principles of the Corpuscularians, especially local motion. And indeed, whatever elements or ingredients men have (that I know of) pitched upon, yet if they take not in the mechanical affections of matter, their principles have been so deficient, that I have usually observed, that the materialists, without at all excepting the chymists, do not only, as I was saying, leave many things unexplained, to which their narrow principles will not extend; but, even in the particulars, they presume to give an account of, they either content themselves to assign such common and indefinite causes, as are too general to signify much towards an inquisitive man's satisfaction; or if they venture to give particular causes, they assign precarious or false ones, and liable to be easily disproved by circumstances, or instances, whereto their doctrine will not agree, as I have often elsewhere had occasion to show. And yet the chymists need not be frighted from acknowledging the prerogative of the mechanical philosophy, since that may be reconcileable with the truth of their own principles, as far as these agree with the phaenomena they are applied to. For these more confined hypotheses may be subordinated to those more general and fertile principles, and there can be no ingredient assigned, that has a real existence in nature, that may not be derived either immediately, or by a row of decompositions, from the universal matter, modified by its mechanical affections. For if, with the same bricks, diversely put together and ranged, several walls, houses, furnaces, and other structures, as vaults, bridges, pyramids &c. may be built, merely by a various contrivement of parts of the same kind; how much more may great variety of ingredients be produced by, or, according to the institution of nature, result from the various coalitions and contextures of corpuscles, that need not be supposed, like bricks, all of the same, or near the same size and shape, but may have amongst them, both of the one and the other, as great a variety as need be wished for, and indeed a greater than can easily be so much as imagined? And the primary and minute concretions, that belong to these ingredients, may, without opposition from the mechanical philosophy, be supposed to have their particles so minute and strongly coherent, that nature of herself does scarce ever tear them asunder; as we see, that mercury and gold may be successively made to put on a multitude of disguises, and yet so retain their nature, as to be reducible to their pristine forms. And you know, I lately told you, that common glass and good enamels, though both of them but factitious bodies, and not only mixed, but decompounded concretions, have yet their component parts so strictly united by the skill of illiterate tradesmen, as to maintain their union in the vitrifying violence of the fire. Nor do we find, that common glass will be wrought upon by aqua fortis, or aqua regis, though the former of them will dissolve mercury, and the latter gold.

From the foregoing discourse it may (probably at least) result, that if, besides rational souls, there are any immaterial substances (such as the heavenly intelligences, and the substantial forms of the Aristotelians,) that regularly are to be numbered among natural agents, their way of working being unknown to us, they can but help to constitute and effect things, but will very little help us to conceive how things are effected; so that by whatever

principles natural things be constituted, it is by the mechanical principles, that their phaenomena must be clearly
explicated. As for instance, though we should grant the
Aristotelians, that the planets are made of a quintessential
matter, and moved by angels, or immaterial intelligences;
yet, to explain the stations, progressions, and retrogradations, and other phaenomena of the planets, we must have
recourse either to eccentricks, epicycles, &c. or to motions
made in elliptical or other peculiar lines; and, in a word,
to theories, wherein the motion and figure, situation, and
other mathematical or mechanical affections of bodies are
mainly employed. But if the principles proposed be corporeal things, they will be then fairly reducible, or reconcilable, to the mechanical principles: these being so general and pregnant, that among things corporeal, there is
nothing real, (and I meddle not with chimerical beings,
such as some of Paracelsus's) that may not be derived
from, or be brought to, a subordination to such comprehensive principles. And when the chymists shall show,
that mixed bodies owe their qualities to the predominancy
of this or that of their three grand ingredients, the Corpuscularians will show, that the very qualities of this, or
that ingredient, flow from its peculiar texture, and the
mechanical affections of those corpuscles it is made up of.
And to affirm, that, because the furnaces of chymists afford
a great number of uncommon productions and phaenomena, there are bodies or operations amongst things purely
corporeal, that cannot be derived from, or reconciled to,
the comprehensive and pregnant principles of the mechanical philosophy, is, as if, because there are a great number
and variety of anthems, hymns, pavins, threnodies, courants, gavots, branles, sarabands, jigs, and other (grave
and sprightly) tunes to be met with in the books and
practices of musicians, one should maintain, that there are
in them a great many tunes, or at least, notes, that have no

dependence on the scale of musick; or, as if, because, besides rhombusses, rhomboids, trapeziums, squares, pentagons, chiliagons, myriagons, and innumerable other polygons, regular, and irregular, one should presume to affirm, that there are among them some rectilinear figures, that are not reducible to triangles, or have affections, that will overthrow what Euclid has taught of triangles and polygons.

To what has been said I shall add but one thing more; that as, according to what I formerly intimated, mechanical principles and explications are for their clearness preferred, even by materialists themselves, to others, in the cases where they can be had; so, the sagacity and industry of modern naturalists and mathematicians having happily applied them to several of those difficult phaenomena, (in hydrostaticks, the practical part of opticks, gunnery, &c.) that before were, or might be referred to occult qualities; it is probable, that when this philosophy is deeplier searched into, and farther improved, it will be found applicable to the solution of more and more of the phaenomena of nature. And on this occasion let me observe, that it is not always necessary, though it be always desirable, that he, that propounds an hypothesis in astronomy, chemistry, anatomy, or other part of physics, be able *a priori,* to prove his hypothesis to be true, or demonstratively to show, that the other hypotheses proposed about the same subject must be false. For as, if I mistake not, Plato said, that the world was God's epistle written to mankind, and might have added, consonantly to another saying of his, it was written in mathematical letters: so, in the physical explications of the parts and system of the world, methinks, there is somewhat like what happens, when men conjectually frame several keys to enable us to understand a letter written in cyphers. For though one man by his sagacity have found out the right key, it will be very difficult for him, either to prove otherwise than by trial, that this or that word is not such, as it is guessed to be by others, according to their keys; or to evince, *a priori*, that theirs are to be rejected, and his to be preferred; yet, if due trial being made, the key he proposes, shall be found so agreeable to the characters of the letter, as to enable one to understand them, and make a coherent sense of them, its suitableness to what it should decypher, is, without either confutations, or extraneous positive proofs, sufficient to make it be accepted as the right key of that cypher. And so, in physical hypotheses, there are some, that, without noise, or falling foul upon others, peaceably obtain discerning men's approbation only by their fitness to solve the phaenomena, for which they were devised, without crossing any known observation or law of nature. And therefore, if the mechanical philosophy go on to explicate things corporeal at the rate it has of late years proceeded at, it is scarce to be doubted, but that, in time, unprejudiced persons will think it sufficiently recommended by its consistency with itself, and its applicableness to so many phaenomena of nature.

A RECAPITULATION

Perceiving, upon a review of the foregoing paper, that the difficulty and importance of the subject, has seduced me to spend many more words about it, than I at first designed; it will not now be amiss to give you this short summary of what came into my mind, to recommend to you the mechanical philosophy, and obviate your fears of seeing it supplanted; having first premised once for all, that presupposing the creation and general providence of God, I pretend to treat but of things corporeal, and do abstract in this paper from immaterial Beings, (which otherwise I very willingly admit,) and all agents and operations miraculous or supernatural.

I. Of the principles of things corporeal, none can be more few, without being insufficient, or more primary, than matter and motion.

II. The natural and genuine effect of variously determined motion in portions of matter is, to divide it into parts of differing sizes, and shapes, and to put them into different motions; and the consequences, that flow from these, in a world framed as ours is, are, as to the separate fragments, posture, order, and situation, and, as to the conventions of many of them, peculiar compositions and contextures.

III. The parts of matter endowed with these catholick affections are, by various associations, reduced to natural bodies of several kinds, according to the plenty of the matter, and the various compositions and decompositions of the principles; which all suppose the common matter they diversify: and these several kinds of bodies, by virtue of their motion, rest, and other mechanical affections, which fit them to act on, and suffer from one another, become endowed with several kinds of qualities, (whereof some are called manifest, and some occult,) and those, that act upon the peculiarly framed organs of sense, whole perceptions, by the animadversive faculty of the soul, are sensations.

IV. These principles, matter, motion, (to which rest is related) bigness, shape, posture, order, texture, being so simple, clear and comprehensive, are applicable to all the real phaenomena of nature, which seem not explicable by any other not consistent with ours. For, if recourse be had to an immaterial principle or agent, it may be such an one, as is not intelligible; and however it will not enable us to explain the phaenomena, because its way of working upon things material, would probably be more difficult to be physically made out, than a mechanical account of the phaenomena. And, notwithstanding the immateriality of a created agent, we cannot conceive, how it should produce changes in a body, without the help of mechanical principles, especially local motion; and accordingly we find not, that the reasonable soul in man is able to produce what changes it pleases in the body, but is confined to such, as it may produce by determining, or guiding the motions of the spirits, and other parts of the body, subservient to voluntary motion.

V. And if the agents, or active principles resorted to, be not immaterial, but of a corporeal nature, they must either in effect be the same with the corporeal principles above-named; or, because of the great universality and simplicity of ours, the new ones proposed, must be less general than they, and consequently capable of being subordinate or reduced to ours, which by various compositions may afford matter to several hypotheses, and by several coalitions afford minute concretions exceedingly numerous and durable, and consequently fit to become the elementary ingredients of more compounded bodies, being in most trials similar, and as it were the radical parts, which may, after several manners, be diversified; as in Latin, the themes are by prepositions, terminations, &c. and in Hebrew, the roots by the haeemantic letters. So that the fear, that so much of a new physical hypothesis, as is true, will overthrow, or make useless the mechanical principles, is, as if one should fear, that there will be a language proposed, that is discordant from, or not reducible to, the letters of the alphabet. [*Works*, IV, 68–78]

10. The Structure of Matter

The following selections, the first from *The Sceptical Chymist* (1661), and the second from the *Origin of Forms and Qualities,* give some indication of Boyle's ideas on the actual structure of matter. It will be seen that he believed in a hierarchy of corpuscles (a not uncommon theory in the seventeenth century), but that what mainly interested him were relatively simple corpuscles and the more complex corpuscles made by a coalition of the simpler ones. The difference between these two kinds of corpuscles is detectable by their chemical behavior. This is the beginning of a theory of simple substances, which slowly began to replace the theory of elements; for the secondary corpuscles are considered as persisting unchanged through complex chemical action and as being recoverable after a series of reactions. The more complex corpuscles are a little like our molecules, but not totally so, for they could be divided in two different ways—they could either be split into their component parts (less complex clusters of corpuscles) or parts of the outer surface could be broken off, when a quite new substance would be formed. Boyle, like most chemists of his day, had somewhat confused ideas about organic substances; thus, both camphor and alcohol (spirit of wine) were considered to be simple substances because of their great inflammability and the fact that they left little or no residue on burning. Antimony is antimony sulphide, the common ore; the metal was known as regulus of antimony. Regulus martis is antimony metal made by reducing the ore in the presence of iron. A menstruum is a solvent.

PROPOSITION I.—It seemes not absurd to conceive, that at
the first production of mixt bodies, the universal matter
whereof they among other parts of the universe consisted, was actually divided into little particles, of several sizes and shapes, variously moved. . . .

. . . Besides that which happens in the generation, corruption, nutrition, and wasting of bodies, that which we
discover partly by our microscopes of the extreme littleness of even the scarce sensible parts of concretes, and
partly by the chymical resolution of mixt bodies, and by
divers other operations of spagyrical fires upon them,
seems sufficiently to manifest their consisting of parts very
minute and of differing figures. And that there does also
intervene a various local motion of such bodies, will scarce
be denied; whether we choose to grant the origin of concretions assigned by Epicurus, or that related by Moses. . . .

PROPOSITION II.—Neither is it impossible that of these minute particles divers of the smallest ˙and neighbouring
ones were here and there associated into minute masses
or clusters, and did by their coalitions constitute great
store of such little primary concretions or masses, as
were not easily dissipable into such particles, as composed them.

To what may be deduced, in favour of this assertion
from the nature of the thing itself, I will add something
out of experience, which, though I have not known it used
to such a purpose, seems to me more fairly to make out
that there may be elementary bodies, than the more ques-
tionable experiments of Peripatetics and Chymists prove,
that there are such. I consider then, that gold will mix and
be colliquated not only with silver, copper, tin and lead,
but with antimony, regulus martis, and many other minerals, with which it will compose bodies very differing

both from gold, and the other ingredients of the resulting concretes. And the same gold will also by common aqua regis, and (I speak it knowingly) by divers other menstruums be reduced into a seeming liquor, insomuch, that the corpuscles of gold will, with those of the menstruum, pass through cap-paper, and with them also coagulate into a crystalline salt. And I have further tried, that with a small quantity of a certain saline substance I prepared, I can easily enough sublime gold into the form of red crystals, of a considerable length; and many other ways may gold be disguised, and help to constitute bodies of very differing natures both from it and from one another, and nevertheless be afterward reduced to the self-same numerical, yellow, fixt, ponderous, and malleable gold it was before its commixture. Nor is it only the fixedest of metals, but the most fugitive, that I may employ in favour of our proposition: for quicksilver will, with divers metals, compose an amalgam; with divers menstruums, it seems to be turned into a liquor; with aqua fortis, it will be brought into either a red or white powder; or precipitate; with oil of vitriol into a pale yellow one; with sulphur it will compose a blood-red and volatile cinnabar; with some saline bodies, it will ascend in form of a salt, which will be dissoluble in water; with regulus of antimony and silver, I have seen it sublimed into a kind of crystals; with another mixture, I reduced it into a malleable body, into a hard and brittle substance by another; and some there are who affirm, that by proper additaments they can reduce quicksilver into oil, nay into glass, to mention no more. And yet out of all these exotic compounds, we may recover the very same running mercury that was the main ingredient of them, and was so disguised in them. Now the reason . . . that I have represented these things concerning gold and quicksilver, is, that it may not appear absurd to conceive, that such little primary masses or

clusters, as our proposition mentions, may remain undissi-
pated, notwithstanding their entering into the composition
of various concretions, since the corpuscles of gold and
mercury, though they be not primary concretions of the
most minute particles of matter, but confessedly mixed
bodies, are able to concur plentifully to the composition
of several very differing bodies, without losing their own
nature or texture, or having their cohesion violated by the
divorce of their associated parts or ingredients. [*Works*, I,
474–75]

1. That there are in the world great store of particles
of matter, each of which is too small to be, whilst single,
sensible; and being entire or undivided, must needs both
have its determinate shape, and be very solid. Insomuch,
that though it be mentally, and by divine Omnipotence
divisible, yet by reason of its smallness and solidity nature
doth scarce ever actually divide it; and these may in this
sense be called *minima* or *prima naturàlia* [least or smallest natural things].

2. That there are also multitudes of corpuscles which
are made up of the coalition of several of the former
minima naturalia; and whose bulk is so small and their
adhesion so close and strict, that each of these little primitive concretions or clusters (if I may so call them) of particles is singly below the discernment of sense, and though
not absolutely indivisible by nature into the *prima naturalia* that composed it, or perhaps into other little fragments, yet, for the reasons freshly intimated, they very
rarely happen to be actually disolved or broken, but remain entire in great variety of sensible bodies, and under
various forms or disguises. As . . . we see that even grosser
and more compounded corpuscles may have such a permanent texture: for quicksilver, for instance, may be
turned into a red powder for a fusible and malleable body,

or a fugitive smoke, and disguised I know not how many
other ways, and yet remain true and recoverable mercury.
And these are, as it were, the seeds or immediate principles of many sorts of natural bodies, as earth, water, salt,
&c. and those singly insensible, become capable, when
united, to affect the sense: as I have tried, that if good
camphor be kept a while in pure spirit of wine, it will
thereby be reduced into such little parts as totally to disappear in the liquor, without making it look less clear
than fair water; and yet, if into this mixture you pour a
competent quantity of water, in a moment the scattered
corpuscles of the camphor will, by reuniting themselves,
become white, and consequently visible, as before their
dispersion.

3. That as well each of the *minima naturalia,* as each of
the primary clusters above mentioned having its own determinate bulk and shape, when these come to adhere to
one another, it must always happen that the size, and
often that the figure of the corpuscle composed by their
juxtaposition and cohesion, will be changed; and not seldom too, the motion either of one or the other, or both,
will receive a new tendency, or be altered as to its veloc-
ity or otherwise: and the like will happen when the corpuscles that compose a cluster of particles are disjoined,
or anything of the little mass is broken off. And whether
anything of matter be added to a corpuscle or taken from
it, in either case (as we just now intimated) the size of
it must necessarily be altered, and for the most part the
figure will be so too, whereby it will both acquire a congruity to the pores of some bodies (and perhaps some of
our sensories) and become incongruous to those of others;
and consequently be qualified, as I shall more fully show
you hereafter, to operate on divers occasions, much otherwise than it was fitted to do before.

4. That, when many of these insensible corpuscles come

to be associated into one visible body, if many or most of them be put into motion, from what cause soever the motion proceeds, that itself may produce great changes and new qualities in the body they compose; for not only motion may perform much even when it makes not any visible alteration in it, as air put into swift motion (as when it is blown out of bellows) acquires a new name, and is called Wind, and to the touch appears far colder than the same air not so formed into a stream; and iron, by being briskly rubbed against wood or other iron, has its small parts so agitated as to appear hot to our sense: but this motion oftentimes makes visible alterations in the texture of the body into which it is received; for always the moved parts strive to communicate their motion, or somewhat of the degree of it, to some parts that were before either at rest or otherwise moved, and oftentimes the same moved parts do thereby either disjoin or break some of the corpuscles they hit against, and thereby change their bulk or shape, or both, and either drive some of them quite out of the body, and perhaps lodge themselves in their places, or else associate them anew with others. Whence it usually follows that the texture is for a while at least, and unless it be very stable and permanent for good and all, very much altered, and especially in that the pores or little intervals intercepted betwixt the component particles will be changed as to bigness or figure, or both, and so will cease to be commensurate to the corpuscles that were fit for them before, and become commensurate to such corpuscles of other sizes and shapes, as till then were incongruous to them. Thus we see that water, by losing the wonted agitation of its parts, may acquire the firmness and brittleness we find in ice, and lose much of the transparency it had whilst it was a liquor. Thus also by very hard rubbing two pieces of resinous wood against one another, we may make them throw out divers of their looser parts into steams and visible smoke; and may, if the attrition be duly continued, make that commotion of the parts so change the texture of the whole, as afterwards to turn the superficial parts into a kind of coal. And thus milk, especially in hot weather, will by the intestine, though languid motions of its parts, be in a short time turned into a thinner sort of liquor than milk, and into cream, and this (last named) will, by being barely agitated in a churn, be turned in a short time into that unctuous and consistent body we call butter, and into thin, fluid and sour butter-milk. And thus (to dispatch) by the bruising of fruit, the texture is commonly so changed, that, as we see particularly in apples, the bruised part soon comes to be of another nature than the sound part, the one differing from the other both in colour, taste, smell, and consistence. So that (as we have already inculcated) local motion hath, of all other affections of matter, the greatest interest in altering and modifying of it; since it is not only the grand agent or efficient among second causes, but is also sometimes one of the principal things that constitutes the form of bodies. As when two sticks are set on fire by long and vehement attrition, local motion is not only that which kindles the wood, and so as an efficient produces the fire, but is that which principally concurs to give the produced stream of shining matter, the name and nature of flame: and so it concurs also to constitute all fluid bodies. . . . [*Works*, III, 29–31]

11. The Theory of Elements

Boyle's definition of an element is so famous that it is included here, though, as he says, there is nothing novel or original about it. It is only reasonable to read this definition in conjunction with his express rejection of the concept of elements. This is largely for experimental reasons, for he did not find that there was any chemical substance which was to be found in *all* substances, as the theory demanded. Seventeenth-century elements were not like twentieth-century ones (see Part One, Chapter 3). This definition and commentary is taken from *The Sceptical Chymist* (1661); it may be profitably compared with Boyle's later statement in the essay "Of the Imperfection of the Chymist's Doctrine of Qualities" from the *Mechanical Origin and Production of Qualities* (1675).

(1)

Though it may seem extravagant, yet it is not absurd to doubt, whether, for aught has been proved, there be a necessity to admit any elements, or hypostatical principles, at all. . . .

And to prevent mistakes, I must advertise you, that I now mean by elements, as those chymists, that speak plainest, do by their principles, certain primitive and simple, or perfectly unmingled bodies; which not being made of any other bodies, or of one another, are the ingredients, of which all those called perfectly mixt bodies are immediately compounded, and into which they are ultimately resolved: now whether there be any one such body to be constantly met with in all, and each, of those, that are said to be elemented bodies, is the thing I now question. . . .

I see not, why we must needs believe that there are any primogeneal and simple bodies, of which, as of pre-existent elements, nature is obliged to compound all others. Nor do I see, why we may not conceive, that she may produce the bodies accounted mixt out of one another, by variously altering and contriving their minute parts, without resolving the matter into any such simple or homogeneous substances, as are pretended. Neither, to dispatch, do I see, why it should be counted absurd to think, that when a body is resolved by the fire into its supposed simple ingredients, those substances, are not true and proper elements, but rather were, as it were, accidentally produced by the fire, which by dissipating a body into minute parts does, if those parts be shut up in close vessels, for the most part necessarily bring them to associate themselves after another manner than before, and so bring them into bodies of such different consistences, as the former texture of the body and concurrent circumstances make such disbanded particles apt to constitute; as experience shows us . . . that as there are some concretes whose parts, when dissipated by fire, are fitted to be put into such schemes of matter as we call oil, and salt, and spirit; so there are others, such as are especially the greatest part of minerals, whose corpuscles being of another size or figure, or perhaps contrived another way, will not in the fire yield bodies of the like consistencies, but rather others of differing textures; not to mention, that from gold and some other bodies, we see not, that the fire separates any distinct substances at all; nor that even those similar parts of bodies, which the chymists obtain by fire, are the elements, whose names they bear, but compounded bodies, upon which, for their resemblance to them in consistence, or some other obvious quality, chymists have been pleased to bestow such appellations. [*Works*, I, 562, 583]

(2)

And now I shall conclude . . . with this summary consideration: that the chymist's salt, sulphur, and mercury themselves are not the first and most simple principles of bodies, but rather primary concretions of corpuscles, or particles more simple than they, as being endowed only with the first, or more radical, (if I may so speak) and most catholick affections of simple bodies, namely, bulk, shape, and motion, or rest; by the different conventions or coalitions of which minutest portions of matter, are made those differing concretions, that chymists name salt, sulphur, and mercury. And to this doctrine it will be consonant, that several effects of this or that spagyrical principle need not be derived from salt, for instance, or sulphur as such, but may be explained by the help of some of those corpuscles, that I have lately called more simple and radical; and such explications being more simple and mechanical, may be thought, upon that score, more fundamental and satisfactory. [*Works*, IV, 281]

12. The Transmutation of Aristotelian Elements

The following, from the *Origin of Forms and Qualities*, is a famous experiment. It was referred to by Newton in Query 30 of the *Opticks* as evidence that all bodies may be made to give off light, since the earth of this experiment could, like all solids, be heated until it shone. In the eighteenth century it was often repeated, especially since it was a stumbling block in the path of the acceptance of elements. The author of the article "Chemistry" in the third edition of the *Encyclopaedia Britannica* (1788–97) got around its difficulties by denying its reliability, on the grounds that Boyle had handed the water over to an assistant for repeated distilling; he wrote: "Here it is evident, that great suspicions must lie against the fidelity of the unknown operator, who no doubt would be wearied out with such a number of distillations. The affair might appear trivial to him; and as he would perhaps know to which side Mr. Boyle's opinion inclined, he might favour it, by mixing some white earth with water. Had the experiment been tried by Mr. Boyle's own hand, his known character would have put the matter beyond a doubt." This is just and ingenious; but in fact, of course, the experiment would succeed exactly as Boyle describes. He himself actually provided a corrective to the conclusions which he drew from the experiment, noting at the conclusion all the objections which might be raised and even pointing out that the "earth" might come, as was indeed the case, from the glass vessel in which the water was heated. It is probable that the chemists who finally found the correct interpretation of this experiment—like Lavoisier in 1770—were merely following Boyle's suggestions.

Considerations and Experiments touching the Origin of Forms and Qualities

Experiment IX

The artificial transmutation of bodies being, as the rarest and difficultest production, so one of the noblest and usefullest effects of human skill and power, not only the clear instances of it are to be diligently sought for and prized, but even the probabilities of effecting such an extraordinary change of bodies are not to be neglected; especially if the version hoped for be to be made betwixt bodies of primordial textures (if I may so call them) and such bodies if by the greatness of their bulk, and by their being to be found in most of the mixed bodies here below, make a considerable part of those that we men have the most immediately to do with. Invited by these considerations . . . I shall venture to give you the account of some observations and trials about the transmuting of water into earth, though it be not so perfect as I wish, and as I hope by God's blessing to make it.

The first occasion afforded me to do anything about this matter was my being consulted by a gentleman (an ancient chymist, but not at all a philosopher) who relating to me how much he had (with the wonted success of such attempts) laboured after the grand *Arcana,*[20] complained to me, among other things, that, having occasion to employ great quantity of putrified rain-water, he obtained from it much less than he wished of the substance that he looked for, but a great deal of a certain whitish excrementitious matter, which he knew not what to make of. This gave me the curiosity first to desire a sight of it, in case he had not thrown it away (which by good fortune he had not) and then, taking notice of the unexpected plenty, and some of the qualities of it, to ask him some questions which were requisite and sufficient to persuade me, that this residence came not from accidental foulness of the water, nor of the vessels it was received in. This I afterwards often thought of, and indeed it might justly enough awaken some suspicions, that the little motes that have been sometimes observed to appear numerous enough in pure rain-water, whilst it is distilling, might not be merely accidental, but really produced, as well as exhibited by the action of the fire. I thought it then worth while to prosecute this matter a little farther; and having put a pretty quantity of distilled rain-water in a clean glass body, and fitted it with a head and a receiver, I suffered it to stand in a digestive furnace, till by the gentle heat thereof the water was totally abstracted, and the vessel left dry; which being taken out of the sand, I found the bottom of the glass covered over with a white (but not so very white) substance, which being scraped off with a knife, appeared to be a fine earth, in which I perceived no manifest taste, and which, in a word, by several qualities seemed to be earth.

This encouraged me to re-distil the rain-water in the same glass body, whose bottom, when the water was all drawn off, afforded me more of the like earth: but though the repetition of the experiment, and my having, for greater caution, tried it all the while in a new glass, that had not been employed before to other uses, confirmed me much in my conjecture, that unless it could be proved, which I think will scarce be pretended, that so insipid a liquor as rain-water should, in so gentle a heat, dissolve the most close and almost indestructible body of glass itself (which such corrosive menstruums as aqua fortis [nitric acid] and aqua regis [nitrohydrochloric acid] are wont to leave unharmed) the earthy powder I obtained from already distilled rain-water, might be a transmutation of some parts of the water into that substance; yet having unhappily lost part of my powder, and consumed almost all the rest (for I kept a little by me, which you may yet see) I should, till

I had more frequently reiterated my experiments (which then I had not opportunity to do, though I had thoughts of doing it also with snow-water that I had put into chymical glasses for that purpose, and with liquor of melted hail, which I had likewise provided) and thereby also obtained some more of this virgin earth (so divers chymists would call it) to make farther trials with, having retained greater suspicions, if I had not afterwards accidentally fallen into discourse of this matter with a learned physician, who had dealt much in rain-water; but he much confirmed me in my conjecture, by assuring me that he had frequently found such a white earth as I mentioned in distilled rain-water, after he had distilled the same numerical liquor (carefully gathered at first) I know not how many times one after another; adding, that he did not find (any more than I had done) any cause to suspect, that if he had continued to re-distil the same portion of water, it would have yielded him more earth.

But the oddness of the experiment still keeping me in suspense, it was not without much delight, that afterwards mentioning it to a very ingenious person, whom without his leave, I think not fit to name, well versed in chymical matters, and whom I suspected to have, in order to some medicines, long wrought upon rain-water, he readily gave me such an account of his proceedings, as seemed to leave little scruple about the transmutation we have been mentioning: for he solemnly affirmed to me, that having observed, as I had done, that rain-water would, even after a distillation or two, afford a terrestrial substance, which may sometimes be seen swimming up and down in the limpid liquor, he had the curiosity, being settled and at leisure, to try how long he could obtain this substance from the water. And accordingly having freed rain-water, carefully collected, from its accidental, and as it were feculent earthiness, which it will deposit at the first slow distillation (and which is oftentimes coloured, whereby it may be distinguished from the white earth made by transmutation) he re-distilled it in very clean glasses, not only eight or ten times, but near two hundred, without finding that his liquor grew weary of affording him the white earth, but rather that the corpuscles of it did appear far more numerous, or at least more conspicuous in the latter distillation than in the former. And when I expressed my curiosity to see this earth, he readily showed me a pretty quantity of it, and presented me with some, which comparing with what I had remaining of mine, I found to be exceeding like it, save that it was more purely white, as having been for the main afforded by rain-water that had been more frequently rectified. And to compare this welcome powder with that I made myself, I tried this with divers things, which I had before tried with my own and (because the quantity presented me was less inconsiderable) some others too. For I observed in this new powder, as I had done with my own, that being put into an excellent microscope, and placed where the sun-beams might fall upon it, it appeared a white meal, or a heap of corpuscles so exceeding, not to say unimaginably small, that in two or three choice microscopes both I and others had occasion to admire it: and their extreme littleness was much more sensibly discerned by mingling some few grains of sand amongst them, which made a mixture that looked like that of pebble stones, and the finest flour. For our earth, even in the microscope, appeared to consist of as small particles, as the finest hair-powder to the naked eye. Nor could we discern this dust to be transparent, though, when the sun shined upon it, it appeared in the microscope to have some particles a little glistering, which yet appearing but in a glaring light, we were not sure to be no *deceptio visus* [trick of the light].

2. I found, that our white powder being cast into water,

would indeed for a while discolour it by somewhat whitening it, which is no more than spaud will do, and the fine dust of white marble and other stones, whose corpuscles, by reason of their minuteness, swim easily for a while in the water; but when it was once settled at the bottom, it continued there undissolved (for aught I could perceive) for some days and nights, as earth would have done.

3. Having weighed a quantity of it, and put it into a new clean crucible, with another inverted over it for a cover, I placed it among quick coals, and there kept the crucible red-hot for a pretty while, causing the fire afterward to be actuated with a blast of a bellows; but taking out the powder, I neither found it melted nor clotted into lumps, nor, when I weighed it again, did I see cause to conclude, that there was much of it wasted, besides what stuck to the sides of the crucible and to a little clay, wherewith I had luted on the cover (and which, to show you that the heat had not been inconsiderable, was in several places burnt red by the vehemence of fire): and when I afterwards kept this powder in an open crucible among glowing coals, neither I, nor one that I employed to assist me, perceived it at all to smoke; and having put a little upon a quick coal, and blown that too, I found that which I had not blown away, to remain fixed (which some bodies will not do) upon quick coals, that will endure the fire in a red-hot crucible.

4. I found this powder to be much heavier in specie than water; for employing a nice pair of gold scales, and a method that would be too long here to describe, I found that this powder weighed somewhat (though not much) more than twice so much common water, as was equal to it in bulk. And lest some corollaries, that seem obviously contained in the common but groundless conceits of the Peripatetics, about the proportions of the elements in density, &c. should make you expect that this powder ought

to have been much more ponderous, I shall add, that having had the curiosity, which I wonder nobody should have before me, to examine the gravity of the earth, which seems the most elementary of any we have, I took some sifted wood-ashes, which I had caused to be three or four times boiled in a plentiful proportion of water, to free them from salt, and having put them very dry into common water, I found them but little heavier than our newly mentioned powder, surpassing in weight water of the same bulk but twice, and a little more than a 6th part (water and it being very little more than as 1 to $2\frac{1}{6}$). And that you may the less doubt of this, I will yet subjoin, that examining the specific gravity of (white) glass itself, I found that compact body to be very little, if at all, more than two times and a half as heavy as water of an equal bigness to it. So that the gravity of that powder, which, borrowing a chymical term, we have been calling virgin earth, being added to its fixedness and other qualities, it may seem no great impropriety of speech to name it earth; at least if by earth we mean not the pure elementary earth of the schools, which many of themselves confess not to be found actually separate, but a body dry, cold, ponderous, enduring the fire, and, which is the main, irresoluble by water and fire into other bodies specifically different.

But to return to the guise of the powder; when I asked this learned man, whether he had observed the glass he distilled in to have been fretted by the liquor, and whether this lost of its substance, according as it deposited more powder, he answered me (and he is a person of unsuspected credit) that he found not his glass to have been injured by the liquor, and that the water wasted (though he was careful it should not do so by evaporation and transfusions) by degrees so much, that there remained by his estimate but about an eight part of the first quantity. And though for certain reasons he kept by him the liquor last distilled, yet he doubted not but that it might be very nigh totally brought into earth, since out of an ounce of distilled rain-water he had already obtained near three quarters of an ounce, if not more, of the often mentioned earth.

These several relations will, I suppose, persuade you . . . that this experiment is hopeful enough to be well worth your pursuing; if not, that perhaps none but such a scrupulous person as I would think the prosecution of it other than superfluous; and if you do acquiesce in what hath been already done, you will, I presume, think it no mean confirmation of the corpuscularian principles and hypotheses; for if, contrary to the opinion that is so much in request among the generality of modern physicians and other learned men, that the elements themselves are transmuted into one another, and those simple and primitive bodies, which nature is presumed to have intended to be the stable and permanent ingredients of the bodies the compounds here below, may be artificially destroyed, and (without the intervention of a seminal and plastic power) generated or produced: if, I say, this may be done, and that by such slight means, why may we not think that the changes and metamorphoses that happen in other bodies, which are acknowledged by the moderns to be far more liable to alterations, may proceed from the local motion of the minute or insensible parts of matter, and the changes of texture that may be consequent thereunto? . . .

But . . . I would not have you wonder, that whilst I was mentioning the many particulars that seem to evince the change of water into earth, I should let fall some words that intimate a diffidence about it. For to disguise nothing unto you, I must confess, that having in spite of an unusual care unluckily lost a whole paper of the powder I had made myself, and having unexpectedly been obliged to remove from my furnaces before I had made half the trials

I judged requisite in so nice a case, I have not yet laid aside all my scruples.

For 1. I would gladly know whether the untransmuted rain-water, by the deposition of so much terrestrial matter, were grown lighter in specie than before, or sharp in taste. Next I would be thoroughly satisfied (which I must confess I am not yet, notwithstanding all that the followers of Angelus Sala[21] have confidently enough written) whether and how far insipid liquors (as rain-water is) may or may not work as menstruums upon stones or earthy bodies: not to question whether the particles of rain-water may not by their mutual attrition, or some other action upon one another, be reduced into shapes and sizes fit to compose such a menstruum as the liquor was not before; as in divers plants that seemed to be nourished only with water, the sap is endowed with a sharp taste and great penetrancy and activity of parts.

2. It were also fit to know whether the glass body, wherein all the distillations are made, do lose of its weight anything near so much as the obtained powder amounts to over and above the decrement of weight which may be imputed to the action of the heat upon the substance of the glass, in case it appear by another glass, kept empty in an equal heat, and for the same time, that the glass loses by such operations anything worth reckoning. And it were also not impertinent to try whether the gravity of the obtained powder be the same in specie with that of the glass wherein the distillations were made (for that it differed but about a fifth part from the weight of crystalline glass I lately mentioned). Which scruple and some of the former I might have prevented, if I had had convenient metalline vessels wherein to make the distillations instead of glass ones.

3. I could wish likewise that it were more demonstrably determined what is on all hands taken for granted (as it

appears highly probable) that distilled rain-water is a perfectly homogeneous body; which if it be not, divers suspicions might be suggested about its transmutation into earth; and if it be, it will be, as a very strange thing, so a matter of very great difficulty to conceive, how a perfectly and exquisitely homogeneous matter should, without any addition, or any seminal and plastic principle, be brought to afford great store of a matter of much more specific gravity than itself; since we see that no aggregate we can make of bodies, but equiponderant in specie with water, doth by virtue of their convention grow specifically heaver than it. . . .

I might . . . subjoin divers other particulars, if it were not too tedious to mention to you all the doubts and considerations that have occurred to me about the recited change of water into earth: which yet are not such as ought to hinder me from giving you the historical account I have set down, since to some of my scruples I could here give plausible answers, but that I cannot do it in few words. And if any part of our white powder prove to be true earth, nobody perhaps yet knows to what the experiment may lead sagacious men: and whether in a strict sence it be true earth or no, yet the phaenomena that are exhibited in the production of it are sufficient to give this ninth experiment a place among the others . . . with which it is associated. For since out of a substance that is universally acknowledged to be elementary and homogeneous, and which manifestly is fluid, transparent, much lighter in specie than earth, moist and fugitive, there is artificially generated or obtained, a substance consistent, white, and consequently opacous, comparatively ponderous, dry, and not at all fugitive: the alteration is so great, and effected in so simple a way, that it cannot but afford us a considerable instance of what the varied texture of the minute parts may perform in a matter confessedly similar. And if

frequently distilled rain-water should not be allowed homogeneous, our experiment will at least show us, better
than perhaps any hath yet done, how little we are bound
to believe what the chymists and others tell us, when they
pretend manifestly to exhibit to us homogeneous principles
and elementary bodies; and how difficult it is to be certain,
when a body is absolutely irresoluble into specifically differing substances, and consequently what is the determinate number of the perfectly simple ingredients of bodies
(supposing that such there are): though I must confess
that my only aim is not to relate what hath been done, but
to procure the prosecution of it. For if the obtained substance be by the rain-water dissolved out of the glass, this
will both prove a noble and surprising instance of what
may be done by insipid menstruums, even upon bodies
that are justly reckoned among the compactest and most
indissoluble that we know of, and may afford us many
other considerable hints that have been partly intimated
already: and if, on the other side, this powder, whether
it be true elementary earth or not, be found to be really
produced out of the water itself, it may prove a *magnale*
[wonder] in nature, and of greater consequence than will
be presently foreseen, and may make the alchymists hopes
of turning other metals into gold appear less wild; since
that by experimentally evincing that two such difficult
qualities to be introduced into a body, as considerable degrees of fixity and weight (whose requisiteness to the making of gold are two of the principal things that have kept
me from easily expecting to find the attempts of alchymists
successful) may, without the mixture of the homogeneous
matter, be generated in it, by varying the texture of its
parts. . . . [*Works*, III, 102–8]

13. The Mechanical Explanation of Qualities

The bulk of Boyle's writing on the corpuscular philosophy was devoted to explaining mechanically all the properties of bodies, chemical and physical, that came within his sphere of interest, or for which he could devise an experimentally grounded explanation. The first of the selections below sets forth some general considerations (taken from the introduction to the *Mechanical Origin and Production of Qualities*, 1675): this is followed by brief examples of explanations (mostly from the same source but also from *Certain Physiological Essays* and the *Usefulness of Experimental Philosophy*) of heat, cohesion, fluidity, firmness, corrosiveness, chemical precipitation, gravity, magnetism, electricity, color, light, and fire. The prefatory "advertisements" give Boyle's theory of presentation of this subject, as well as his philosophy of explanation and the advantages of the mechanical philosophy for this purpose. Most of the selections below are examples of the experimental evidence which Boyle normally annexed to any theoretical discussion of his corpuscular philosophy. The *Enquiry and Experiments about Electricall Bodys* is a hitherto unpublished plan of research. The discussion of color is all drawn from the *Experiments and Considerations touching Colours*, published in 1664 (for other selections from this work, see Section III). This is one of the most important of Boyle's works; it was filled with really excellent examples, nicely balanced between easy experiments which would catch the layman's eye and more important experiments which would genuinely contribute to the advancement of science. *Lignum nephriticum*, whose opalescent solution so interested Boyle (his is one of the best descriptions of its optical properties, before that in Newton's *Opticks*) was a New World wood of supposedly valuable medical properties. It was actually far more helpful as a chemical reagent than as a relief for disease of the kidney. *The New Experiments to Make Fire and Flame Stable and Ponderable* (1673) is better seen as an experimental treatise on the mechanical explanation of fire than as an unsuccessful attempt to explain combustion. Boyle saw it as one more example of the mechanical solution of the problem of the origin of forms; the corporeality of fire was one more blow against occult qualities. Boyle here displays a truly remarkable quantitative technique. His units of weight were troy or apothecary units; thus 1 drachm equals 60 grains, 1152 grains equal one troy ounce, and 12 ounces equals one pound. One grain is approximately equal to 60 milligrams. Weighing to one grain was about the outside limit of accuracy of the apothecary's balance; Boyle used more accurate balances, but probably did not bother with an assayer's balance, which at this time was often accurate to the nearest 0.1 to 0.03 grams (6 to 2 milligrams). The reason he failed to notice that air played a role was not lack of quantitative technique—his accuracy was of the right order of magnitude—but an *a priori* conviction that air was not a chemical reactant, while fire was; hence it must be the fire which combined with the metal to form the calx (oxide). Boyle was in fact making the error for which he so often, and rightly, censured his opponents; unfortunately the experimental results appeared to support his theoretical convictions.

Advertisements Relating to the Following Treatise

To obviate some misapprehensions that may arise concerning the ensuing notes about particular qualities, it may not be improper . . . to premise to the particular experiments some few general advertisements about them.

And I. we may consider, that there may be three differing ways of treating historically of particular qualities. For either one may in a full and methodical history prosecute the phaenomena; or one may make a collection of various experiments and observations, whence may be gathered divers phaenomena to illustrate several, but not all of the heads or parts of such an example or methodical history; or, in the third place, one may in a more confined way content one's self to deliver such experiments and observations of the productions, or the destruction or change of this or that quality, as being duly reasoned on, may suffice to show, wherein the nature of that quality doth consist, especially in opposition to those erroneous conceits, that have been entertained about it. Of the first of these three ways of treating of a quality I pretend not to have given any complete example; but you will find, that I have begun such histories in my specimens about fluidity and firmness, and in the experiments, observations, &c. that I have put together about cold. The second sort of historical writings I have given an instance of in my experiments about colours; but in these ensuing notes, the occasion I had to make them, having obliged me chiefly to have an eye to the disproval of the errors of the peripateticks and the chymists about them, I hope I shall not be thought to have fallen very short in my attempt, if I have (here and there) performed, what may be required in the third way of writing historically of a quality; my present design being chiefly to give an intelligent and historical account of the possible mechanical origination, not of the various phaenomena of the particular qualities succinctly mentioned in these notes; though my secondary end being to become a benefactor to the history of qualities by providing materials for myself or better architects, I have not scrupled to add to those, that tend more directly to discover the nature or essence of the quality treated of, and to derive it from mechanical principles, some others (which happened to come in my way) that acquaint us but with some of the less luciferous phaenomena.[22]

II. That you may not mistake what is driven at in many of the experiments and reasonings delivered or proposed in the ensuing notes about particular qualities, I must desire you to take notice with me, what it is, that I pretend to offer you some proofs of. For if I took upon me to demonstrate, that the qualities of bodies cannot proceed from (what the schools call) substantial forms, or from any other causes but mechanical, it might be reasonably enough expected, that my argument should directly exclude them all. But since, in my explications of qualities, I pretend only, that they may be explicated by mechanical principles, without enquiring, whether they are explicable by any other; that, which I need to prove, is, not that mechanical principles are the necessary and only things, whereby qualities may be explained, but that probably they will be found sufficient for their explication. And since these are confessedly more manifest and more intelligible, than substantial forms and other scholastic entities (if I may so call them) it is obvious, what the consequence will be of our not being obliged to have recourse to things, whose existence is very disputable, and their nature very obscure.

There are several ways, that may be employed, some on one occasion, and some on another, either more directly to reduce qualities (as well as divers other things in nature) to mechanical principles; or, by showing the insufficiency of the Peripatetick and chymical theories of qualities, to recommend the Corpuscularian doctrine of them.

For further illustration of this point, I shall add on this occasion, that there are three distinct sorts of experiments (besides other proofs) that may be reasonably employed, (though they be not equally efficacious) when we treat of the origin of qualities. For some instances may be brought to show, that the proposed quality may be mechanically introduced into a portion of matter, where it was not before. Other instances there may be to show, that by the same means the quality may be notably varied as to degrees, or other not essential attributes. And by some instances also it may appear, that the quality is mechanically expelled from, or abolished in, a portion of matter, that was endowed with it before. Sometimes also by the same operation the former quality is destroyed, and a new one is produced. And each of these kinds of instances may be usefully employed in our notes about particular qualities. For as to the first of them, there will be scarce any difficulty. And as to the second, since the permanent degrees, as well as other attributes of qualities are said to flow from (and do indeed depend upon) the same principles, that the quality itself does; if, especially in bodies inanimate, a change barely mechanical does notably and permanently alter the degree or other considerable attribute; it will afford, though not a clear proof, yet a probable presumption, that the principles, whereon the quality itself depends; are mechanical. And lastly, if, by a bare mechanical change of the internal disposition and structure of a body, a permanent quality, confessed to flow from its substantial form, or inward principle, be abolished, and, perhaps, also immediately succeeded by a new quality mechanically producible; if, I say, this come to pass in a body inanimate, especially, if it be also, as to sense similar, such a phaenomenon will not a little favour that hypothesis, which teaches, that these qualities depend upon certain contextures, and other mechanical affections of the small parts of the bodies, that are endowed with them, and consequently may be abolished when that necessary modification is destroyed. This is thus briefly premised to show the pertinency of alledging differing kinds of experiments and phaenomena, in favour of the corpuscular hypothesis about qualities.

What has been thus laid down, may, I hope, facilitate and shorten most of the remaining work of this preamble, which is to show, though but very briefly, that there may be several ways, not impertinently employable to recommend the corpuscularian doctrine of qualities.

For first, it may sometimes be shown, that a substantial form cannot be pretended to be the necessary principle of this or that quality; as will, for instance, hereafter be made manifest in the asperity and smoothness of bodies, and in the magnetical virtue, residing in a piece of iron, that has been impregnated by a loadstone. It is true, that the force of such instances is indirect, and that they do not expressly prove the hypothesis, in whose favour they are alledged; but yet they may do it good service, by disproving the grounds and conclusions of the adversaries, and so (by removing prejudices) making way for the better entertainment of the truth.

Secondly, we may sometimes obtain the same, or the like quality, by artificial and sometimes even temporary compositions, which, being but factitious bodies, are by learned adversaries confessed, not to have substantial forms, and can indeed reasonably be presumed to have but resulting temperaments: as will be hereafter exemplified in the production of green and by compounding blue and yellow, and in the electrical faculty of glass; and in the temporary whiteness produced by beating clear oil and fair water into an ointment, and by beating water into a froth, and, more permanently, in making coral white by flawing it with heat; and in divers other particulars, that will more properly be elsewhere mentioned.

Thirdly then, in some cases the quality proposed may be either introduced, or varied, or destroyed, in an inanimate body, when no change appears to be made in the body, except what is mechanical, and what might be produced in it, supposing such a parcel of matter were artificially framed and constituted as the body is, though without any substantial form, or other such like internal principle. So when a piece of glass, or of clarified rosin, is, by being beaten to powder, deprived of its transparency, and made white, there appears no change to be made in the pulverized body, but a comminution of it into a multitude of corpuscles, that by their number, and the various situations of their surfaces are fitted copiously to reflect the sincere light several ways, or give some peculiar modification to its rays; and hinder that free passage of the beams of light, that is requisite to transparency.

Fourthly, as in the cases belonging to the foregoing number there appears not to intervene in the patient or subject of the change, any thing but a mechanical alteration of the mechanical structure or constitution; so in some other cases it appears not, that the agent, whether natural or factitious, operates on the patient, otherwise than mechanically, employing only such a way of acting, as may proceed from the mechanism of the matter, which itself consists of, and that of the body it acts upon. As when goldsmiths burnish a plate or vessel of silver, that having been lately boiled looked white before, though they deprive it of the greatest part of its colour, and give it a new power of reflecting the beams of light and visible objects, in the manner proper to specular bodies; yet all this is done by the intervention of a burnishing tool, which often is but a piece of steel or iron conveniently shaped; and all that this burnisher does, is but to depress the little prominencies of the silver, and reduce them, and the little cavities of it, to one physically level or plain superficies. And so when a hammer striking often on a nail, makes the head of it grow hot, the hammer is but a purely mechanical agent, and works by local motion. And when by striking a lump of glass, it breaks it into a multitude of small parts, that compose a white powder, it acts as mechanically in the production of that whiteness, as it does in driving in a nail to the head. And so likewise, when the powdered glass, or colophony [rosin] lately mentioned, is, by the fire, from a white and opacous body, reduced into a colourless (or a reddish) and transparent one, it appears not, that the fire, though a natural agent, need work otherwise than mechanically, by colliquating the incoherent grains of powder into one mass; wherein, the ranks of pores not being broken and interrupted as before, the incident beams of light are allowed every way a free passage through them.

Fifthly, the like phaenomena to those of a quality to be explicated, or at least as difficult in the same kind, may be produced in bodies and cases, wherein it is plain we need not recur to substantial forms. Thus a varying colour, like that, which is admired in a pigeon's neck, may be produced in a changeable taffety, by a particular way of ranging and connecting silk of several colours into one piece of stuff. Thus we have known opals casually imitated and almost excelled by glass, which luckily degenerated in the furnace. And somewhat the like changeable and very delightful colour I remember to have introduced into common glass, with silver or with gold and mercury. So likewise merely by blowing fine crystal-glass, at the flame of a lamp, to a very extraordinary thinness, we have made it to exhibit, and that vividly, all the colours (as they speak) of the rainbow; and this· power of pleasing by diversifying the light, the glass, if well preserved, may keep for a long time. Thus also by barely beating gold into such thin leaves, as artificers and apothecaries are wont to employ, it will be brought to exhibit a green colour, when you hold it against the light, whether of the day, or of a good candle; and this kind of greeness, as it is permanent in the foliated

gold, so I have found by trial, that if the sun-beams, somewhat united by a burning-glass be trajected through the
expanded leaf, and cast upon a piece of white paper, they
will appear there, as if they had been tinged in their passage. Nay, and sometimes a slight and almost momentary
mechanical change will seem to over-rule nature, and introduce into a body the quite opposite quality to that she had
given it: as when a piece of black horn is, only by being
thinly scraped with the edge of a knife, or a piece of glass,
reduced to permanently white shavings. And to these instances of colours, some emphatical, and some permanent,
might be added divers belonging to other qualities, but
that I ought not to anticipate what you will elsewhere
meet with.

There is yet another way of arguing in favour of the
Corpuscularian doctrine of qualities, which, though it do
not afford direct proofs of its being the best hypothesis,
yet it may very much strengthen the arguments drawn
from other topics, and thereby serve to recommend the
doctrine itself. For, the use of an hypothesis being to render
an intelligible account of the causes of the effects, or
phaenomena proposed, without crossing the laws of nature,
or other phaenomena; the more numerous, and the more
various the particulars are, whereof some are explicable by
the assigned hypothesis, and some are agreeable to it, or
at least, are not dissonant from it, the more valuable is the
hypothesis, and the more likely to be true. For it is much
more difficult, to find an hypothesis, that is not true, which
will suit with many phaenomena, especially, if they be of
various kinds, than but with a few. And for this reason, I
have set down among the instances belonging to particular
qualities, some such experiments and observations, as we
are now speaking of, since, although they be not direct
proofs of the preferableness of our doctrine, yet they may
serve for confirmation of it; though this be not the only,

or perhaps the chief reason of their being mentioned. For, whatever they may be as argument, since they are matters of fact, I though it not amiss to take this occasion of preserving them from being lost; since, whether or no they contribute much to the establishment of the mechanical doctrine about qualities, they will, at least, contribute to the natural history of them.

III. I shall not trouble the reader with a recital of those unlucky accidents that have hindered the subjects of the following book from being more numerous; and I hope he will the more easily excuse their paucity, if he be advertised, that although the particular qualities, about which some experiments and notes, by way of specimens, are here presented, be not near half so many as were intended to be treated of; yet I was careful to choose them such, as might comprehend in a small number of great variety; there being scarce one sort of qualities, of which there is not an instance given in this small book, since therein experiments and thoughts are delivered about heat and cold, which are the chief of the four first qualities; about tastes and odours, which are of those, that, being the immediate objects of sense, are wont to be called sensible qualities; about volatility and fixity, corrosiveness and corrosibility, which, as they are found in bodies purely natural, are referable to those qualities, that many physical writers call second qualities, and which yet, as they may be produced and destroyed by the chemists are, may be styled chemical qualities and the spagyrical ways of introducing, or expelling them, may be referred to chemical operations, of which there is given a more ample specimen in the mechanical account of chemical precipitations. And lastly, some notes are added about magnetism and electricity, which are known to belong to the tribe of occult qualities.

IV. If a want of apt coherence, and exact method, be discovered in the following essays, it is hoped, that defect will be easily excused by those, that remember and consider, that these papers were originally little better than a kind of rhapsody of experiments, thoughts, and observations, occasionally thrown together by way of annotations, upon some passages of a discourse, (about the differing parts and redintegration of nitre) wherein some things were pointed at, relating to the particular qualities, that are here more largely treated of. And though the particulars, that concern some of these qualities, were afterwards (to supply the place of those borrowed by other papers whilst these lay by me) encreased in number; yet it was not to be expected, that their accession should as well correct the form as augment the matter of our annotations. And as for the two tracts, that are inserted among these essays about qualities; I mean, the discourse of the imperfection of the chymical doctrine of them, and the reflections on the hypothesis of acidum and alcali, the occasion of their being made parts of this book, is so far expressed in the tracts themselves, that I need not here trouble the reader with a particular account of it.

V. I do not undertake, that all the following accounts of particular qualities would prove to be the very true ones, nor every explication the best, that can be devised. For besides that the difficulty of the subject, and incompleteness of the history we yet have of qualities, may well deter a man, less diffident of his own abilities than I justly am, from assuming so much to himself, it is not absolutely necessary to my present design. For, mechanical explications of natural phaenomena do give so much more satisfaction to ingenious minds, than those, that must employ substantial forms, sympathy, antipathy, &c. that the more judicious of the vulgar philosophers themselves prefer them before all others, when they can be had (as is elsewhere shown at large); but then they that look upon them either as confined to mechanical engines, or at least, but as reaching to very few of nature's phaenomena, and, for that reason, unfit to be received as physical principles. To remove therefore this grand prejudice and objection, which seems to be the chief thing, that has kept off rational inquiries from closing with the mechanical philosophy, it may be very conducive, if not sufficient, to propose such mechanical accounts of particular qualities themselves, as are intelligible and possible, and are agreeable to the phaenomena whereto they are applied. And to this it is no more necessary, that the account proposed should be the truest and best, that can possibly be given, than it is to the proving, that a clock is not acted by a vital principle (as those Chinese thought, who took the first, that was brought them out of Europe, for an animal,) but acts as an engine, to do more than assign a mechanical structure made up of wheels, a spring, a hammer, and other mechanical pieces, that will regularly show and strike the hour, whether this contrivance be, or be not, the very same with that of the particular clock proposed; which may indeed be made to move either with springs or weights, and may consist of a greater or lesser number of wheels, and those differingly situated and connected; but for all this variety, it will still be but an engine. I intend not therefore by proposing the theories and conjectures ventured at in the following papers, to debar myself of the liberty either of altering them, or of substituting others in their places, in case a further progress in the history of qualities shall suggest better hypotheses or explications. And it was but agreeable to this intention of mine, that I should, as I have done, on divers occasions in the following notes, employ the word *or*, and express myself somewhat doubtingly, mentioning more than one cause of a phaenomenon, or reason of an opinion, without dogmatically declaring for either; since my purpose in these notes was rather to show, it was not necessary to betake ourselves to the scholastick or chymical doctrine about qualities, than to act the umpire between the differing hypotheses of the Corpuscularians; and, provided I kept myself within the bounds of mechanical philosophy, my design allowed me a great latitude in making explications of the phaenomena I had occasion to take notice of. [*Works*, IV, 231–36]

Heat

The nature of [heat] . . . seems to consist mainly, if not only, in that mechanical affection of matter we call local motion mechanically modified, which modification, as far as I have observed, is made up of three conditions.

The first of these is, that the agitation of the parts be vehement, by which degree of rapidness the motion proper to bodies, that are hot, distinguishes them from bodies, that are barely fluid. For these, as such, require not near so brisk an agitation, as is wont to be necessary to make bodies deserve the name of hot. Thus we see, that the particles of water, in its natural (or usual) state, move so calmly, that we do not feel it at all warm, though it could not be a liquor, unless they were in a restless motion; but when water comes to be actually hot, the motion does manifestly and proportionably appear more vehement, since it does not only briskly strike our organs of feeling, but ordinarily produces store of very small bubbles, and will melt butter or coagulated oil cast upon it, and will afford vapours, that, by the agitation they suffer, will be made to ascend into the air. . . . Thus, in a heated iron, the vehement agitation of the parts may be easily inferred, from the motion and hissing noise it imparts to drops of water, or spittle, that fall upon it. For it makes them hiss and boil, and quickly forces their particles to quit the form of a liquor, and fly away into the air in the form of steams. And, lastly, fire, which is the hottest body we know, consists of parts so vehemently agitated, that they perpetually and swiftly fly abroad in swarms, and dissipate or shatter all the combustible bodies they meet with in their way; fire making so fierce a dissolution, and great a dispersion of its own fuel, that we may see whole piles of solid wood (weighing perhaps many hundred pounds) so dissipated, in very few hours, into flame and smoke, that, oftentimes, there will not be one pound of ashes remaining, and this is the first condition required to heat.

The second is this, that the determinations be very various, some particles moving towards the right, some to the left hand, some directly upwards, some downwards, and some obliquely, &c. . . .

And it will be convenient to begin with an instance or two of the production of heat, wherein there appears not to intervene anything in the part of the agent or patient, but local motion, and the natural effects of it. And as to this sort of experiments, a little attention and reflection may make some familiar phaenomenon apposite to our present purpose. When, for example, a smith does hastily hammer a nail, or such like piece of iron, the hammered metal will grow exceeding hot, and yet there appears not anything to make it so, save the forcible motion of the hammer, which impresses a vehement, and variously determined agitation of the small parts of the iron; which being a cold body before, by that superinduced commotion of its small parts, becomes in divers senses hot; first, in a more lax acceptation of the word in reference to some other bodies, in respect of whom it was cold before, and then sensibly hot; because this newly gained agitation, surpasses that of the parts of our fingers. And in this instance, it is not to be overlooked, that oftentimes neither the hammer, by which, nor the anvil, on which a cold piece of iron is forged, (for all iron does not require precedent ignition to make it obey the hammer) continue

cold, after the operation is ended; which shows, that the
heat acquired by the forged piece of iron was not com-
municated by the hammer or anvil as heat, but produced
in it by motion, which was great enough to put so small
a body as the piece of iron, into a strong and confused
motion of its parts, without being able to have the like
operation upon so much greater masses of metal, as the
hammer and the anvil; though, if the percussion were
often and nimbly renewed, and the hammer were but
small, this also might be heated (though not so soon, nor
so much, as the iron); by which one may also take notice,
that it is not necessary, a body should be itself hot, to be
calorific. And now I speak of striking an iron with a hammer, I am put in mind of an observation, that seems to
contradict, but does indeed confirm our theory: namely,
that if a somewhat large nail be driven by a hammer into
a plank, or piece of wood, it will receive divers strokes on
the head before it grow hot; but when it is driven to the
head, so that it can go no further, a few strokes will suffice
to give it a considerable heat; for whilst, at every blow of
the hammer, the nail enters further and further into the
wood, the motion, that is produced, is chiefly progressive,
and is of the whole nail tending one way; whereas, when
that motion is stopped, then the impulse given by the
stroke, being unable either to drive the nail further on,
or destroy its entireness, must be spent in making a various, vehement and intestine commotion of the parts
among themselves, and in such an one we formerly observed the nature of heat to consist. [*Works*, IV, 244-45,
249-50]

Cohesion, Fluidity, Firmness

As to what is very confidently, as well as plausibly pretended, that a substantial form is requisite to keep the

parts of a body united, without which it would not be one body; I answer, That the contrivance of conveniently figured parts, and in some cases their juxtaposition, may, without the assistance of a substantial form, be sufficient for this matter. . . . [*Works*, III, 45]

The qualifications, that conduce most to the fixity of a portion of matter, seem to be these.

First, the grossness, or the bulk of the corpuscles it consists of. . . .

The next is the ponderousness, or solidity of the corpuscles it is made up of. . . .

The third qualification, that conduces to the fixity of a body, belongs to its integral parts, not barely as they are several parts of it, but as they are aggregated or contexted into one body. For, the qualification, I mean, is the ineptitude of the component corpuscles for avolation, by reason of their branchedness, irregular figures, crookedness, or other inconvenient shape, which entangles the particles among one another, and makes them difficult to be extricated; by which means, if one of them do ascend, others, wherewith it is complicated, must ascend with it; and, whatever be the account, on which divers particles stick firmly together, the aggregate will be too heavy or unwieldy to be raised. Which I therefore take notice of, because that, though usually it is on the roughness and irregularity of corpuscles, that their cohesion depends; yet it sometimes happens, that the smoothness and flatness of their surfaces makes them so stick together, as to resist a total divulsion. . . . [*Works*, IV, 306–7]

A body then seems to be fluid, chiefly upon this account, that it consists of corpuscles, that touching one another in some parts only of their surfaces (and so being incontiguous in the rest) and separately agitated to and fro, can by reason of the numerous pores or spaces necessarily left betwixt their contiguous parts, easily glide along each other's superficies, and by reason of their motion diffuse themselves, till they meet with some hard or resting body; to whose internal surface, by virtue of that motion, their smallness, and either their gravity, or something analogous or equivalent to it, they exquisitely, as to sense, accommodate themselves. . . . [Works, I, 378–79]

The firmness or stability of a body consists principally in this, that the particles that compose it, besides that they are most commonly somewhat gross, either do so rest, or are so intangled between themselves, that there is among them a mutual cohesion, whereby they are rendered unapt to flow or diffuse themselves. . . . [Works, I, 401]

Corrosiveness

The attributes, that seem the most proper to qualify a liquor to be corrosive, are all of them mechanical, being such as are these, that follow:

First, that the menstruum consist of, or abound with corpuscles not too big to get in at the pores or commissures of the body to be dissolved; not yet be so very minute, as to pass through them, as the beams of light do through glass; or to be unable, by reason of their great slenderness and flexibility, to disjoin the parts they invade.

Secondly, that these corpuscles be of a shape fitting them to insinuate themselves, more or less, into the pores or commissures above mentioned, in order to the dissociating of the solid parts.

Thirdly, that they have a competent degree of solidity to disjoin the particles of the body to be dissolved; which solidity of solvent corpuscles is somewhat distinct from their bulk, mentioned in the first qualification; as may appear, by comparing a stalk of wheat and a metalline wire of the same diameter, or a flexible wand of osier, of the bigness of one's little finger, with a rigid rod of iron of the same length and thickness.

Fourthly, that the corpuscles of the menstruum be agile and advantaged for motion, (such as is fit to disjoin the parts of the invaded body) either by their shape, or their minuteness, or their fitness to have their action befriended by adjuvant causes; such as may be (first) the pressure of the atmosphere, which may impel them into the pores of bodies not filled with a substance so resisting as common air . . . and (secondly) the agitation, that the intruding corpuscles may be fitted to receive in those pores or commissures, by the transcursion of some subtile aetherial matter; or by the numerous knocks and other pulses of the swimming or tumbling corpuscles of the menstruum itself (which, being a fluid body, must have its small parts perpetually and variously moved), whereby the engaged corpuscles, like so many little wedges and levers, may be enabled to wrench open, or force asunder the little parts between which they have insinuated themselves. . . . [*Works*, IV, 314–15]

Chemical Precipitation

By precipitation is here meant, such an agitation or motion of a heterogeneous liquor, as in no long time makes the parts of it subside, and that usually in the form of a powder, or other consistent body. . . .

As for the causes of precipitation, the very name itself, in its chemical sense, having been scarce heard of it in the Peripatetic schools, it is not to be expected, that they should have given us an account of the reasons of the thing. And it is like, that those few Aristotelians, that

have, by their converse with the laboratories or writings
of chymists, taken notice of this operation, would, according to their custom on such occasions, have recourse for
the explication of it to some secret sympathy or antipathy
between the bodies, whose action and reaction intervenes
in this operation.

But if this be the way proposed of accounting for it, I
shall quickly have occasion to say somewhat to it, in considering the ways proposed by the chymists, who were
wont to refer precipitation, either, as is most usual, to a
sympathy betwixt the precipitating body and the menstruum, which makes the solvent run to the embraces of
the precipitant, and so let fall the particles of the body
sustained before; or (with others) to a great antipathy,
or contrariety between the acid salt of the menstruum and
the fixed salt of the oil, or solution of calcined tartar,
which is the most general and usual precipitant they
employ.

But I see not, how either of these causes will either
reach to all the phaenomena, that have been exhibited, or
give a true account even of some of those, to which it
seems applicable. For first, in precipitations, wherein what
they call a sympathy between the liquors is supposed to
produce the effect, this admired sympathy does not (in
my apprehension) evince such a mysterious occult quality, as is presumed, but rather consists in a greater congruity, as to bigness, shape, motion, and pores of the minute parts between the menstruum and the precipitant,
than between the same solvent and the body it kept before
dissolved. And though this sympathy, rightly examined,
may be allowed to have an interest in some such precipitations, as let fall the dissolved body in its pristine nature
and form, and only reduced into minute powder; yet I find
not, that, in the generality of precipitations, this doctrine
will hold; for in some, that we have made of gold and

silver in proper menstruums, after the subsiding matter
had been well washed and dried, several precipitates of
gold made, some with oil of tartar, which abounds with
a fixed salt, and is the usual precipitant, and some with
an urinous spirit,[23] which works by virtue of a salt highly
fugitive or volatile, I found the powder to exceed the
weight of the gold and silver I had put to dissolve; and
the eye itself sufficiently discovers such precipitates not
to be mere metalline powders, but compositions, whose
consisting, not (as hath been by somebody suspected) of
the combined salts alone, but of the metalline parts also,
may be strongly concluded, not only from the ponderousness of divers of them, in reference to their bulk, but also
manifestly from the reduction of true malleable metals
from several of them. [*Works*, IV, 329–30]

Gravity

Though the effects of gravity be very obvious, yet the
cause and nature of it are as obscure, as those of almost
any phenomenon it can be brought to explicate. . . . A
stone may be said to strive to descend . . . either by the
magnetical steams of the earth, or the pressure of some
subtile matter incumbent upon it, or by whatever else
may be the cause of gravity. . . . [*Works*, II, 36–37,39]

Magnetism

Though the virtues of the loadstone be none of the least
famous of occult qualities, and are perhaps the most justly
admired; yet I shall venture to offer something to make
it probable, that some, even of these, may be introduced
into bodies by the production of mechanical changes in
them. . . .

We elsewhere observe which perhaps you also may

have done, that the iron bars of windows, by having stood very long in an erected posture, may at length, grow magnetical, so that, if you apply the north point of a poised and excited needle to the bottom of the bar, it will drive it away, and attract the southern; and if you raise the magnetic needle to the upper part of the bar, and apply it as before, this will draw the northern extreme, which the other end of the bar expelled; probably because, as it is elsewhere declared, the bar is in tract of time, by the continual action of the magnetical effluvia of the terr-aqueous globe, turned into a kind of magnet, whose lower end becomes the north pole of it, and the other the southern. Therefore, according to the magnetical laws, the former must expel the northern extreme of the needle, and the latter draw it. . . .

As may be often, though not always, observed in tongs, and such like iron utensils, that, having been ignited, have been set to cool, leaning against some wall or other prop, that kept them in an erected posture, which makes it probable, that the great commotion of the parts, made by the vehement heat of the fire, disposed the iron, whilst it was yet soft, and had its pores more lax, and parts more pliable, disposed it, I say, to receive much quicker impressions from the magnetical effluvia of the earth, than it would have done, if it had still been cold. [*Works*, IV, 340–43]

Electricity

MECHANICAL ORIGIN

In electrical attraction, not only effluvia are emitted by the electrical body, but these effluvia fasten upon the body to be drawn, and that in such a way, that the intervening viscous strings, which may be supposed to be made up of those cohering effluvia are, when their agitation ceases, contracted or made to shrink inwards, towards both ends, almost as a highly stretched lutestring does, when it is permitted to retreat into shorter dimensions. But the conjecture itself was much more easy to be made, than the experiment requisite to examine it. [*Works*, IV, 349]

ENQUIRY AND EXPERIMENTS ABOUT ELECTRICALL BODYS

What Bodys are Electricall and what not. What are the differing kinds of Electricall Bodys as Amber, Jett, Resins, Sulphurs, Diamonds, Christall, Sparse,[24] Glasse, Cornelians, &c.

Whether all Gums, as Gum Arabeck, and those only that are soluble in water and aqueous Liquors, and whether those Gums that are soluble both in water and Oyle, and whether also all Sulphurs, as that of Antimony, and of Mars,[25] are Electricall.

Whether the same Body may be Magneticall and Electricall, which question is to be determin'd by the Glasse of Iron made at the Smelting mill, and by vitrify'd Steel.

Whether the same Body may be made without addition (by a bare change of Texture) to be sometimes Electricall, and sometimes not Electricall (to be try'd in Glasse of Lead and in that of Copper or of Silver made per se).

To try the Operations of two Electricall Bodys plac'd at opposite places of the Body to be attracted, and either of equal force or of differing, and plac'd at aequall or unaequall distances, &c.

Whether a large and strong Electricall Body will attract without being at all rub'd and whether it will doe soe at all seasons of the year and in all kinds of weather without excepting frosty.

Whether Quicklime and Minium colliquated into a vitreous Saturnis, will compose an Electrical Body.[26]

Whether Amber &c. will be excited by haveing its small parts put into motion by any moderate heat (as of the Sun) or even that of warme water, without [there] being the intervention of frication.

To measure the attractive power of Electricall Bodys by a nice pair of Scales, to one of which the Body to be attracted is to be conveniently ty'd or fasten'd.

To try whether Electricall Bodys will at all attract under water, or other Liquors.

To try whether the extract of red Amber will be more Electricall than the Amber itself was; and whether Amber unbroken being infus'd in pure spirit of wine often renue'd till the Liquor will yeeld no more tincture, the remaining Lump will have its Electricall vertue lessen'd, encreas'd or neither.

Whether the Colophony,[27] if I may soe call it, that may be obtained from Amber distill'd warily and per se, will after the recesse of the salt and volatile oyle, and of the phlegme & spirit, be Electricall, and more or lesse so then Amber it self was.

Whether the mixture of differing Electricall Bodys as hard wax & Rosin, will make the composition more or less Electrical than the Ingredients; whether this mixture be made by fire, or by dissolving them both in rectify'd spirit of wine; and afterwards totally and slowly abstracting the menstruum.

Whether in case Oyle of Amber, or the Balsome of it made per se,[28] can by a mixture of snow and salt be made to freeze, that frozen Liquor will be Electricall.

Whether the parts of distill'd Amber Distill'd per se being reunited into a kind of Resin, will be Electricall; and if they be, whether the mixture will be more or lesse soe, then the Amber it self was.

Whether in case Oyle of Turpentine can by salt of Amber, or any other Salts, be reduc'd to a consistent Body, that will be Electricall. The like Enquiry may be made concerning all other Oyles and Balsoms, as also Bodys too soft to be fit for brisk rubbing, as Palm Oyle, Beeswax, expressed Oyle of Mace, &c.

Whether the various maners of nealing Glasse soe as to make it more or lesse brittle, will encrease or diminish the Electricity of it, and in what proportions.

Whether Glasse either made red hot, or considerably heated, will retain all its Electricall facultie, or any part of it.

What difference will be made in Amber &c. by operating upon it with Spirit of Urine and Sal Armoniack & other volatile salt or else with Spirit of Salt or Nitre or Oyle of Vitriol instead of spirit of wine.

What are the severall degrees of attractive power in Electricall Bodys of differing kinds.

Of the Sphere of activity of Electricall Bodys how far it reaches.

In what proportion if in any the attractive power in Electricall Bodys decreases according as the Body to be drawne is remoter from it.

What kind or measure of friction dos give an Electricall Body its highest power of attracting; by what degrees of friction it attains that power, and if it be heated by friction beyond what is requisite to its utmost energies, by what degree its attractive power will be impair'd.

Whether a Lump of Amber will attract a small Needle or a peece of it whilst it is red hot.

Whether an Electricall Body will retain its attractive vertue intire or unimpair'd in our Receiver when it is carefully empty'd of Aire.

Whether a peace of Amber being turn'd into a solid Globe there will be anything remarkable discovered by that figure in reference to the way and force of Electrical Effluviums.

Whether Electricall Bodys attract more forcibly in any

one position than in another, accounting for the differing gravity which the Body to be drawne may have according to its differing Scituations.

Whether the action of an Electricall Body or the motion of the effluviums by which it is perform'd be made in any certain lines as straight, circular, ellipticall, &c. which may be try'd, by severall ways, as by small bitts of downe fasten'd to soft wax, or by Liquors to whose smooth surface the Body may be apply'd.

Whether a strong Electricall Body will attract the surface of the Liquors, especially good spirit of wine and oyle.

Whether an Electricall Body will attract all light Bodys indifferently, and particularly . . . flame either of a Taper or spirit of wine.

Whether an Electricall Body being suspended at a nice pair of scales, and rub'd till it emit an Effluvium, not only strongly attractive, but such as may be smelt, will loose anything discernable of its weight. [Royal Society Boyle Papers, Vol. XXII]

Color

Colour is so far from being an inherent quality of the object in the sense that is wont to be declared by the schools, or even in the sense of some modern Atomists, that, if we consider the matter more attentively, we shall see cause to suspect, if not to conclude, that though light do more immediately affect the organ of sight, than do the bodies that send it thither, yet light itself produces the sensation of colour, but as it produces such a determinate kind of local motion in some part of the brain; which, though it happen from the motion whereinto the slender strings of the retina are put, by the appulse of light; yet if the like motion . . . be produced by any other cause, wherein the light concurs not at all, a man shall think he sees the same colour. For proof of this, . . . it is usual for dreaming men to think they see the images that appear to them in their sleep, adorned . . . with this and . . . that lively colour, whilst yet, both the curtains of their bed, and those of their eyes, are close drawn. And I might add the confidence with which distracted persons do oftentimes, when they are awake, think they see black fiends in places, where there is no black object in sight without them. But I will rather observe, that not only when a man receives a great stroke upon his eye, or a very great one upon some other part of his head, he is wont to see, as it were, flashes of lightning, and little vivid, but vanishing flames, though perhaps his eyes be shut: but the like apparitions may happen, when the motion proceeds not from something without, but from something within the body, provided the unwonted fumes that wander up and down in the head, or the propagated concussion of any internal part in the body, do cause, about the inward extremities of the optic nerve, such a motion as is wont to be there produced, when the stroke of the light upon the retina makes us conclude, that we see either light or such and such a colour. [This is exemplified by coughing in the night (observation on himself); bright flashes of light said by a lady to precede hysterical attacks; sign of approaching attack of plague.] [*Works*, I, 71–72]

THE NATURE OF WHITENESS AND BLACKNESS

Whiteness then considered as a quality in the object seems chiefly to depend upon this, that the superficies of the body, that is called white, is asperated by almost innumerable small surfaces; which being of an almost specular nature, are also so placed, that some looking this way, and some that way, they yet reflect the rays of light that fall on them, not towards one another, but outwards to-

wards the spectator's eye. In this rude and general account
of whiteness, it seems, that besides those qualities, which
are common to bodies of other colours, as for instance the
minuteness and number of the superficial parts, the two
chief things attributed to bodies as white are made to be,
first, that little protuberances and superficial parts be
of somewhat a specular nature, that they may, as little
looking-glasses, each of them reflect the beams it receives
(or the little picture of the sun made on it) without otherwise considerably altering them; whereas in most other
colours, they are wont to be much changed, by being also
refracted, or by being returned to the eye, mixt with
shades or otherwise. And next, that its superficial parts
be so situated, that they retain not the incident rays of
light by reflecting. them inwards, but send them almost
all back; so that the outermost corpuscles of a white
body, having their various little surfaces of a specular nature, a man can from no place behold the body, but that
there will be among those innumerable *superficielculae*,[29]
that look some one way, and some another, enough of
them obverted to his eye, to afford, like a broken looking-
glass, a confused idea, or representation of light, and make
such an impression on the organ, as that for which men
are wont to call a body white . . . indeed it seems, that
as that, which makes a body white, is chiefly such a disposition of its parts, that it reflects (I mean without much
interruption) more of the light that falls on it, than bodies
of any other colour do; so that, which makes a body black
is principally a peculiar kind of texture, chiefly of its superficial particles, whereby it does as it were dead the
light that falls on it, so that very little is reflected outwards
to the eye. . . .

And the better to show that white bodies reflect store of
light, in comparison of those that are otherwise coloured,
I did in . . . [a] darkened room . . . hold not far off from

the hole, at which the light was admitted, a sheet only of white paper, from whence casting the sun-beams upon a white wall, whereunto it was obverted, it manifestly appeared both to me, and to the person I took for a witness of the experiment, that it reflected a far greater light, than any of the other colours I formerly mentioned; the light so thrown upon the wall notably enlightening it, and by it a good part of the room. And yet further to show you, that white bodies reflect beams from them, and not towards themselves, let me add, that ordinary burning glasses, such as are wont to be employed to light tobacco, will not in a great while burn, or so much as discolour a sheet of white paper. Insomuch that even when I was a boy, and loved to make trials with burning-glasses, I could not but wonder at this odd phaenomenon, which set me very early upon guessing at the nature of whiteness; especially because I took notice, that the image of the sun upon a white paper was not so well defined (the lighting seeming too diffused) as upon black, and because I tried, that blacking over the paper with ink, not only the ink would be quickly dried up, but the paper, that I could not burn before, would be quickly set on fire. I have also tried, that my exposing my hand with a thin black glove over it to the warm sun, it was thereby very quickly and considerably more heated, than if I took off the glove, and held my hand naked, or put on it another glove of thin but white leather. . . .

And to show, that the beams, that fall on black bodies, as they do not rebound outwards to the eye, so they are reflected towards the body itself, as the nature of those erected particles, to which we have imputed blackness, requires, we will add another experiment, that will also confirm our doctrine touching whiteness; namely, we took a broad and large tile, and having whitened over one half of the superficies of it, and blacked the other, we exposed it to the summer's sun; and having let it lie there a convenient time (for the difference is more apparent, if it have not lain there too long) we found, as we expected, that whilst the whited part of the tile remained cool enough, the blacked part of the same tile was grown not only sensible, but very hot (sometimes to a strong degree). And to satisfy some of our friends the more, we have sometimes left upon the surface of the tile, besides the white and black parts thereof, a part, that retained the native red of the tile itself; and exposing them to the sun, we observed this last mentioned to have contracted a heat in comparison of the white, but a heat inferior to that of the black; of which the reason seems to be, that the superficial particles of black bodies, being, as we said, more erected, than those of white or red ones, the corpuscles of light falling on their sides, being for the most part reflected inward from one particle to another, and thereby engaged as it were, and kept from rebounding upwards, they communicate their brisk motion, wherewith they were impelled against the black body (upon whose account, had they fallen upon a white body, they would have been reflected outwards) to the small parts of the black body, and thereby produce in those small parts such an agitation, as (when we feel it) we are wont to call heat. . . . And with this doctrine accords very well, that rooms hung with black are not only darker than else they would be, but are wont to be warmer too; insomuch that I have known a great lady, whose constitution was somewhat tender, complain, that she was wont to catch cold, when she went out into the air, after having made any long visits to persons, whose rooms were hung with black. [*Works*, I, 697, 699, 704]

LIGHT AND COLORS

October the 11th, About ten in the morning in sun-shiny weather (but not without fleeting clouds) we took several sorts of paper stained, some of one colour, and some of another; and in a darkened room, whose window looked southward, we cast the beams, that came in at a hole about three inches and a half in diameter, upon a white wall, that was placed on one side, about five foot distance from them.

The white gave much the brightest reflection.

The green, red, and blue being compared together, the red gave much the strongest reflection, and manifestly enough also threw its colour upon the wall: the green and blue were scarce discernible by their colours, and seemed to reflect an almost equal light.

The yellow, compared with the two last named, reflected somewhat more light.

The red and purple being compared together, the former manifestly reflected a good deal more light.

The blue and purple being compared together, the former seemed to reflect a little more light, though the purple colour were more manifestly seen. . . . [*Works*, I, 725]

AN AMUSING EXPERIMENT ON WHITENESS AND BLACKNESS

That a solution of silver does dye hair of a black colour, is a known experiment, which some persons, more curious than dexterous, have so unluckily made upon themselves as to make their friends very merry. And I remember, that the other day I made myself some sport by an improvement of this observation; for having dissolved some pure silver in aqua fortis, and evaporated the *menstruum ad siccitatem*,[30] as they speak, I caused a quantity of fair water to be poured upon the calx two or three several times, and to be at each evaporated, till the calx was very dry, and all the greenish blueness, that is wont to appear in common crystals of silver, was quite carried away. Then I made those I meant to deceive, moisten some part of their skin with their own spittle, and slightly rub the moistened parts with a little of this prepared silver; whereupon they admired to see, that a snow-white body laid upon the white skin should presently produce a deep blackness, as if the stains had been made with ink; especially considering, that this blackness could not, like that produced by ordinary ink, be readily washed off, but required many hours, and part of it some days, to its oblivion. [*Works*, I, 714]

Color in Solution—Experiment X

Take Lignum Nephriticum, and with a knife cut it into thin slices; put about a handful of these slices into two, three or four pounds of the purest spring-water; let them infuse there a night; but if you be in haste, a much shorter time may suffice. Decant this impregnated water into a clear glass phial; and if you hold it directly between the light and your eye, you shall see it wholly tincted, (excepting the very top of the liquor, wherein you will sometimes discern a sky-coloured circle) with an almost golden colour, unless your infusion have been made too strong of the wood; for in that case it will against the light appear somewhat dark and reddish, and requires to be diluted by the addition of a convenient quantity of water. But if you hold this phial from the light, so that your eye be placed betwixt the window and the phial, the liquor will appear of a deep and lovely ceruleous colour, of which also the drops, if any be lying on the outside of the glass, will seem to be very perfectly. . . . If you so hold the phial over against your eyes, that it may have a window on one side of it, and a dark part of the room both before it and on the other side, you shall see the liquor partly of a bluish and partly of a golden colour. If turning your back to the window, you pour out some of the liquor towards the light and towards your eyes, it will seem at the coming out of the glass to be perfectly ceruleous, but when it is fallen down a little way, the drops may seem parti-coloured,

according as the beams of light do more or less fully penetrate and illustrate them. [*Works*, I, 729–30]

New Experiments to Make Fire
and Flame Stable and Ponderable

A Preface; showing the Motive, Design,
and Parts of the ensuing Tract.

The inducements which put me upon the attempt expressed in the title of this essay, were chiefly these:

First, I considered that the interstellar part of the universe, consisting of air and aether, or fluids analogous to
one of them, is diaphanous; and that the aether is, as it
were, a vast ocean, wherein the luminous globes, that here
and there, like fishes, swim by their own motion, or like
bodies in whirlpools are carried about by their ambient,
are but very thinly dispersed, and consequently, that the
proportion that the fixed stars and planetary bodies bear
to the diaphanous part of the world, is exceeding small,
and scarce considerable, though we should admit the sun
and fixed stars to be opacous bodies, upon the account of
their terminating our sight; which diffident expression I
employ, because I have elsewhere shown by two or three
experiments, purposely devised, that a body may appear
opacous to our eyes, and yet allow free passage to the
beams of light.

I further considered, that there being so vast a disproportion between the diaphanous part of the world, and
the globes, about which it is every way diffused, and with
which it is sometimes in great portions mingled, as in the
water, which, together with the earth, makes up the globe
we inhabit; and the nature of a diaphanous body's being
such, that when the sun, or any other luminous body illus-

trates them, that which we call light does so penetrate, and mix itself *per minima,*[31] with them, that there is no sensible part of the transparent body unenlightened; I thought it worth the inquiry, whether a thing so vastly diffused as light is, were something corporeal, or not? and, whether in case it be, it may be subjected to some other of our senses, besides our sight, whereby we may examine, whether it hath any affinity with other corporeal things that we are acquainted with here below? . . .

To compass, then, what I aimed at, I thought it was fit, in the first place, to try what I could do by the union of the sunbeams, they being on all hands confessed to be portions (as I may so speak) of true and celestial light; and then I thought fit to try what could be obtained from flame; not only, because that is acknowledged to be a luminary, but because I hoped the difficulties I foresaw in the other trials might be, in some measure, avoided in those made with flame; and if both sorts of them should succeed, the latter and former would serve to confirm each other. According to the method I proposed of handling these two subjects, I should begin with some account of what I attempted to perform in the sunbeams. But the truth is, that when I chanced to fall upon the inquiry that occasioned this paper, besides that the time of the year itself was not over-favourable, the weather proved so extraordinary dark and unseasonable, that it was wondered at; so that, though I was furnished with good burning glasses, and did several times begin to make trials upon divers bodies, as lead, quicksilver, antimony, &c. yet the frequent interposition of clouds and mists did so disfavour my attempts, that, however they were not all alike defeated, yet I could not prosecute the greatest part of them to my own satisfaction. And therefore, being unwilling to build on them as yet, I shall reserve an account of them for another opportunity; and now proceed to the mention of that sort of experiments, which, depending less on casualties, it was more in my power to bring to an issue. . . .

A piece of copper-plate not near so thick as a half-crown, and weighing two drachms and twenty-five grains, was so placed with its broad part horizontal, in a crucible, whose bottom had a little hole in it for fumes to get out at, that it could not be removed from its position, nor be easily made to drop down or lose its level to the horizon, though the crucible were turned upside down; then about an ounce and half of common sulphur being put into a taller and broader crucible, that wherein the copper stuck was inverted into the orifice of it, that the sulphur being kindled, the flame, but not the melted brimstone, in substance, might reach the plate, and have some vent beyond it at the above-mentioned hole. This brimstone burned about two hours, in which time it seemed all to have been resolved into flame, no flowers of sulphur appearing to have sublimed into the inside of the upper crucible; and though the copper-plate were at a considerable distance from the ignited sulphur, yet the flame seemed to have really penetrated it, and to have made it visibly swell or grow thicker; which appeared to be done by a real accession of substance; since, after we had wiped off some little adhering sordes, and with them divers particles of copper that stuck close to them, the plate was found to weigh near two-and-thirty grains more than at first, and consequently to have increased its former weight by above a fifth part.

Into a crucible whose sides had been purposely taken down to make it very shallow, was put one ounce of copper-plates; and this being put into our cupelling-furnace, and kept there two hours, and then being taken out, we weighed the copper (which had not been melted) having first blown off all the ashes, and we found it to weigh one ounce and thirty grains.

EXPERIMENT IV

Supposing that copper, being reduced to filings, and thereby gaining more of superficies in proportion to its bulk, would be more exposed to the action of the fire than when it is in plates, as it was formerly, we took an ounce of that metal in filings, and putting them upon a very shallow crucible, and under a muffler, we kept them there about three hours (whilst other things that required so long a time were cupelling); and afterwards taking them off, we found them of a very dark colour, not melted, but caked together in one lump, and increased in weight (the ashes and dust being blown off) no less than about forty-nine grains. Part of which increment, above that obtained by the copper-plates in the former experiment, may not improbably be due to the longer time, that in this experiment the filed copper was kept in the fire.

EXPERIMENT VI

Upon a good cupel we put one ounce of English tin of the better sort, and having placed it in the furnace under the muffler, though it presently melted, yet it did not forsake its place, but remained upon the concave surface of the cupel, till at the end of about two hours, it appeared to have been well calcined; and then being taken out and weighed by itself, the ounce of metal was found to have gained no less than a drachm.

EXPERIMENT IX

Iron being a metal, that experience had informed me will more easily be wrought on by fluids that have particles of a saline nature in them, than is commonly believed; it was not unreasonable to expect that flame would have a greater operation on it (especially if it were beforehand reduced to small parts) than on any of the bodies hitherto described. Which supposition will be confirmed by the short ensuing note.

Four drachms of filings of steel being kept two hours on a cupel under a muffler, acquired one drachm six grains and a quarter increase of weight.

After having shown, that either flame, or the analogous effluxions of fire, will be, what chymists would call corporated with metals and minerals exposed naked to its action; I thought it would be a desirable thing to discover, whether this flame or igneous fluid were subtile enough to exercise any such operation upon the light bodies sheltered from its immediate contact, by being included in close vessels; but it being very difficult to expose bodies in glasses to such vehement fires, without breaking or melting the glass, and thereby losing the experiment; I thought fit, first, to employ crucibles carefully luted together, that nothing might visibly get in or out; and of that attempt I find among my notes the following account.

EXPERIMENT XIV

We took an ounce of steel freshly filed from a lump of that metal, that the filings might not be rusty, and having included them betwixt two crucibles, as formerly, kept them for two hours in a strong fire, and suffered them to continue there until the fire went out; the crucibles being unluted, the filings appeared hard-caked together, and had acquired a dark colour, somewhat between black and blue, and were increased five grains in weight.

The foregoing experiment being the first I mention of this kind, it will not be amiss to confirm it, by annexing the following memorial.

An ounce of filings of steel being put between the crucibles luted together, after they had been kept about an hour and half in the fire, were taken out, and being weighed, were found to have gained six grains.

Most of the experiments hitherto recited having been made, as it were, upon the by with others, whose exigencies it was fit these should comply with; very few of the exposed bodies were kept in the cupelling-fire above two hours, or thereabouts. Upon which account, I thought fit to try, how much some bodies that had been already exposed to the fire, would gain in weight, by being again exposed to it; especially considering, that most calcinable bodies (for I affirm it not of all) which yield rather calces than ashes, by being without additament reduced in the fire to fine powder, seemed to be by that operation opened, or (as a chymist would speak) unlocked, and therefore, probably, capable of being further wrought upon, and increased in weight, by such a menstruum, as I supposed flame and igneous exhalations to be. And about this conjecture, I shall subjoin the ensuing trials.

EXPERIMENT XIX

One ounce of calx of tin that had been made *per se*, for an experiment in our own laboratory, being put in a new cupel, and kept under the muffler for about two hours, was taken out hot, and put into the scales, where the powder appeared to have gained in weight one drachm, and thirty-five grains, by the operation of the fire, which made it also look much whiter than it did before, as appeared by comparing it with some of the calx that had not been exposed to the second fire; no part of the putty was, as we could perceive, melted by the vehemencies of the fire, much less reduced into metal.

EXPERIMENT XX

Out of a parcel of filings of steel that had been before exposed to the fire, and had its weight thereby increased some grains, not scruples; we took an ounce, and having exposed it at the same time with the calx of tin, and, for the same time, kept it in the fire, we took it out at the two hours end; and found the weight to be increased two drachms, and two-and-twenty grains. The filings were very hard baked together, and the lump being broken, looked almost like iron. [*Works*, III, 708–17, passim]

A Discovery of the Perviousness of Glass
to Ponderable Parts of Flame

EXPERIMENT II

Because it seems evident enough, that whatever chymists tell us of the hypostatical sulphur,[32] common brimstone is a body heterogeneous enough, having in it some parts of an oily or inflammable nature, and others acid, and very near of kin to the spirits of vitriol; I thought it fit to vary our experiment, by making it with a liquor that is generally reputed to be as homogeneous as chymists themselves are wont to render any, I mean with a spirit of wine, or some such liquor as will totally flame away without affording soot, or leaving any drop of phlegm behind it. In prosecution of this design, we carefully weighed out an ounce of filings of block-tin, and put them into a glass retort, fit for the purpose, whose neck was afterwards drawn out to a great slenderness; and we also provided a conveniently shaped metalline lamp, such as that the flame of this ardent spirit might commodiously burn in it, and yet not melt or crack it; which lamp, though furnished with a cotton wick, afforded no soot, because, as long as it was supplied with liquor enough, it remained unburnt. These things being in readiness, the retort was warily approached to the flame, and the metal was thereby in a short time melted. After which, the glass being kept exposed to the same flame for near two hours in all, the sealed apex of the retort was broken off, and there appeared to have been produced a not inconsiderable quantity of calx, that lay loose about the remaining part of the tin, which, upon its growing cold, was hardened into a lump. This, and the calx, being taken out of the retort with care, that no little fragment of glass should at all impose upon us, was weighed in the same scales as formerly, and found to have gained four grains and a half, besides the dust, that stuck in the inside of the retort, of which we reckoned enough to make about half a grain more; so that of so fine and pure a flame, as of this totally ardent spirit, enough to amount to five grains, was arrested, and in good measure fixed by its operation on the tin it had wrought upon.

EXPERIMENT III

For confirmation of the former trial, wherein we had employed the spiritus ardens of sugar, we made the like experiment with highly rectified spirit of wine, only substituting an ounce of lead instead of one of tin. The event, in short, was this; that after the metal had been for two hours or better kept in the flame, the sealed neck of the retort being broken off, the external air rushed in with a noise (which showed the vessel to have been very tight) and we found pretty store of the lead, for it was above seven scruples, turned into a greyish calx, which together with the rest of the metal being weighed again, there was very near, if not full six grains of increase acquired by the operation. . . .

Corollary I

Confirming this paradox, that flame may act as a menstruum, and make coalitions with the bodies it works on.

The experiments we have made and recited, of the permeating of flame (as to some of its parts) through glass vessels, and of its working on included metals, may much confirm the paradox I have elsewhere proposed, that flame may be a menstruum, and work on some bodies at the rate of being so; I mean, not only by making a notable comminution and dissipation of the parts, but by a coalition of its own particles with those of the fretted body, and thereby permanently adding substance and weight to them. Nor is it repugnant to flame's being a menstruum, that in our experiment the lead and tin, exposed to it, were but reduced to powder, and not dissolved in the form of a liquor, and kept in that state. For, besides that the interposed glass hindered the igneous particles from getting through in plenty enough; I consider that it is not necessary, that all menstruums should be such solvents, as the objection supposes. For whether it be (as I have sometimes suspected) that menstruums, that we think simple, may be compounded of very differing parts, whereof one may precipitate what is dissolved by the other; or for some other cause, I have not now time to discuss. Certain it is, that some menstruums corrode metals and other bodies, without keeping dissolved all, or perhaps, any considerable part; as may be seen, if you put tin in a certain quantity of aqua fortis, which will in a very short time reduce it almost totally to a very white substance, which, when dry, is a kind of calx. And so by a due proportion of oil of vitriol, abstracted from quicksilver by a strong fire, we have divers times reduced the main body of the mercury into a white powder, whereof but an inconsiderable part would be dissoluble in water....

COROLLARY II

Proposing a Paradox about Calcination, and Calces

Another consequence, deducible from our discovery of the perviousness of glass to flame, may be this, that there is cause to question the truth of what is generally taken for granted about calcination, and particularly of the notion, that not only others but chymists themselves, have entertained about the calces of metals and minerals. For whereas it is commonly supposed, that in calcination the greater part of the body is driven away, and only the earth, to which chymists add the fixed salt, remains behind; and whereas even mechanical philosophers (for two or three of them have taken notice of calcination) are of opinion, that much is driven away by the violence of the fire, and the remaining parts, by being deprived of their more radical and fixed moisture, are turned into dry and brittle particles: whereas these notions, I say, are entertained about calcination, it seems, that they are not well framed, and do not universally hold; since, at least, they are not applicable to the metals our experiments were made on. For, it does not appear by our trials, that any proportion, worth regarding, of moist and fugitive parts, was expelled in the calcination; but it does appear very plainly, that by this operation the metals gained more weight than they lost; so that the main body of the metal remained entire, and was far from being, either as a Peripatetic would think, elementary earth, or a compound of earth and fixed salt, as chymists commonly suppose the calx of lead to be. From which very erroneous hypothesis they are wont to infer the sweet vitriol of lead, which they call saccharum Saturni,[33] to be but the sweet salt of it extracted only by the spirit of vinegar, which does indeed plentifully enough concur to compose it. Whence I conclude, that the calx of a metal even made, as they speak, *per se,* that is, by fire without additament, may be, at least in some cases, not the *caput mortuum,* or *terra damnata,* but a magistery[34] of it. For, in the sense of the most intelligible of the chymical writers, that is properly a magistery, wherein the principles are not separated, but the bulk of the body being preserved, it acquires a new and convenient form by the addition of the menstruum, or solvent, employed about the preparation. And, not here to borrow any argument from my notes about particular qualities, you may guess how true it is that the greatest part of the body, or all the radical moisture, is expelled in calcination, which therefore turns the metal into an arid, unfusible powder; by this, that I have several times, from calx of lead, reduced corporeal lead. And I remember, that having taken what I guessed to be but about a third, or fourth part of the calx of lead, produced by the third experiment, found by a trial purposely devised, that without any flux-powder, or any additament, but merely by the application of the flame of highly rectified spirit of wine, there could, in a short time, be obtained a considerable proportion of malleable lead; whereof the part I had the curiosity to examine, was true malleable lead; so little was the arid powder, whence this was reduced, deprived by the foregoing calcination of the supposed radical moisture requisite to a metal. . . . [*Works,* III, 724–29]

14. Early Chemistry

The following letters, written to Lady Ranelagh, give the earliest information we have on Boyle's first interest in chemistry. The moralizing tone is characteristic of all his writing in this period, when he was not much more than twenty years old. These letters clearly show how rapidly he found that chemistry was not only his favorite science, but a most absorbing pursuit.

That great earthern furnace, whose conveying hither has taken up so much of my care, and concerning which I made bold very lately to trouble you, since I last did so, has been brought to my hands crumbled into as many pieces, as we into sects; and all the fine experiments, and castles in the air, I had built upon its safe arrival, have felt the fate of their foundation. Well, I see I am not designed to the finding out the philosophers stone, I have been so unlucky in my first attempts at chemistry. My limbecks, recipients, and other glasses have escaped indeed the misfortune of their incendiary, but are now, through the miscarriage of that grand implement of Vulcan, as useless to me, as good parts to salvation without the fire of zeal. Seriously, Madam, after all the pains I have taken, and the precautions I have used, to prevent this furnace the disaster of its predecessors, to have it transported a thousand miles by land, that I may after all

this receive it broken, is a defeat, that nothing could recompense, but that rare lesson it teaches me, how brittle
that happiness is, that we build upon earth.

March 6, 1646/7

[*Works,* I, xxxvi–xxxvii]

My sister,

I must confess that I should be as much in your debt
for letters, though I had answered every one of yours, as
he is in his creditors, who for two angels has paid back
but two shillings: for certainly, if any where, it is in the
productions of the mind, that the quality ought to measure
extent, and assign number, and equity to multiply excellency, where wit has contracted it. I could easily evince
this truth, and the justness of the application too, did I
not apprehend that your modesty would make you mind
me, that the nature of my disease forbids all strains. I am
here, God be praised, upon the mending hand, though not
yet exempted either from pain or fears; the latter of which
I could wish (but believe not) as much enemies to my
reason, as I find the former to my quiet. I intend notwithstanding, by God's blessing, as soon as I have here re-
cruited and refreshed my purse and self, to accomplish
my designed removal to London; my hoped arrival at
which I look on with more joy, as a fruit of my recovery,
than a testimony of it. Sir William and his son went hence
this morning, having by the favour (or rather charity) of
a visit, made me some compensation for the many I have
lately received from persons, whose visitations (I think
I may call them) in spite of my averseness to physic, make
me find a greater trouble in the congratulations than the
instruments of my recovery. You will pardon, perhaps, the
bitterness of this expression, when I have told you, that
having spent most of this week in drawing (for my particular use) a quintessence of wormwood, those disturbers

of my work might easily shake some few drops into my ink. I will not now presume to entertain you with those moral speculations, with which my chemical practices have entertained me; but if this last sickness had not diverted me, I had before this presented you with a discourse (which my vanity made me hope would not have displeased you) of the theological use of natural philosophy, endeavouring to make the contemplation of the creatures contributory to the instruction of the prince, and to the glory of the author of them. But my blood has so thickened my ink, that I cannot make it run; and my thoughts of improving the creatures have been very much displaced by those of leaving them. Nor has my disease been more guilty of my oblivion, than my employment since it has begun to release me: for Vulcan has so transported and bewitched me, that as the delights I taste in it make me fancy my laboratory a kind of Elysium, so as if the threshold of it possessed the quality the poets ascribed to that Lethe, their fictions make men taste of before their entrance into those seats of bliss, I there forget my standish and my books, and almost all things, but the unchangeable resolution I have made of continuing till death,

Sister, your
R. B.

Stalb, August the last, 1649

[*Works*, VI, 49–50]

15. The Uses of Chemistry

The following selections give some idea of Boyle's concept of the nature and purpose of chemical study. The first is an undated letter to an unidentified friend, intended as a preface to a collection of recipes or processes which was never, in fact, published. It gives some notion of the layman's picture of what chemical work was like, as contrasted with Boyle's view of chemistry as a branch of natural philosophy. The second selection, as its title indicates, was intended to show how chemistry could be of use to the natural philosopher in promoting the corpuscular philosophy; it was the preface to the "Essay on Nitre," one of the *Physiological Essays*. The "Advertisements about the Experiments and Notes relating to Chemical Qualities" is taken from the *Mechanical Origin and Production of Qualities*, and indicates the kind of theoretical chemistry which interested Boyle, and about which he had long intended to write at length. It is clear that Boyle was often criticized for the unpretentiousness of his experiments, which he defends so warmly as being the most instructive, because the easiest to repeat. He had no use for secrets, real or imaginary, such as Spagyrical chymists boasted of discovering; his interest was always in natural philosophy.

Sir,

I confess you are not the only person among my friends, to whom it hath seemed somewhat strange, that I, who have spent many of my thoughts, some of my money, and, what I value far more, of my time too, upon chemistry, as well as divers other parts of learning, have not been taken notice of to have found any particulars, as chemists speak, or other lucriferous experiments upon metals and minerals, nor have pretended to be possessor of those difficult and compounded experiments, that are magnified by chemists as excellent Hermetic Arcana.

But, Sir, since I find you in the list of those that have made the newly-mentioned reflection, I am content to give you such a summary account of my comportment, as may at least lessen your wonder at it. I must inform you then, that when, among other studies, I applied myself to the cultivating of natural philosophy, I soon perceived, that some insight into chemical operations was, though not absolutely necessary, yet highly conducive to the true knowledge of nature, and especially to the indagation of several of her most abstruse mysteries. On this score I was induced to make a nearer inspection into chemistry than virtuosi are wont to think it worth while to do; and I did not repent me of my labour. But as a cultivated chemistry, not so much for itself, as for the sake of natural philosophy, and in order to it, so most of the experiments I devised and pursued, were generally such as tended not to multiply processes or gain the reputation of having store of difficult and elaborate ones; but to serve for foundations, and other useful materials for an experimental history of nature, on which a solid theory may in process of time be superstructed. For this purpose I judged, that plain and easy experiments, and as simple, or as little compounded as may be, would, *caeteris paribus,* be the fittest, as being the most easy to be tried (and, if need be, repeated) and to be judged of, both in relation to their causes, and to their effects. And for these reasons, though I had by me a not inconsiderable number of more compounded and elaborate processes, some of which I had made, and others I received as great secrets from noted artists; I purposely forbore to mention any number of them in my writings about physics, being desirous rather to increase knowledge, than make any ostentation of any that I thought would puzzle most readers more than it would instruct them.

This, Sir, I hope, will appear to you a fair account of your not finding my physical discourses larded with long and intricate processes, some of which may, I willingly grant, produce notable effects, and for that reason are valuable, but are less fit than far more simple ones to discover the causes of things, which yet is the chief scope of a naturalist, as such. And to those that think it strange, that among my other experiments about metals and minerals, I have not produced those gainful ones, that chemists call particulars, it may, I hope, suffice to represent, that being a bachelor, and through God's bounty furnished with a competent estate for a younger brother, and freed from any ambition to leave my heirs rich, I had no need to pursue lucriferous experiments, to which I so much preferred luciferous ones, that I had a kind of ambition (which I now perceive to have been a vanity) of being able to say, that I cultivated chemistry with a disinterested mind, neither seeking nor scarce caring for any other advantages by it, than those of the improvement of my own knowledge of nature, the gratifying of the curious and industrious, and the acquist of some useful helps to make good and uncommon medicines.

If I may be allowed to judge of courses by the success, the entertainment, that the public has been pleased to give my endeavours to serve it, will not make me repent of the way I have made choice of to do it in. But, however, since I find myself now grown old, I think it time to comply with my former intentions to leave a kind of Hermetic legacy to the studious disciples of that art, and to deliver candidly, in the annexed paper, some processes chemical and medicinal, that are less simple and plain than those barely luciferous ones I have been wont to affect, and of a more difficult and elaborate kind than those I have hitherto published, and more of kin to the noblest Hermetic secreta, or as Helmont styles them, *arcana majora.* Some of these I have made and tried; others I have, (though not without much difficulty) obtained, by exchange or otherwise, from those that affirm they knew them to be real, and were themselves competent judges, as being some of them disciples of true adepts, or otherwise admitted to their acquaintance and conversation. Most of these processes are clearly enough delivered; and of the rest there is plainly set down, without deceitful terms, as much as may serve to make what is literally taught to be of great utility, though the full and complete uses are not mentioned, partly because, in spite of my philanthropy, I was engaged to secrecy, as to some of these uses, and partly because I much ingenuously confess it, I am not yet, or perhaps ever shall be acquainted with them myself. The knowledge I have of your great affection for the public good, and your particular kindness for me, invites me, among the many virtuosi, in whose friendship I am happy, to instruct the following papers in your hands, earnestly desiring you to impart them to the public faithfully, and without envy, *verbatim,* in my own expressions, as a monument of my good affections to mankind, as well in my chemical capacity, as in the others, wherein I have been solicitous to do it service. I am, with sincere respect,

Sir,

Your most faithful and most humble servant,

Robert Boyle

[*Works,* I, cxxx–cxxxi]

Some Specimens of an Attempt to make Chymical Experiments useful to illustrate the notions of the Corpuscular Philosophy

The Preface

Giving an account of the two following treatises, and proposing the desireableness of a good intelligence betwixt the Corpuscularian Philosophers and the Chymists.

There are many learned men, who being acquainted with chymistry but by report, have from the illiterateness, the arrogance and the impostures of too many of those, that pretend skill in it, taken occasion to entertain so ill an opinion, as well of the art, as of those that profess it, that they are apt to repine, when they see any person, capable of succeeding in the study of solid philosophy, addict himself to an art they judge so much below a philosopher, and so unserviceable to him: nay, there are some, that are troubled when they see a man, acquainted with other learning, countenance by his example sooty empirics, and a study, which they scarce think fit for any but such, as are unfit for the rational and useful parts of physiology. I now take notice of these things, because they gave occasion to the two following treatises. For perceiving divers years ago, that some learned men of the temper above described thought it strange (if not amiss also) that one, of whose studies they were pleased to have too favourable an expectation, should spend upon chymical trials (to which I then happened to be invited by the opportunity of some furnaces and leisure) much of those endeavors, which they seemed to think might be far more usefully employed, than upon such empty and deceitful study: perceiving this, I say, I thought it not amiss to endeavor to manifest, that without seeking after the elixir, that alchymists generally hope and toil for (but which they, that knew me, knew to be not at all in my aim) I did not in the prosecution of chymical trials do any thing either without an end, or unsuitable to the design I had of attempting to promote men's knowledge of the works of nature, as well as their power over them. In order to do this, I did not think it enough to show, that by an insight into chymistry one may be enabled to make some meliorations (I speak not of transmutations) of mineral and metalline bodies, and many excellent medicines for the health of men, besides divers other preparations of good use in particular trades, and in several occurrences of human life; I did not, I say, think it enough to do this, because, that though this might suffice to evince that a rational man might without losing his time employ some of it to understand and promote chymistry; yet this would scarce suffice to manifest it to be useful to philosophy. And therefore there seemed requisite some specimens, which might show that chymical experiments might be very assistant even to the speculative naturalist in his contemplations and inquiries. . . .

I considered, that the Atomical and Cartesian hypotheses, though they differed in some material points from one another, yet in oposition to the Peripatetic and other vulgar doctrines they might be looked upon as one philosophy: for they agree with one another, and differ from the schools in this grand and fundamental point, that not only they take care to explicate things intelligibly; but that whereas those other philosophers give only a general and superficial account of the phenomena of nature from certain substantial forms, which the most ingenious among themselves confess to be incomprehensible, and certain real qualities, which knowing men of other persuasions think to be likewise unintelligible; both the Cartesians and the Atomists explicate the same phenomena by little bodies variously figured and moved. I know, that these

two sects of modern naturalists disagree about the notion
of body in general, and consequently about the possibility
of a true vacuum; as also about the origin of motion, the
indefinite divisibleness of matter, and some other points
of less importance than these: but in regard that some of
them seem to be rather metaphysical and physiological
notions, and that some others seem rather to be requisite
to the explication of the first origin of the universe, than
of the phaenomena of it, in the state wherein we now find
it; in regard of these, I say, and some other considerations,
and especially for this reason, that both parties agree
in deducing all the phaenomena of nature from matter
and local motion; I esteemed that, notwithstanding these
things, wherein the Atomists and the Cartesians differed,
they might be thought to agree in the main, and their
hypotheses might by a person of a reconciling disposition
be looked on as, upon the matter, one philosophy. Which
because it explicates things by corpuscles, or minute
bodies, may (not very unfitly) be called corpuscular;
though I sometimes style it the Phoenician philosophy,
because some ancient writers inform us, that not only before Epicurus and Democritus, but even before Leucippus
taught in Greece, a Phoenician naturalist was wont to
give an account of the phaenomena of nature by the motion and other affections of the minute particles of matter.
Which because they are obvious and very powerful in
mechanical engines, I sometimes also term it the mechanical hypothesis or philosophy.

By such considerations then, and by this occasion, I was
invited to try, whether, without pretending to determine
the above mentioned controverted points, I could, by the
help of the corpuscular philosophy, in the sense newly
given of that appellation, associated with chymical experiments, explicate some particular subjects more intelligibly,
than they are wont to be accounted for, either by the

schools or the chymists. And however since the vulgar philosophy is yet so vulgar, that it is still in great request with the generality of scholars; and since the mechanical philosophers have brought so few experiments to verify their assertions: and the chymists are thought to have brought so many on behalf of theirs, that of those, that have quitted the unsatisfactory philosophy of the schools, the greater number, dazzled as it were by the experiments of Spagyrists, have embraced their doctrines instead of those they deserted: for these reasons, I say, I hoped I might at least do no unseasonable piece of service to the corpuscular philosophers, by illustrating some of their notions with sensible experiments, and manifesting, that the things by me treated of may be at least plausibly explicated without having recourse to inexplicable forms, as the three chymical principles. . . .
real qualities, the four peripatetic elements, or so much
And indeed I freely confess, that I shall think myself to have done no useless service to the commonwealth of learning, if I prove so fortunate, as by these or any other writings of mine to the like purpose, to beget a good understanding betwixt the chymists and the mechanical philosophers, who have hitherto been too little acquainted with one another's learning; there being to this very day a great and almost general misunderstanding betwixt the corpuscular philosophers and the chymists; most of those (on the one hand) looking upon the Spagyrists as a company of mere and irrational operators, whose experiments may indeed by serviceable to apothecaries, and perhaps to physicians, but are useless to a philosopher, that aims at curing no disease but that of ignorance; and most of the Spagyrists (on the other hand) looking upon the Corpuscularians (if I may so call them) as a sort of empty and extravagant speculators, who pretend to explicate the great book of nature, without having so much as looked

upon the chiefest and the difficultest part of it; namely, the phaenomena, that their art has added to the former edition of this vast and obscure volume. But that some of the principal of the hermetic opinions may be more handsomely accommodated by the notions of the Phoenician hypotheses than by the common philosophy of elements and substantial forms (which yet their writers so frequently allude to and otherwise employ) may appear from hence, that whereas the schools generally declare the transmutation of one species into another, and particularly that of baser metals into gold, to be against nature, and physically impossible; the corpuscular doctrine rejecting the substantial forms of the schools, and making bodies to differ but in the magnitude, figure, motion, or rest, and situation of their component particles, which may be always infinitely varied, seems much more favourable to the chymical doctrine of the possibility of working wonderful changes, and even transmutations in mixt bodies. And on the other side, there are scarce any experiments, that may better accommodate the Phoenician principle, than those, that may be borrowed from the laboratories of chymists. For first, chymistry enabling us to depurate bodies, and in some measure to analyze them, and take asunder their heterogeneous parts, in many chymical experiments we may better than in others know what manner of bodies we employ, art having made them more simple or uncompounded, than nature alone is wont to present them us. And next, many chymical operations being performed in close, and yet in transparent vessels, we may better know what concurs to the effects produced, because adventitious bodies (or at least all grosser ones) are kept from intruding upon those, whose operations we have a mind to consider. And lastly, the bodies employed by the chymists being for the most part active ones, the progress of nature in an experiment, and the series of successive alterations, through which the matter passes from first to last, is wont to be made more nimbly, and consequently becomes the more easy to be taken notice of and comprehended. So that all this considered, I hope it may conduce to the advancement of natural philosophy, if, as I said, I be so happy, as, by any endeavours of mine, to possess both chymists and Corpuscularians of the advantages, that may redound to each party by the confederacy I am meditating between them, and excite them both to enquire more into one another's philosophy, by manifesting, that as many chymical experiments may be happily explicated by corpuscularian notions, so many of the corpuscularian notions may be commodiously either illustrated, or confirmed by chymical experiments. . . . [*Works*, I, 354–59]

Advertisements about the Experiments and Notes relating to Chemical Qualities

When, after I had gone through the common operations of chemistry, I began to make some serious reflections on them, I thought it was a pity, that instruments, that might prove so serviceable to the advancement of natural philosophy, should not be more studiously and skilfully made use of to so good a purpose. I saw indeed, that divers of the chymists had, by a diligent and laudable employment of their pains and industry, obtained divers productions, and lighted on several phaenomena, considerable in their kind, and indeed more numerous, than, the narrowness and sterility of their principles considered, could well be expected. But I observed too, that the generality of those, that busy themselves about chemical operations; some, because they practice physick, and others, because they either much wanted, or greedily coveted money, aimed, in their trials, but at the preparation of good medicines for the human body, or to discover the ways of curing the diseases or imperfections of metals, without referring their trials to the advancement of natural philosophy in general; of which most of the alchymists seem to have been so incurious, that not only did they not institute experiments for that purpose, but overlooked and despised those undesigned ones, that occurred to them, whilst they were prosecuting a preparation of a medicine, or a transmutation of metals. The sense I had of this too general omission of the chymists, tempted me sometimes to try, whether I could do anything towards the repairing of it by handling chemistry, not as a physician, or an alchymist, but as a mere naturalist, and so by applying chemical operations to philosophical purposes. And, in pursuance of these thoughts, I remember I drew up a scheme of what I ventured to call a *chemia philosophica,* not out of any affectation of a splendid title, but to intimate, that the chemical operations, there treated of, were not directed to the usual scopes of physicians, or transmuters of metals, but partly to illustrate, or confirm some philosophical theories by such operations; and partly to explicate those operations, by the help of such theories.

But before I had made any great progress in the pursuit of this design, the fatal pestilence that raged in London, and in many other parts of England, in the years 1664 and 65, obliging me, among the rest, to make several removes, which put me upon taking new measures, and engaging me in other employments of my time, made me so long neglect the papers I had drawn up, that, at last, I knew not where to find them, (though, I hope, they are not yet mislaid beyond recovery) which I was the less troubled at, because the great difficulties, to be met with in such an undertaking, did not a little discourage me, such a task requiring, as well as deserving, a person better furnished, than I had reason to think myself, with abilities, leisure, chemical experiments, and conveniences, to try as many more, as should appear needful. But yet, to break the ice for any, that may hereafter think fit to set upon such a work, or, to shorten my own labour, if I should see cause to resume it myself, I was content to throw in, among my notes about other particular qualities, some experiments and observations about some of those, that I have elsewhere called chemical qualities, because it is chiefly by the operations of chymists, that men have been induced to take special notice of them. Of these notes I have assigned to some qualities more, and to some fewer, as either the nature or importance of the subject seemed to require, or my leisure and other circumstances would permit. And though I have not here handled the subjects they belonged to, as if I intended such a *chemia philosophica;* as I lately mentioned, because my design did not make it necessary, but did, perhaps, make it impertinent for me to do so; yet, in some of the larger notes . . . I have given some little specimens of the theorical part of a philosophical account of those qualities, or operations, that, I hope, will not be wholly useless. I know, it may be objected, that I should have employed, for instances, some more considerable experiments, if not arcana; but, though possibly I am not altogether unfurnished with such, yet, aiming rather to promote philosophy, than appear a possessor of elaborate processes, I declined several experiments, that required either more skill, or more time, or more expence, than could well be expected from most readers, and chose rather to employ such experiments, as may be more easily or cheaply tried; and, which is mainly to be considered, being more simple, are more clearly intelligible, and more fit to have notions and theories built upon them; especially considering, that the doctrine of qualities being itself conversant about some of the rudimental parts, if I may so call them, of natural philosophy, it seemed unfit to employ intricate experiments, and whose causes were liable to many disputes, to settle a theory of them. In short, my design being to hold a taper, not so much to chymists, as to the naturalists, it was fit I should be less sollicitous to gratify the former, than to inform the latter. [*Works*, IV, 292-93]

16. Chemical Experiment

The following selections give some notion of the range and utility of Boyle's actual chemical work as distinct from his chemical theory. The first, on chemical indicators, is from the *Experiments and Considerations touching Colours* (1664), ostensibly addressed to Boyle's nephew. Boyle's discovery of the several indicators which permitted him to differentiate between acid, alkaline, and neutral substances was extremely important both in determining chemical composition and in helping to establish a useful form of chemical classification. A "sulphureous" salt is an alkaline one; this is a "chymical" term, presumably drawn from the soapy feel of alkalies. Salt or spirit of urine is ammonia, also called spirit of hartshorn or of soot; sal ammoniac is ammonium chloride. Lixiviate salts are alkalies, properly those leached from ashes, the carbonates, also called potash, salt of tartar, and fixed vegetable salts. Spirit of vitriol (oil of vitriol) is sulphuric acid; spirit of salt is hydrochloric acid; and spirit of nitre is nitric acid. Mercury sublimate (mercuric chloride) gives orange mercuric oxide with carbonates and white ammonium mercury chloride with ammonia.

The second selection contains the bulk of Boyle's investigation of phosphorus, published as the *Aerial Noctiluca* and the *Icy Noctiluca*. It well illustrates the depth and range of his chemical technique and the use to which he put his newly discovered methods of chemical identification. It is a far more thorough investigation than that made by any other chemist on the subject for two centuries. The utilitarian spirit which so often animated Boyle is amusingly illustrated by his opening remarks.

The third selection gives Boyle's suggestions for the best procedure to use in examining mineral waters, one of the most important kinds of chemical analysis in this period. Here he makes full use of his chemical and physical knowledge.

Indicators

A COROLLARY OF THE TENTH EXPERIMENT

That this experiment, Pyrophilus, may be as well useful as delightful to you, I must mind you, Pyrophilus, that in the newly mentioned observation, I have hinted to you a new and easy way of discovering in many liquors (for I dare not say in all) whether it be an acid or sulphureous salt, that is predominant; and that such a discovery is oftentimes of great difficulty, and may frequently be of great use, he that is not a stranger to the various properties and effects of salts, and of how great moment it is to be able to distinguish their tribes, may readily conceive. But to proceed to the way of trying other liquors by an infusion of our wood, take it briefly thus. Suppose I have a mind to try whether I conjecture aright, when I imagine that alum, though it be plainly a mixt body, does abound rather with acid than sulphureous salt: to satisfy myself herein, I turn my back to the light, and holding a small phial full of the tincture of Lignum Nephriticum, which, looked upon in that position, appears ceruleous, I drop into it a little of a strong solution of alum made in fair water; and finding upon the affusion and shaking of this new liquor, that the blueness formerly conspicuous on our tincture does presently vanish. I am thereby incited to suppose, that the salt predominant in alum belongs to the family of sour salts. But if on the other side I have a mind to examine whether or no I rightly conceive that salt of urine, or of hartshorn is rather of a saline sulphureous (if I may so speak) than of an acid nature, I drop

a little of the saline spirit of either into the nephritic tincture, and finding that the ceruleous colour is rather
thereby deepened than destroyed, I collect that the salts,
which constitute these spirits, are rather sulphureous than
acid. And to satisfy myself yet farther in this particular,
I take a small phial of fresh tincture, and placing both it
and myself in reference to the light as formerly, I drop
into the infusion just as much distilled vinegar, or other
acid liquor as will serve to deprive it of its blueness
(which a few drops, if the sour liquor be strong, and phial
small, will suffice to do;) then without changing my posture, I drop and shake into the same phial a small proportion of spirit of hartshorn or urine, and finding that
upon this affusion the tincture immediately recovers its
ceruleous colour, I am thereby confirmed in my former
opinion, of the sulphureous nature of these salts. And so,
whereas it is much doubted by some modern chymists to
what sort of salt, that which is predominant in quick-lime
belongs, we have been persuaded to refer it rather to lixiviate than acid salts; and having observed, that though an
evaporated infusion of it will scarce yield such a salt, as
ashes and other alcalizate bodies are wont to do, yet if
we deprive our nephritic tincture of its blueness by just
so much distilled vinegar as is requisite to make that
colour vanish, the lixivium of quick-lime will immediately
upon its affusion recall the banished colour, but not so
powerfully as either of the sulphureous liquors formerly
mentioned. And therefore I allow myself to guess at the
strength of the liquors examined by this experiment, by
the quantity of them which is sufficient to destroy or restore the ceruleous colour of our tincture. But whether
concerning liquors, wherein neither acid nor alcalizate
salts are eminently predominant, our tincture will enable
us to conjecture any thing more than that such salts are
not predominant, in them, I take not upon me to deter-

mine here, but leave to further trial; for I find not that
spirit of wine, spirit of tartar freed from acidity, or chymical oil of turpentine (although liquors which must be
conceived very saline, if chymists have, which is here no
place to dispute, rightly ascribed tastes to the saline principles of bodies) have any remarkable power either to
deprive our tincture of its ceruleous colour, or restore it,
when upon the affusion of spirit of vinegar it has dis-
appeared.

Experiment XX

Take good syrup of violets, impregnated with the tincture of the flowers, drop a little of it upon a white paper
(for by that means the change of colour will be more
conspicuous and the experiment may be practised in
smaller quanties) and on this liquor let fall two or three
drops of spirit either of salt or vinegar, or almost any other
eminently acid liquor, and upon the mixture of these you
shall find the syrup immediately turn red: and the way
of effecting such a change has not been unknown to divers
persons, who have produced the like, by spirit of vitriol,
or juice of lemons, but have groundlessly ascribed the
effect to some peculiar quality of those two liquors,
whereas (as we have already intimated) almost any acid
salt will turn syrup of violets red. But to improve the
experiment, let me add what has not (that I know of)
been hitherto observed, and has, when we first showed it
them, appeared something strange, even to those that
have been inquisitive into the nature of colours; namely,
that if instead of spirit of salt or that of vinegar, you drop
upon the syrup of violets a little oil of tartar per deliquium, or the like quantity of solution of pot-ashes, and rub
them together with your finger, you shall find the blue
color of the syrup turned in a moment into a perfect green;

and the like may be performed by divers other liquors,
as we may have occasion elsewhere to inform you.

ANNOTATION UPON THE TWENTIETH EXPERIMENT

The use of what we lately delivered, concerning the
way of turning syrup of violets red or green, may be this:
that, though it be a far more common and procurable
liquor than the infusion of Lignum Nephriticum, it may
yet be easily substituted in its room, when we have a mind
to examine, whether or no the salt predominant in a liquor
or other body, wherein it is loose and abundant, belong
to the tribe of acid salts or not. For if such a body turn
the syrup of a red or reddish purple colour, it does for the
most part argue the body (especially if it be a distilled
liquor) to abound with acid salt. But if the syrup be made
green, that argues the predominant salt to be of a nature
repugnant to that of the tribe of acids. For, as I find that
either spirit of salt, or oil of vitriol, or aqua fortis, or spirit
of vinegar, or juice of lemons, or any of the acid liquors
I have yet had occasion to try, will turn syrup of violets
of a red, or at least of a reddish colour; so I have found,
that not only the volatile salts of all animal substances I
have used, as spirit of hartshorn, of urine, of sal ammoniac,
of blood, &c. but also all the alcalizate salts I have employed, as the solution of salt of tartar, of pot-ashes, of
common wood-ashes, lime-water, &c. will immediately
change the blue syrup into a perfect green. And by the
same way (to hint that upon the by) I elsewhere show
you, both the changes that nature and time produce, in
the more saline parts of some bodies, may be discovered,
and also how even such chemically prepared bodies, as
belong not either to the animal kingdom, or to the tribe
of alcalies, may have their new and superinduced nature
successfully examined. In this place I shall only add, that

not alone the changing the colour of the syrup requires, that the changing body be more strong of the acid, or other sort of salt, that is predominant in it, than is requisite for the working upon the tincture of Lignum Nephriticum; but that in this also, the operation of the formerly mentioned salts upon our syrup, differs from their operation upon our tinctures; that in this liquor, if the ceruleous colour be destroyed by an acid salt, it may be restored by one that is either volatile or lixiviate; whereas in the syrup of violets, though one of these contrary salts will destroy the action of the other, yet neither of them will restore the syrup to its native blue; but each of them will change it into the colour which itself doth (if I may so speak) affect. . . .

Experiment XL

The experiment I am now to mention to you, Pyrophilus, is that which both you, and all the other Virtuosi that have seen it, have been pleased to think very strange; and indeed of all the experiments of colours I have yet met with, it seems to be the fittest to recommend the doctrine proposed in this treatise, and to show that we need not suppose, that all colours must necessarily be inherent qualities, flowing from the substantial forms of the bodies they are said to belong to, since by a bare mechanical change of texture in the minute parts of bodies, two colours may in a moment be generated quite *de novo*, and utterly destroyed. For there is this difference betwixt the following experiment, and most of the others delivered in these papers, that in this, the colour that the body already had, is not changed into another, but betwixt two bodies, each of them apart devoid of colour, there is in a moment generated a very deep colour, and which, if it were let alone, would be permanent; and yet by a very small parcel of a third body, that has no colour of its own (lest some may pretend I know not what antipathy betwixt colours) this otherwise permanent colour will be in another trice so quite destroyed, that there will remain no footsteps either of it or of any other colour in the whole mixture.

The experiment is very easy, and it is thus performed: take good common sublimate, and fully satiate with it what quantity of water you please, filtre the solution carefully through clean and close paper, that it may drop down as clear and colourless as fountain water. Then, when you'll show the experiment, put of it about a spoonful into a small wine-glass, or any other convenient vessel made of clear glass, and dropping in three or four drops of good oil of tartar per deliquium, well filtred, that it may likewise be without colour: these two limpid liquors will in the twinkling of an eye turn into an opaceous mixture of a deep orange colour, which by keeping the glass continually shaking in your hand, you must preserve from settling too soon to the bottom; and when the spectators have a little beheld this first change, then you must presently drop in about four or five drops of the oil of vitriol, and continuing to shake the glass pretty strongly, that it may the nimbler diffuse itself, the whole colour, if you have gone skilfully to work, will immediately disappear, and all the liquor in the glass will be clear and colourless as before, without so much as a sediment at the bottom. But for the more graceful trial of this experiment, it will not be amiss to observe, first, that there should not be taken too much of the solution of sublimate, nor too much of the oil of tartar dropped in, to avoid the necessity of putting in so much oil of vitriol as may make an ebullition, and perhaps run over the glass. Secondly, that it is convenient to keep the glass always a little shaking, both for the better mixing of the liquors, and to keep the yellow substance from subsiding, which else it would in a short time do; though when it is subsided it will retain its colour, and also be capable of being deprived of it by the oil newly mentioned. Thirdly, that if any yellow matter stick at the sides of the glass, it is but inclining the glass, till the clarified liquor can wash along it, and the liquor will presently imbibe it, and deprive it of its colour.

Many have sometimes wondered, how I came to light upon this experiment; but the notions or conjectures I have about the differing natures of the several tribes of salts, having led me to devise the experiment, it will not be difficult for me to give you the chemical reason, if I may so speak, of the phaenomenon. Having then observed, that mercury, being dissolved in some menstruums, would yield a dark yellow precipitate, and supposing that, as to this, common water, and the salts that stick to the mercury would be equivalent to those acid menstruums, which work upon the quicksilver, upon the account of their saline particles, I substituted a solution of sublimate in fair water, instead of a solution of mercury in aqua fortis, or spirit of nitre, that simple solution being both clearer and free from that very offensive smell, which accompanies the solutions of mercury made with those other corrosive liquors. Then I considered, that that which makes the yellow colour, is indeed but a precipitate made by the means of the oil of tartar, which we drop in, and which, as the chymists know, does generally precipitate metalline bodies corroded by acid salts: so that the colour in our case results from the coalition of the mercurial particles with the saline ones, wherewith they were formerly associated, and with the alcalizate particles of the salt of tartar that swim up and down in the oil. Wherefore considering also, that very many of the effects of the lixiviate liquors, upon the solutions of other bodies, may be destroyed by acid menstruums, as I elsewhere more particularly declare, I concluded, that if I chose a very potently acid liquor, which by its incisive power might undo the work of the oil of tartar, and disperse again those particles, which the other had by precipitation associated, into such minute corpuscles as were before singly inconspicuous, they would become inconspicuous again, and consequently leave the liquor as colourless as before the precipitation was made.

This, as I said, Pyrophilus, seems to be the chymical reason of this experiment; that is, such a reason, as, supposing the truth of those chymical motions I have elsewhere I hope evinced, may give such an account of the phaenomena as chymical notions can supply us with: but I both here and elsewhere make use of this way of speaking, to intimate that I am sufficiently aware of the difference betwixt a chymical explication of a phaenomenon, and one that is truly philosophical or mechanical; as in our present case, I tell you something, when I tell you that the yellowness of the mercurial solution, and the oil of tartar, is produced by the precipitation occasioned by the affusion of the latter of those liquors, and that the destruction of the colour proceeds from the dissipation of that curdled matter, whose texture is destroyed, and which is dissolved into minute and invisible particles by the potently acid menstruum: which is the reason, why there remains no sediment in the bottom, because the infused oil takes it up, and resolves it into hidden or invisible parts, as water does salt or sugar. But when I have told you all this, I am far from thinking I have told you all that such an inquisitive person as yourself would know: for I presume you would desire, as well as I, to learn (at least) why the particles of the mercury, of the tartar, and of the acid salts convening together, should make rather an orange colour than a red, or a blue, or a green. For it is not enough to say what I related a little before, that divers ..mercurial solutions, though otherwise made, would yield a yellow precipitate, because the question will recur concerning them; and to give it a satisfactory answer is, I freely acknowledge, more than I dare as yet pretend to.

But to confirm my conjecture about the chymical reason of our experiment, I may add, that . . . with saline liquors of another kind and nature than salt of tartar (namely, with spirit of urine, and liquors of kin to that) I can make the mercury precipitate out of the first simple solution quite of another colour than that hitherto mentioned; nay, if instead of altering the precipitating liquor, I altered the texture of the sublimate in such a way as my notions about salt required, I could produce the same phaenomenon. For having purposely sublimed together equal parts (or thereabout) of sal ammoniac and sublimate, first diligently mixed, the ascending flowers being dissolved in fair water, and filtered, gave a solution limpid and colourless, like that of the other sublimates, and yet an alcali dropped into this liquor did not turn it yellow but white. And upon the same grounds we may with quicksilver, without the help of common sublimate, prepare another sort of flowers dissoluble in water without discolouring it, with which I could likewise do what I newly mentioned; to which I shall add (what possibly you will somewhat wonder at) that so much does the colour depend upon the texture resulting from the convention of the several sorts of corpuscles, that though, in our experiment, oil of vitriol destroys the yellow colour, yet with quicksilver and fair water, by the help of oil of vitriol alone, we may easily make a kind of precipitate of a fair and permanent yellow . . . And I may further add, that I chose oil of vitriol, not so much for any other or peculiar quality, as for its being, when it is well rectified (which is somewhat hazardous to bring it to be) not only devoid of colour and ill smells, but extremely strong and incisive. For . . . aqua fortis . . . made exceeding strong, by being carefully dephlegmed, will do it pretty well, though not so well as oil of vitriol; which is so strong, that even without rectification it may for a need be made use of. I will not here tell you what I have tried, that I may be able to deprive at pleasure the precipitate that one of the sulphureous liquors had made, by the copious affusion of the other; because I found, though this experiment is too ticklish to let me give a full account of it in a few words, I shall therefore tell you, that it is not only for once, that the other above-mentioned experiment may be made, the same numerical parcels of liquor being still employed in it. For after I have clarified the orange-coloured liquor, by the addition of as little of the oil of vitriol as will suffice to perform the effect, I can again at pleasure reproduce the opacous colour, by the dropping in of fresh oil of tartar, and destroy it again by the re-affusion of more of the acid menstruum; and yet oftener, if I please, can with these two contrariant liquors recall and disperse the colour, though the reason of the addition of so much new liquor, in reference to the mercurial particles, the colour will at length appear more dilute and faint.

REFLECTIONS UPON THE XLTH EXPERIMENT, COMPARED WITH THE XTH AND XXTH

The knowledge of the distinction of salts which we have proposed, whereby they are discriminated into acid, volatile, or salfuginous (if I may for distinction sake so call the fugitive salts of animal substances) and fixed or alcalizate, may possibly (by that little part which we have already delivered, of what we could say of its applicableness) appear of so much use in natural philosophy (especially in the practic part of it) that I doubt not but it will be no unwelcome corollary of the preceding experiment, if by the help of it I teach you to distinguish which

of those salts is predominant in chymical liquors, as well
as whether any of them be so or not. For though in our
notes upon the tenth and twentieth experiments I have
shown you a way, by means of the tincture of Lignum
Nephriticum, or of syrup of violets, to discover whether a
propounded salt be acid or not; yet you can thereby only
find in general that such and such salts belong not to the
tribe of acids, but cannot determine whether they belong
to the tribe of urinous salts (under which, for distinction
sake, I comprehend all those volatile salts of animal or
other substances that are contrary to acids) or to that of
alcalies. For as well the one as the other of these salino-
sulphureous salts will restore the ceruleous colour to the
tincture of Lignum Nephriticum, and turn that of syrup
of violets into green. Wherefore this XLth experiment
does opportunely supply the deficiency of those. For being
solicitous to find out some ready ways of discriminating
the tribes of chymical salts, I found that all those I thought
fit to make trial of, would, if they were of a lixiviate nature, make with sublimate dissolved in fair water an
orange tawny precipitate; whereas, if they were of an
urinous nature, the precipitate would be white and milky.
So that having always by me some syrup of violets and
some solution of sublimate, I can by the help of the first
of those liquors discover in a trice, whether the propounded salt or saline body be of an acid nature or no;
if it be, I need (you know) inquire no further; but if it
be not, I can very easily, and as readily distinguish between the other two kinds of salts, by the white or
orange colour that is immediately produced, by letting
fall a few drops or grains of the salt to be examined, into
a spoonful of the clear solution of the sublimate. For
example, it has been supposed by some eminently learned,
that when sal ammoniac being mingled with an alcali is
forced from it by the fire in close vessels, the volatile salt

that will thereby be obtained (if the operation be skill-
fully performed) is but a more fine and subtile sort of sal
ammoniac, which, it is presumed, this operation does but
more exquisitely purify than common solutions, filtrations,
and coagulations. But this opinion may be easily shown
to be erroneous, as by other arguments, so particularly by
the lately delivered method of distinguishing the tribes of
salts. For the saline spirit of sal ammoniac, as it is in many
other manifest qualities very like the spirit of urine, so
like, that it will in a trice make syrup of violets of a lovely
green, turn a solution of good verdigrease into an excellent azure, and make the solution of a sublimate yield a
white precipitate; insomuch that in most (for I say not
all of the experiments) where I aim only at producing a
sudden change of colour, I scruple not to use spirit of
sal ammonaic when it is at hand, instead of spirit of urine,
as indeed it seems chiefly to consist (besides the phlegm
that helps to make it fluid) of the volatile urinous salt
(yet not excluding that of soot) that abounds in the sal
ammoniac, and is set at liberty from the sea-salt wherewith it was formerly associated, and clogged, by the operation of the alkali, that divides the ingredients of sal ammoniac, and retains that sea-salt with itself: what use may
be made of the like way of exploration in that inquiry
which puzzles so many modern Naturalists, whether the
rich pigment (which we have often had occasion to mention) belongs to the vegetable or animal kingdom, you
may find in another place, where I give you some account
of what I tried about cochineal. But I think it needless
to exemplify here our method, by any other instances,
many such being to be met with in divers parts of this
treatise; but I will rather advertise you, that by this way
of examining chemical liquors, you may not only in most
cases conclude affirmatively, but in some cases negatively.
As since spirit of wine, and, as far as I have tried, those

chemical oils which artists call essential, did not (when
I used them as I had used the several families of salts
upon that syrup) turn syrup of violets red or green, nor
the solution of sublimate white or yellow; I inferred it
may thence be probably argued, that either they are destitute of salt, or have such as belongs not to either of the
three grand families often already mentioned. When I
went to examine the spirit of oak, or of such like concretes
forced over through a retort, I found by this means
amongst others, that (as I elsewhere show) those chymists
are much mistaken in it, that account it a simple liquor,
and one of their hypostatical principles. For not to mention what phlegm it may have, I found that with a few
drops of one of this sort of spirits mixed with a good proportion of syrup of violets, I could change the colour and
make it purplish, by the affinity of which colour to redness,
I conjectured that this spirit had some acid corpuscles in
it; and accordingly I found, that as it would destroy the
blueness of a tincture of Lignum Nephriticum, so being
put upon corals, it would corrode them, as common spirit
of vinegar, and other acid liquors are wont to do. And
farther to examine whether there were not a great part
of the liquor that was not of an acid nature, having separated the sour or vinegar-like part from the rest, which
(if I mistake not) is far the more copious; we concluded,
as we had conjectured, the other or remaining part, though
it had a strong taste as well as smell, to be of a nature
differing from that of either of the three sorts of salts
above-mentioned, since it did as little as spirit of wine,
and chymical oils, alter the colour either of syrup of violets
or solution of sublimate: whence we also inferred, that
the change that had been made of that syrup into a purple
colour, was effected by the vinegar, that was one of the
two ingredients of the liquor, which was wont to pass for
a simple or uncompounded spirit. And, upon this account,

it was of the spirit of oak (and the like concretes) freed
from its vinegar, that I elsewhere told you, that I had
not then observed it (and I have repeated the trial but
very lately) to destroy the ceruleous tincture of Lignum
Nephriticum. But this was only *en passant;* for the chief
thing I had to add was this: that by the same way may
be examined and discovered divers changes that are produced in bodies, either by nature only, or by art; either
of them being able, by changing the texture of some concretes I could name, to qualify them to operate after a
new manner upon the above–mentioned syrup, or solution,
or both: and by this means, to tell you that, upon the by,
I have been able to discover, that there may be made
bodies, which though they run per deliquium, as readily
as salt of tartar, belong in other respects not to the family
of alcalies, much less to that of salfuginous or that of acid
salts. Perhaps too, I may know a way of making a highly
operative saline body, that shall neither change the colour
of syrup of violets nor precipitate the solution of sublimate; and I can likewise, if I please, conceal by what
liquors I perform such changes of colour, as I have been
mentioning to you, by quite altering the texture of some
ordinary chymical productions, the exploration of which
is the main use of the fortieth experiment, which I think
teaches not a little, if it teach us to discover the nature
of those things (in reference to salt) that are obtained by
the ordinary chymical analysis of mixed bodies, though
perhaps there may be other bodies prepared by chymistry,
which may have the same effects in the change of colours,
and yet be produced not from what chymists call the
resolution of bodies, but from their composition. But the
discoursing of things of this nature is more proper for another place. I shall now only add, what might perhaps
have been more seasonably told you before; that the reason why the way of exploration of salts hitherto delivered

succeeds as well in the solutions of sublimate, depends upon the particular texture of that solution, as well as upon the differing natures of the saline liquors employed to precipitate it. For gold dissolved in aqua regis, whether you precipitate it with oil of tartar, which is an alcali, or with spirit of urine, or sal ammoniac, which belongs to the family of volatile salts, will either way afford a yellow substance: though with such an acid liquor as, I say not spirit of salt, the body that yields it being upon the matter an ingredient of aqua regis, but oil of vitriol itself, I did not find that I could precipitate the metal out of the solution, or destroy the colour of it; though the same oil of vitriol would readily precipitate silver dissolved in aqua fortis. And if you dissolve pure silver in aqua fortis, and suffer it to shoot into crystals, the clear solution of these made in fair water, will afford a very white precipitate, whether it be made with an alcali or an acid spirit, as that of salt; whereas, which may seem somewhat strange, with spirit of sal ammoniac (that I used was made of quick-lime) I could obtain no such white precipitate: that volatile spirit, nor (as I remember) that of urine, scarce doing any more than striking down a very small quantity of matter, which was neither white nor whitish; so that the remaining liquor being suffered to evaporate till the superfluous moisture was gone, the greatest part of the metalline corpuscles with the saline ones that had imbibed them, concoagulated into salt, as is usual in such solutions, wherein the metal has not been precipitated. [*Works*, I, 733–34, 743–44, 761–64, 765–67]

Phosphorus, or Aerial and Icy Noctilucas

The uses, that may be made of noctilucas, especially of the consistent, are not, in all probability, all of them to be easily foreseen and declared; especially by me, who have not yet had time and ability to make those improvements of self-shining substances, that, by the assistance of the father of lights, I hope will, in process of time, be attained. If the lucid virtue of the constant noctiluca could be (as I see not, why it may not be) considerably invigorated, it may prevent a great deal of danger, to which men of war, and other ships are exposed, by the necessity men often have to come into the gun-room with common flames or fires, to take out powder, which has occasioned the blowing up of many a brave ship. Our light may, perhaps, be of use to those, that dive in deep waters; and also may very safely and conveniently be let down into the sea, to what depth one pleases, and kept there a long time, to draw together the fishes, that are wont to resort to the light of a fire or candle; as in divers parts of Scotland and Ireland is well known to the fisherman, who get much profit by this resort. The same self-shining substance, which in our aerial noctiluca affords a light, that, as faint as it yet is, was able, when I waked in the night, to show me distinctly enough the bigness and shape of some joints of my fingers, and to discover itself in the shape of a capital letter of the alphabet, that was cut out of a piece of blacked paper pasted upon the vial; this light, I say, may probably (at least when somewhat invigorated) suffice to show the hour of the night when one wakes, (with eyes unaccustomed to light), if it be placed, instead of a lamp or candle, behind an index, where the figure employed to mark the hours are cut out. It may also serve to make a guide knowable at a good distance off, in spite of tempestuous winds and great showers, and this in the darkest night. Divers ludicrous experiments, very pleasant and surprising, may be made with the noctiluca, by him that has enough of it. But these trifles, though very pretty in their kind, I purposely pass over: as also an use, that may be of great, but I fear of mischievous, consequences; re-

serving what I have further to say of the usefulness of
these self-shining substances, till time shall give me more
information and leisure. In the mean while I shall only
intimate, that probably the utilities, that so subtle and
noble a substance may be brought to afford in medicine,
may be more considerable than any of its other particular
uses; and that though our noctiluca had none of these, yet
it may be highly valuable, if it shall (as in all likelihood
it will) be found conductive to discover the nature of so
noble a subject as light, whose encomiums would require
more time than I can allow this writing. And perhaps they
will seem needless, when I shall have observed, that light
was the first corporeal thing the great creator of the universe was pleased to make; and that (as our excellent
Bacon well noted, to another purpose) he was pleased to
allot the whole first day to the creation of light alone, without associating with it in that honour any other corporeal
thing. . . .

New Phaenomena Exhibited by an Icy Noctiluca; or, Solid, Self-shining Substance

SOME QUALITIES OF THE NOCTILUCA ITSELF

1. And first, though it usually came over in distillation
in the form of divers little grains or fragments, differing
for the most part from one another, both in bigness (some
being of the size of grains of corn, and others of pease,
or large cherry stones), and also as to their shapes, which
most commonly were irregular, as concretions are wont
to be, that are casually produced; yet when the distillation
was carried on prosperously, we obtained the desired matter in greater lumps, sometimes as large as small beans,
and sometimes at least three or four times as large, but
not proportionately thick.

2. These lumps, whether small or great, were colour-less, and usually, when they were held against the light, transparent; so that divers bodies, placed beyond them at a convenient distance, might be plainly seen through them. And some of the bigger appeared so like such fragments of ice, as being thin, are oftentimes very clear, and almost quite destitute of manifest bubbles, that, because of this great resemblance, and for distinction sake, I thought it not amiss to call our consistent self-shining substance, the icy or glacial noctiluca (and for variety phosphorus); which name I chose to give it, rather than that of crystal-line, because this epithet is not unfrequently given to every diaphanous liquor, as well as to transparent solids. But when I said, that our noctiluca was transparent and colourless, I meant it only in reference to what usually appeared. For whether it were any real difference in the texture or constitution of the body itself, or the effect of some casual junctures of circumstances, I am not sure; but this occurred to us, that sometimes, especially by candlelight, some lesser fragments appeared not diaph-anous, nor always either colourless, nor of the same colour. For sometimes the matter looked reddish, sometimes of a faint, but pleasing blue, and sometimes too of a colour to which I cannot easily assign a known name.

3. Our icy noctiluca or phosphorus, is manifestly heavier in specie than common water, in which being put, it readily sinks to the bottom, and quietly lies there.

4. The ice-like body, though consistent, is not hard, be-ing far less so, than common ice; but yet it is not so soft, but that it is brittle, and will more easily be broken in pieces by the pressure of one's fingers, than receive shapes from them; and yet by him, that goes somewhat warily to work, it may be spread upon a solid body, almost like the unmelted tallow of a candle.

5. The consistent phosphorus is fusible enough. For

though in the air it will not be brought to melt, without some difficulty and waste, yet by the help of hot liquors, and even of water itself, it may with a little care and dexterity be brought to melt, which is an observation of good use; because by means of fusion, several fragments (if the matter be pure enough) may be brought to run into one lump, and in that condition may both be the better preserved, and become fit to be applied to some considerable uses, which cannot so well, if at all, be made of lesser, though numerous fragments.

6. This glacial noctiluca is, as to sense, cold, but of a texture, that disposes it to be easily agitated, and by agitation become incalescent, as will appear hereafter. When this solid noctiluca is held in the free air, though perhaps its superficies be wet, it affords a very vivid light, usually surpassing that of the aerial noctiluca; and this light seems to proceed from, if not altogether to reside in, the body itself.

7. When our icy phosphorus is taken out of its receptacle, and exposed to the immediate contact of the free air, it usually emits a wonderful deal of smoke, discernable by the light of the body it ascends from; and this plentiful emission of effluviums usually lasts as long as the phosphorus is kept in the air.

8. But it is pleasant to observe, and deserves to be considered, that as soon as it is plunged in water, so as to be quite covered with that liquor, it ceases not only to smoke as before, but to shine, as if a thoroughly kindled coal were suddenly quenched in water. And if it were not for this, our noctiluca would effluviate so fast, that it would be quickly wasted; whereas the water, fencing it from the contact of the air, keeps it from spending itself as formerly, and yet does really make but a seeming and temporary extinction of this anomalous fire. For as soon as it is again taken out of the water (though it have lain there perhaps

a great while) it falls to shine again, even whilst it is yet dropping wet.

9. And I have sometimes had the pleasure to observe, that when I had so large a piece of noctiluca, that I could conveniently hold one half of it under the surface of the water, and the other half above it, whilst the immersed part afforded no light, the extant part shone vividly. . . .

OBSERVATIONS ABOUT THE WATER WHEREIN THE NOCTILUCA WAS KEPT

Because I guessed, that the water, wherein the noctiluca had been long kept covered, to fence it from the air, though it did not manifestly dissolve the mass, yet might be impregnated at least with the more saline, and, on that account, resoluble parts of it, I thought fit to make a few trials upon this liquor.

I. And first, I found, that it had a strong and penetrant taste, that seemed near of kin to that of sea-salt, but was more piercing, as if brine were mingled with spirit of salt, and it relished also somewhat of vitriol.

II. Being put into a small concave vessel of refined silver upon lighted coals and ashes, it evaporated very slowly, and would not be brought to shoot into crystals, nor yet to afford a dry salt, but coagulated into a substance, sometimes like a jelly, and sometimes, as to consistence, like whites of eggs; which substance was easily melted by heat.

III. When this substance was kept a while on a hotter fire, it only boiled at first, but soon after began, as I guessed it would, to make a crackling noise; wherein this was remarkable and pretty, that the explosions were accompanied with flashes of fire and light, which, if they were small, were generally very blue like the flames of sulphur, but more vivid, and sometimes also more blue; but

the greater cracks, whose noise was considerable, were
wont to appear of a yellow colour and very luminous. . . :

WHAT LIQUORS WOULD OR WOULD NOT, DISSOLVE THE ICY NOCTILUCA

Among other ways of investigating the nature of our
icy phosphorus, I thought fit to try, whether or no it would
be dissolved in some liquors of differing kinds, hoping,
that if it would be so, in any of them, it might somewhat
assist us to guess at its texture.

I. We found then by trial, that common water would
not, in the cold, dissolve it, though the liquor was thereby
impregnated. . . .

II. Afterwards we put a grain, or two, of our lucid matter into a little urinous spirit of sal ammoniac, but it
seemed not to make any conflict with it, nor manifestly to
work upon it, though, to give the liquor time to make a
solution, we left them together for several days. But, as
soon as we had poured aside the spirit, it appeared, that
it had not, by any contrariety, destroyed the power of the
noctiluca, which began readily to shine as formerly. . . .

III. Seeing a volatile and urinous salt would not work
sensibly upon our phosphorus, we thought fit to try, what
corrosive liquors would do; and accordingly, we put a
grain or two of our splendent matter into a very small
phial, wherein was a little oil of vitriol, that menstruum
appearing, in many cases, more corrosive than other vulgar
acids: but neither did this menstruum dissolve our icy
noctiluca. . . .

IV. Afterwards we put a small fragment of our icy phosphorus into aqua fortis; and though we kept it in that
menstruum two or three days, and set the phial, that contained them, for many hours in a warm place (the chimney corner) yet we found the matter so little altered, as

to its visible appearance, that we doubted, whether the liquor had dissolved any sensible quantity of it.

Having tried saline menstruums upon our icy phosphorus, I thought fit to try oils, and also spirit of wine, that is reckoned by chymists to be of great affinity with them.

V. Whereupon I put a little of our noctiluca into some oil of turpentine, which not dissolving it in the cold, the small phial, that contained it, was left all night in the chimney, upon warm ashes. But though, the next day, none of the phosphorus appeared any longer in the glass, yet we could not perceive, by two or three differing trials, that the oil was much altered by it, and particularly I observed, that though the glass were unstopped, and kept so for a while, yet the ingress of air did not produce any sensible light, nor did we perceive the upper part of the glass to be full of white fumes, as is usual in divers other liquors impregnated with our noctiluca, when they are unstopped.

It has rendered the experiments, made with aerial noctiluca, much less acceptable, than otherwise they would have been, to the delicate sort of spectators, especially to ladies, that the light they produced was accompanied with a very unpleasant smell, that issued out of the phial, whenever it was unstopped to let in the air. But, by the help of our icy noctiluca, I found a way to prevent this ungrateful concomitant of our artificial light. But, not being discouraged by the bad success of the forementioned experiment, I hoped an aromatical oil might do, what subtle oils had not done.

And therefore having, in a very small phial, put about a grain of noctilucal matter, and covered it with as much pure essential oil of cinnamon, as would swim less than a finger's breadth above it, we carefully stopped our little phial, and having warily held the bottom of it against a fire, till the phosphorus began to melt, I suffered it to cool; and then unstopping it in a dark place, had the pleasure to see produced a vanishing indeed, but a vivid light. So that by this means I could afterwards show the production of light to the nearest persons of quality, not only without offending their noses, whilst their eyes were gratified, but with adding to the pleasure of a delightful apparition that of a fragrant smell. But because oil of cloves is more easy to be had good than the oil of cinnamon, and is also much cheaper, I tried the experiment more fully with that. . . .

OF A WAY OF SUDDENLY PRODUCING LIGHT IN COMMON WATER, BY THE HELP OF ANOTHER, NOT LUMINOUS

LIQUOR

I come now to recite to you a phaenomenon, which, I presume, may not displease you. I had a hint of it from a casual observation made by my industrious laborant. For having, to encourage him, allowed him, for his own use, some fragments of our icy noctiluca, he mingled a portion of this shining substance with a spiritous medicinal liquor, that he had prepared, by extracting several drugs with it; and having afterwards, upon some occasion or other, diluted it with water, it afforded him a phaenomenon, at which being surprised, he came to acquaint me with it, bringing me withal some of the liquor. But I thinking, that the phaenomenon did not depend upon the peculiar nature of the liquor, whose being very compounded and high coloured, made me judge it not fit for luciferous experiments, but proceeded from the vinous spirits, wherein that liquor abounded, I thought fit to make the experiment with a liquor, as colourless and as simple as I could; the effects of such liquors being more easy to be discerned, and judged of, and reasoned upon. And accordingly we weighed out, in a tender balance, one grain of our glacial phosphorus, wiped dry, and broken in four or five pieces, for the easier dissolution. And to these, in a crystalline phial, we put a convenient quantity of highly rectified vinous spirit, and stopping the phial close, we suffered the things contained in it to remain for many hours, sometimes (and indeed for the most part) in the cold, and sometimes in the warm sun, but perceived not, that near a total dissolution was made of the noctilucal matter by the liquor, in which it lay, even one of the lesser fragments appearing, as well as the others, undissolved in the bottom of it. However, since a body, consisting of such subtle parts, may communicate many of them to a contiguous liquor, without any diminution of its bulk, observable by the eye, I thought fit to try what effects this body had upon the vinous spirit.

I. And first, I observed that it did not manifestly discolour the liquor, but left it transparent and limpid, as before; save that there appeared some very small earthy corpuscles, like dust, at the bottom of the liquor, when being a little shaken, (to raise them) it was attentively viewed.

II. We did not observe, that, upon the unstopping of the phial, and the restored commerce between the inward and outward air, there appeared any flame or luminous exhalations, as is usual upon opening phials, that contain the liquid aerial noctiluca.

III. But the phaenomenon I chiefly intended to relate was this, that, having in a dark night, dropped a little of this impregnated spirit into a small china cup, with common water in it, though the spirit, neither in the phial, nor in its passage through the air, disclosed any degree of luminousness, yet, as soon as ever the drops came to touch the liquor, they would be, as it were, kindled by the cold water, and afford little flashes of light, which was more vivid than the noctiluca itself, affording a splendour, that made not only the brims of the cup, but divers of the neighboring objects manifestly visible, not to say conspicuous. But these coruscations had the property of other lightning, to vanish almost as soon as they appeared, nor would the water that produced them, by being agitated, shine; but others might immediately be produced, by letting fresh drops fall into the same water, upon whose surface they seemed to diffuse themselves, and would sometimes leave, for a little while, a faintly luminous, as it were, film or membrane. . . .

EXPERIMENTS DISCOVERING A STRANGE SUBTILTY OF PARTS IN THE GLACIAL NOCTILUCA

But what has been above recited, is not all that I thought fit to try with the shining matter, that I told you we dissolved in spirit of wine; for after having, as I lately recited, brought one grain to impregnate between four and five ounces of alcohol, as the chymists call the high rectified spirit of wine, which did at least two thousand times exceed the weight of the noctilucal matter, I presumed, that this very parcel of spirit of wine, wherein the shining matter was already diffused and scattered into so many thousand corpuscles, as sufficed to impregnate all the liquor, would yet communicate to a good quantity of water particles enough to make it shine, when agitated: wherefore when we had weighed out in a very trusty balance one dram of our impregnated spirit of wine, we mixed it with, and shook it in as much fair water as we thought fit (but not all at once) that is, till we had to our dram of spirit of wine put above fifty times its weight of water; and that alcohol itself weighing at least two thousand times as much as the noctilucal matter, that impregnated it, it follows (though it may seem strange it should be true), that the single grain of icy noctiluca was able to diffuse itself through, and impregnate full a hundred thousand grains of liquor, so as (when duly ordered) to make it luminous. For having presently after the last water was put into the glass, stopped the vessel close with a good cork, and shaken it a little in a dark place, the whole phial appeared to be full of light, which though it were not more than ordinary intense, yet, by reason of the bulk of the liquor, made a glorious show, and discovered divers of the neighboring objects. And after we had done shaking that phial, not only the upper part, which was filled with exhalations and vapours, shined like those other liquid phosphoruses formerly mentioned, but what was not observed in them, the water itself had a luminousness, though of an inferior degree, of its whole mass; which yet will not keep me from thinking of some expedient, that may satisfy those, who may suspect, as I did, that some of this light proceeded from the exhalations, that shined through that diaphanous water, though this did not seem the only, nor perhaps the chief cause of its appearing luminous, since when the glass was shaken, the whole mass of the liquor appeared to shine, so that we could plainly see through the sides of the vessel the conical figure of the bottom.

After this, I prosecuted the experiment a good way further, increasing the proportion of the water to fresh impregnated spirit; and I found (what perhaps you will think strange) that one part of the noctiluca, being first dissolved in alcohol of wine, and afterwards briskly shaken into a convenient quantity of water, rendered luminous as much liquor as upon calculation amounted to four hundred thousand times its weight. And this did not seem to proceed from the irradiation of the luminous corpuscles or exhalations, shining in the empty space at the top of the glass; because the phial was so near filled with liquor, that there was but little room left for vapour; and because also the vapours, that did play in that space, shined but very faintly, and when the glass was at rest much less than a minute of an hour, the light would reach but a little way downwards in the water, and yet was there so dim, as to be scarce discernable. Whereas in our experiment, not only the agitated liquor appeared luminous throughout, but the light was brisk enough, insomuch that the conical figure of the bottom of the glass was clearly visible by help of it.

But lest some should think, if this experiment had been further and further prosecuted, the luminousness would have still extended to greater and greater quantities of water, I shall add, that when I increased the proportion of this liquor to the noctilucal matter to be dispersed through it by putting in near three or four ounces of water more than I guessed would be convenient, the luminous matter seemed to be, as it were drowned or lost in so much liquor; for though we gave it much more agitation, than had in the former experiments been needful to produce light, yet no luminousness at all appeared in the mixture. Wherefore, taking some fresh spirit, and shaking it into such a quantity of water as I thought it might serve to impregnate, I found by supputation, that the luminous mass of liquor thereby produced amounted to no less, but a pretty deal more, than five hundred times the weight of the noctilucal matter dispersed through it, which is a visible expansion, very much greater, than, I think, has been hitherto observed in any corporeal substance dissolved in a visible liquor, since it four times exceeds that expansion of cochineal, which I many years since imparted to the ingenious, and which several of them have in their writings, been pleased to take notice of, as a prodigious thing; one part of cochineal, ordered as I there mention, having in that experiment produced a discernable colour in an hundred twenty-five thousand parts of water. . . .

I come now to another way, by which I thought the great subtilty of parts in our noctilucal matter might appear with good advantage, and possibly you will think by the success, that I missed not of what I expected from the intended trial.

We carefully weighed out a small lump of our shining matter, amounting to three grains, and having purposely broken it into divers lesser fragments, perhaps six or seven at least, we laid them upon a flat bottomed glass, that was broader at the top than the bottom, and shallow too (not being near an inch deep) that the matter might be more fully exposed to free air. This glass we placed in a south window, laying it very shelving, that the liquor to be produced by its resolution in the moist air might presently run down, and not hinder the free evaporation of the remaining matter. . . . The vessel being thus placed, about ten of the clock at night, all the fragments of the noctiluca shined briskly, and so continued to do, till most of them were resolved into other substances, and the biggest of them continued to shine, till they were reduced to such a smallness, that they would scarce have been seen, had not their own light made them visible. But the main thing, that I am to take notice of in this experiment (and which perhaps will somewhat surprise you) is, that so little quantity of noctilucal matter continued to emit fumes for a good many more than an hundred and fifty hours, and this with circumstances, that made the thing more strange. . . .

To examine somewhat particularly, to what family, or sort of salts, the saline of our noctilucal matter either does belong, or has most cognation with (for I thought it might not fully agree with any known species of salts, but have somewhat peculiar to itself) I suffered a little of the small stock, I then had, to resolve itself per deliquium[35] into a clear liquor, and then made with it some of the trials elsewhere delivered, by which I am wont to examine what species a salt belongs to, guessing this liquor by the taste, and the manner how it was made to be somewhat, though not altogether, of the nature of spirit of sea-salt; I dropt a little of it upon a convenient proportion of syrup of violets, and found, that it turned not green, as a volatile urinous salt would have done, but of a fine carnation colour, such as that syrup is wont to acquire, upon the mixture of an acid spirit with it. I found also, that a very little of our anomalous liquor presently destroyed the blue colour, and not the other of a tincture of Lignum Nephriticum.

I also put some of this liquor, that came by deliquium from the noctiluca, upon some filings of copper, which being thoroughly wetted, and some of them covered with it, I exposed in a hollow glass for two or three days to the air; and by this means had, as I expected, without the help of heat, a solution of some of the filings of copper, the colour of which was not a deep azure, as if it had been made with a volatile urinous salt, but seemed to partake of green and blue, and to be an intermediate or compounded colour.

To make the saline nature of this liquor more manifest, I put some of it upon powder of red coral, which it presently fell upon, and corroded with noise and froth; and putting another parcel of the same liquor upon some dry salt of tartar, there presently ensued a fierce conflict between them, whereby some noise and much froth was produced; so that I thought it needless to waste any more of the noctilucal matter (wherewith I was but slenderly stored) to make it more apparent, that our liquor was not, as most chymists would have expected, of an urinous nature, but belonged to the family of acid salts, and seemed to be near of kin to that branch of them, to which the spirituous part of common or sea salt belongs. . . .

The Conclusion

And now I have acquainted you with all the chief things, that I have hitherto been able to try or observe, about our icy noctiluca, or solid phosphorus: and though I have been obliged to deliver them without any exact method, yet perhaps their novelty will serve to make them acceptable to you. Light is so noble a thing, that the matter our phosphorus affords it to reside in being endued with some uncommon qualities, and particularly with a strange, and almost incredible subtilty of parts, I cannot but hope, that, if improvements, upon such a matter, were more industriously attempted, by persons better qualified for such a work, than I (especially in my present circumstances) pretend to be, something would be produced, tending to the discovery of the nature, not only of light, but divers other bodies, and perhaps also, of good use to human life. If some unwelcome circumstances did not, for the present, discourage me, I would contribute my weak endeavours towards such a design. For, sometimes I think a naturalist's pen ought to be like a merchant's ship, that comes from time to time into port to rest, but not always to stay there, but to take in new lading, and refit itself for a new voyage to the same, or other parts. [*Works*, IV, 384, 475–95]

Experimental History of Mineral Waters
TITLES

For the natural history of a mineral water proposed, considered as being drawn out of its spring or receptacle: (being the second, or physio-chemical, part of the designed work). . . .

1. Of the actual coldness or heat of the mineral water proposed.

2. Of the specific gravity of the mineral water proposed.

3. Of the transparency, the muddiness, or the opacity of the mineral water.

4. Whether the mineral water will, by standing for a competent time, let fall of itself any ochre, or other earthy substance, especially though the liquor be kept from the air?

5. Whether anything, and if anything, what can be discovered in the mineral water by the help of the best microscopes adapted to view liquors?

6. Of the colour or colourlessness of the mineral water.

7. Of the odour of the mineral water, as acetous, winy, sulphureous, bituminous, &c.

8. Of the taste of the mineral water, as acid, ferruginous, vitriolate, lixivial, sulphureous, &c.

9. Whether any change will be produced in the transparency, colour, odour, or taste of the mineral water, by its being taken up at the spring-head or other receptacle; or removed to some distance, by its being kept stopped or unstopped for a greater or lesser space of time; and, by its being much warmed or refrigerated, and also, by naturally or artificially produced cold, turned into ice and thawed again?

10. Of the thinness or viscosity of the mineral water.

11. Whether the mineral water will be more easy to be heated and cooled, and to be dilated and condensed, than common water?

12. Whether the mineral water will of itself putrify, and, if it will, whether sooner or later, than common water, and with what kind or degree of stink and other phaenomena?

13. Of the change of colours producible in the mineral water by astringent drugs, as galls, pomegranate peels, balaustium, red roses, myrobolans, oaken leaves, &c. as also by some liquors or juices of the body.[36]

14. Whether anything will be precipitated out of the mineral waters by salts or saline liquors, whether they be acid, as spirit of salt, of nitre, aqua fortis, &c. or volatile alcalies, as strong spirit of urine, sal-ammoniac, &c. or lixiviate salts, as oil of tartar per deliquium, fixed nitre, &c.

15. How to examine with evaporation, whether the mineral water contain common salt, and, if it do, whether it contains but little or much?

16. How to examine, without evaporation, whether the mineral water have any acidity, though it be but very little?

17. Of the liquor or liquors afforded by the mineral water by distillation in balneo, and other ways.

18. Of the residence, caput mortuum of the mineral water, when the liquor is totally evaporated or distilled off; and whether the caput mortuum be the same in quantity and quality, if produced by either of those ways?

19. Whether the proposed water being, in glass vessels exactly luted together, slowly and warily abstracted to a thickish substance; this being reconjoined to the distilled liquor, the mineral water will be redintegrated, and have again the same texture and qualities it had at first?

20. Whether a glass full of mineral water being hermetically sealed, and boiled in common water, deep enough to keep it always covered, will have its texture so altered, as to suffer an observable change in any of its manifest qualities? And if it do, in what qualities, and to what degree of alteration?

21. Of the proportion of the dry caput mortuum to the mineral water, that affords it.

22. Of the division of the caput mortuum into saline and terrestrial, and other parts not dissoluble in water, in case it contain both or more sorts.

23. Of the proposition of the saline part of the caput mortuum to the terrestrial.

24. Of the fixity or volatility of the saline part in strong fires.

25. Whether the saline part will shoot into crystals or no? And, if it will, what figure the grains will be of? And, if it will not, whether being combined with a salt, that will (as purified sea-salt, saltpetre, &c), it will then crystallize; and if it do, into what figures it will shoot, especially if any of them be reducible to those of any species of salt known to us?

26. To examine, whether the saline part be, *ex praedominio,* acid, alcalisate, or adiaphorous?[37]

27. Of the observables in the terrestrial portion of the caput mortuum, as, besides its quantity in reference to the saline, its colour, odour, volatility or fixity in strong fire; its being soluble, or not dissoluble by divers menstruums, as spirit of vinegar, spirit of urine, oil of tartar, &c.

28. Whether, and (if anything) how much the mineral water's earth loses by strong and lasting ignition? What changes of colour, &c. it thereby receives? Whether it be capable of vitrification per se? And what colour (if any) it will impart to fine and well powdered Venice glass, if they be exactly mixed and fluxed into a transparent glass?

29. Of the oeconomical and mechanical uses of the mineral water, as in brewing, baking, washing of linen, tanning of leather, or drying of cloth, callicoes, silks, &c as these may assist in discovering the ingredients and qualities of the liquor proposed.

30. Of the imitation of natural medicinal waters, by chymical and other artificial ways, as that may help the physicians to guess at the quality and quantity of the ingredients, that impregnate the natural water proposed. [*Works,* IV, 801–2]

17. New Experiments Physico-Mechanical, Touching the Spring of the Air and its Effects; Made, for the most Part, in a New Pneumatical Engine. Written by Way of a Letter to the Right Honourable Charles Lord Viscount of Dungarvan, eldest Son of the Earl of Cork

The following, consisting of the preface and a number of the more significant experiments contained therein, is taken from Boyle's first published (1660) scientific work. All the experiments were made between 1657, when he first heard of Otto von Guericke's invention of the air pump, and December, 1659, when the text was written. The work begins with an elaborate description of the air pump (omitted here) and of its use; Boyle generously intended the reader to learn how to construct his own pump, and how to make pneumatical experiments. The experiments Boyle includes are a fair sample of those he had been working on (though he had more available than he here published); those chosen here particularly relate to the "spring" (elasticity) of the air. The performing of the Torricellian experiment in the air pump was, as Boyle here indicates, regarded by him as the conclusive proof of the role of the pressure of the atmosphere in creating the Torricellian vacuum. The interest that this and other experiments aroused among the Oxford scientists is indicated by the references to their presence at many of the more important trials.

To the Reader

Although the following treatise being far more prolix than becomes a letter, and than I at first intended it, I am very unwilling to increase the already excessive bulk of the book by a preface; yet there are some particulars, that I think myself obliged to take notice of, to the reader, as things that will either concern him to know, or me to have known.

In the first place then: If it be demanded why I publish to the world a letter, which, by its style and divers passages, appears to have been written as well for, as to a particular person; I have chiefly these two things to answer; the one, that the experiments therein related, having been many of them tried in the presence of ingenious men, and by that means having made some noise among the Virtuosi (insomuch that some of them have been sent into foreign countries, where they have had the luck not to be despised) I could not, without quite tiring more than one amanuensis, give out half as many copies of them as were so earnestly desired, that I could not civilly refuse them. The other, that intelligent persons in matters of this kind persuade me, that the publication of what I had observed touching the nature of the air, would not be useless to the world; and that in an age so taken with novelties as is ours, these new experiments would be grateful to the lovers of free and real learning: so that I might at once comply with my grand design of promoting experimental and useful philosophy, and obtain the great satisfaction of giving some to ingenious men; the hope of which is, I confess, a temptation, that I cannot easily resist.

Of my being somewhat prolix in many of my experiments, I have these reasons to render: that some of them being altogether new, seemed to need the being circumstantially related, to keep the reader from distrusting them: that divers circumstances I did here and there set down for fear of forgetting them, when I may hereafter have occasion to make use of them in my other writings: that in divers cases I thought it necessary to deliver things circumstantially, that the person I addressed them to might, without mistake, and with as little trouble as possible, be able to repeat such usual experiments: and that after I consented to let my observations be made public, the most ordinary reason of my prolixity was, that foreseeing, that such a trouble as I met with in making those trials carefully, and the great expence of time that they necessarily require (not to mention the charges of making the engine, and employing a man to manage it) will probably keep most men from trying again these experiments, I thought I might do the generality of my readers no unacceptable piece of service, by so punctually relating what I carefully observed, that they may look upon these narratives as standing records in our new pneumatics, and need not reiterate themselves an experiment to have as distinct an idea of it, as may suffice them to ground their reflexions and speculations upon. . . .

Ever since I discerned the usefulness of speculative geometry to natural philosophy, the unhappy distempers of my eyes have so far kept me from being much conversant with it, that I fear I shall need the pardon of my mathematical readers for some passages, which, if I had been deeply skilled in geometry, I should have treated more accurately.

And indeed, having for reasons elsewhere deduced, purposely kept myself a stranger to most of the new hypotheses in philosophy, I am sensible enough, that the engine I treat of hath prevailed with me to write of some subjects which are sufficiently remote from those I have been most conversant in. And having been reduced to write the greatest part of the ensuing letter at a distance, not only from my library, but from my own manuscripts, I cannot but fear, that my discourses do not only want many choice things, wherewith the learned writings of others might have enriched or embellished them; but that . . . it is possible I may have mentioned some notions already published by others, without taking notice of the authors, not out of any design to defraud deserving men, but for want of knowing such particulars to have been already published by them; especially the experiments of our engine being themselves sufficiently to hint such notions as we build upon them. . . .

The Elasticity of the Air

We took then a lamb's bladder large, well dried, and very limber, and leaving in it about half as much air as it could contain, we caused the neck of it to be strongly tied, so that none of the included air, though by pressure, could get out. This bladder being conveyed into the receiver, and the cover luted on, the pump was set on work, and after two or three exsuctions of the ambient air (whereby the spring of that which remained in the glass was weakened) the imprisoned air began to swell in the bladder; and as more and more of the air in the receiver was, from time to time, drawn out; so did that in the bladder more and more expand itself, and display the folds of the formerly flaccid bladder: so that before we had exhausted the receiver near so much as we could, the bladder appeared as full and stretched, as if it had been blown up with a quill.

And that it may appear, that this plumpness of the bladder proceeded from the surmounting of the debilitated spring of the ambient air remaining in the vessel, by the stronger spring of the air remaining in the bladder; we returned the key of the stop-cock, and by degrees allowed the external air to return into the receiver, whereupon it happened, as was expected, that as the air came in from

without, the distended air in the bladder was proportionably compressed into a narrower room, and the sides of
the bladder grew flaccid, till the receiver having re-ad-
mitted its wonted quantity of air, the bladder appeared
as full of wrinkles and cavities as before. . . .

To try then . . . both what it was that expanded the bladder, and what a powerful spring there is even in the air we
are wont to think uncompressed; we caused a bladder
dry, well tied and blown moderately full, to be hung in
the receiver by one end of a string, whose other end was
fastened to the inside of the cover: and upon drawing
out the ambient air that pressed on the bladder; the internal air not finding the wonted resistance, first swelled
and distended the bladder, and then broke it, with so
wide and crooked a rent, as if it had been forcibly torn
asunder with hands. After which a second bladder being
conveyed in, the experiment was repeated with like success: and I suppose it will not be imagined, that in this
case the bladder was broken by its own fibres, rather than
by the imprisoned air.

And of this experiment these two phaenomena may be
taken notice of: the one, that the bladder at its breaking
gave a great report, almost like a cracker; and the other,
that the air contained in the bladder had the power to
break it with the mentioned impetuosity, long before the
ambient air was all, or near all, drawn out of the receiver. . . .

Having thus seen, that the air hath an elastical power,
we were next desirous to know in some measure, how far
a parcel of air might by this its own spring be dilated.
And though we were not provided of instruments fit to
measure the dilation of the air any thing accurately, yet
because an imperfect measure of it was more desirable than
none at all, we devised the following method as very
easily practicable.

We took a limber lamb's bladder, which was thoroughly
wetted in fair water, what the sides of it being squeezed
together, there might be no air left in its folds; (as indeed we could not afterwards upon trial discern any).
The neck of this bladder was strongly tied about that of
a small glass (capable of holding five full drachms of
water), the bladder being first so compressed, that all the
included air was only in the glass, without being pressed
there. Then the pump being set on work, after a few exsuctions, the air in the little phial began to dilate itself,
and produce a small tumour in the neck of the bladder;
and as the ambient air was more and more drawn away,
so the included air penetrated farther and farther into
the bladder, and by degrees lifted up the sides and displayed its folds, till at length it seemed to have blown it
up to its full extent: whereupon the external air, being
permitted to flow back into the receiver, repulsed the air
that had filled the bladder into its former narrow receptacle, and brought the bladder to be again flaccid and wrin-
kled as before. Then taking out the bladder, but without
severing it from the glass, we did, by a hole made at the
top of the bladder, fill the vessel, they both made up,
with water, whose weight was five ounces five drachms and
a half: five drachms whereof were above mentioned to be
the contents of the bottle. So that in this experiment, when
the air had most extended the bladder, it possessed in all
above nine times as much room as it did when it was put
into the receiver. And it would probably have much en-
larged its bounds, but that the bladder by its weight, and
the sticking together of the sides, did somewhat resist its expansion: and, which was more considerable, the bladder
appeared tumid enough, whilst yet a pretty deal of air was
left in the receiver, whose exsuction would, according to
our former observation, probably have given way to a
farther expansion of the air, especially supposing the dilation not to be restrained by the bladder. . . .

The Torricellian Experiment

Proceed we now to the mention of that experiment, whereof the satisfactory trial was the principal fruit I promised myself from our engine, it being then sufficiently known, that in the experiment *de vacuo*, the quicksilver in the tube is wont to remain elevated, above the surface of that whereon it leans, about 27 digits [inches]. I considered, that, if the true and only reason why the quicksilver falls no lower, be, that at that altitude the mercurial cylinder in the tube is in aequilibrium with the cylinder of air supposed to reach from the adjacent mercury to the top of the atmosphere; then if this experiment could be tried out of the atmosphere, the quicksilver in the tube would fall down to a level with that in the vessel, since then there would be no pressure upon the subjacent, to resist the weight of the incumbent mercury. Whence I inferred (as easily I might) that if the experiment could be tried in our engine, the quicksilver would subside below 27 digits, in proportion to the exsuction of air, that should be made out of the receiver. For, as when the air is shut into the receiver, it doth (according to what hath above been taught) continue there as strongly compressed, as it did whilst all the incumbent cylinder of the atmosphere leaned immediately upon it; because the glass, wherein it is penned up, hinders it to deliver itself, by an expansion of its parts, from the pressure wherewith it was shut up. So if we could perfectly draw the air out of the receiver, it would conduce as well to our purpose, as if we were allowed to try the experiment beyond the atmosphere.

Wherefore (after having surmounted some little difficulties, which occurred at the beginning) the experiment was made after this manner: we took a slender and very curiously blown cylinder of glass, of near three foot in length, and whose bore had in diameter a quarter of an inch, wanting a hair's breadth: this pipe being hermetically sealed at one end, was, at the other, filled with quicksilver, care being taken in the filling, that as few bubbles as was possible should be left in the mercury. Then the tube being stopt with the finger and inverted, was opened, according to the manner of the experiment, into a somewhat long and slender cylindrical box (instead of which we are now wont to use a glass of the same form) half filled with quicksilver: and so, the liquid metal being suffered to subside, and a piece of paper being pasted on level with its upper surface, the box and tube and all were by strings carefully let down into the receiver: and then, by means of the hole formerly mentioned to be left in the cover, the said cover was slipt along as much of the tube as reached above the top of the receiver; and the interval, left betwixt the sides of the hole and those of the tube, was very exquisitely filled up with melted (but not over-hot) diachylon, and the round chink, betwixt the cover and the receiver, was likewise very carefully closed up: upon which closure there appeared not any change in the height of the mercurial cylinder, no more than if the interposed glass-receiver did not hinder the immediate pressure of the ambient atmosphere upon the inclosed air; which hereby appears to bear upon the mercury, rather by virtue of its spring than of its weight; since its weight cannot be supposed to amount to above two or three ounces, which is inconsiderable in comparison to such a cylinder of mercury as it would keep from subsiding.

All things being thus in a readiness, the sucker was drawn down; and, immediately upon the egress of a cylinder of air out of the receiver, the quicksilver in the tube did, according to expectation, subside: and notice being carefully taken (by a mark fastened to the outside) of the place where it stopped, we caused him that managed the pump to pump again, and marked how low the quicksilver fell at the second exsuction; but continuing this work we were quickly hindered from accurately marking the stages made by the mercury in its descent, because it soon sunk below the top of the receiver, so that we could henceforward mark it no other ways than by the eye. And thus, continuing the labour of pumping for about a quarter of an hour, we found ourselves unable to bring the quicksilver in the tube totally to subside; because, when the receiver was considerably emptied of its air, and consequently that little that remained grown unable to resist the irruption of the external, that air would (in spite of whatever we could do) press in at some little avenue or other; and though much could not thereat get in, yet a little was sufficient to counterbalance the pressure of so small a cylinder of quicksilver, as then remained in the tube.

Now (to satisfy ourselves farther, that the falling of the quicksilver in the tube to a determinate height, proceedeth from the aequilibrium, wherein it is at that height with the external air, the one gravitating, the other pressing with equal force upon the subjacent mercury) we returned the key and let in some new air; upon which the mercury immediately began to ascend (or rather to be impelled upwards) in the tube, and continued ascending, till, having returned the key, it immediately rested at the height which it had attained: and so, by turning and returning the key, we did several times at pleasure impel it upwards, and check its ascent. And lastly, having given a free egress at the stop-cock to as much of the external air as would come in, the quicksilver was impelled up almost to its first height: I say almost, because it stopped near a quarter of an inch beneath the paper-mark formerly mentioned; which we ascribed to this, that there was (as is usual in this experiment) some little particles of air engaged among those of the quicksilver; which particles, upon the descent of the quicksilver, did manifestly rise up in bubbles towards the top of the tube, and by their pressure, as well as by lessening the cylinder by as much room as they formerly took up in it, hindered the quicksilver from regaining its first height.

This experiment was a few days after repeated, in the presence of those excellent and deservedly famous Mathematic Professors, Dr. Wallis, Dr. Ward, and Mr. Wren, who were pleased to honour it with their presence; and whom I name, both as justly counting it an honour to be known to them, and as being glad of such judicious and illustrious witnesses of our experiment; and it was by their guess, that the top of the quicksilver in the tube was destined to be brought within an inch of the surface of that in the vessel.

And here, for the illustration of the foregoing experiment, it will not be amiss to mention some other particulars relating to it.

First then, when we endeavoured to make the experiment with the tube closed at one end with diachylon instead of an hermetical seal, we perceived, that upon the drawing of some of the air out of the receiver, the mercury did indeed begin to fall, but continued afterwards to subside, though we did not continue pumping. When it appeared, that though the diachylon, that stopt the end of the tube, were so thick and strong, that the external air could not press it in, (as experience taught us that it would have done, if there had been but little of it;) yet the subtler parts of it were able (though slowly) to insinuate themselves through the very body of the plaster, which it seems was not of so close a texture, as that which we mentioned ourselves to have successfully made use of, in the experiment *de vacuo* some years ago. So that now we begin to suspect, that perhaps one reason, why we cannot perfectly pump out the air, may be, that when the vessel is almost empty, some of the subtler parts of the external air may, by the pressure of the atmosphere, be strained through the very body of the diachylon into the receiver. But this is only conjecture.

Another circumstance of our experiment was this, that if (when the quicksilver in the tube was fallen low) too much ingress were, at the hole of the stop-cock, suddenly permitted to the external air; it would rush in with that violence, and bear so forcibly upon the surface of the subjacent quicksilver, that it would impel it up into the tube rudely enough to endanger the breaking of the glass.

We formerly mentioned that the quicksilver did not, in its descent, fall as much at a time, after the two or three first exsuctions of the air, as at the beginning. For, having marked its several stages upon the tube, we found, that at the first suck it descended an inch and $\frac{3}{8}$, and at the second an inch and $\frac{3}{8}$; and when the vessel was almost emptied, it could scarce at one exsuction be drawn down above the breadth of a barley-corn. And indeed we found it very difficult to measure, in what proportion these decrements of the mercurial cylinder did proceed; partly, because (as we have already intimated) the quicksilver was soon drawn below the top of the receiver; and partly because, upon its descent at each exsuction, it would immediately reascend a little upwards; either by reason of the leaking of the vessel at some imperceptible hole or other, or by reason of the motion of the restitution in the air, which, being somewhat compressed by the fall as well as the weight of the quicksilver, would repel it a little upwards, and make it vibrate a little up and down, before they could reduce each other to such an aequilibrium as both might rest in.

But though we could not hitherto make observations accurate enough, concerning the measures of the quicksilver's descent, to reduce them into any hypothesis, yet would we not discourage any from attempting it; since, if it could be reduced to a certainty, it is probable, that the discovery would not be unuseful.

And, to illustrate this matter a little more, we will add, that we made a shift to try the experiment in one of our . . . small receivers, not containing a quart; but (agreeably to what we formerly observed) we found it as difficult to bring this to be quite empty as to evacuate the greater; the least external air that could get in (and we could not possibly keep it all perfectly out) sufficing, in so small a vessel, to display a considerable pressure upon the surface of the mercury, and thereby hinder that in the tube from falling to a level with it. But this is remarkable, that having two or three times tried the experiment in a small vessel upon the very first cylinder of air that was drawn out of the receiver, the mercury fell in the tube 18 inches and a half, and another trial 19 inches and a half.

But on this occasion, I hold it not unfit to give your Lordship notice, that I hoped from the descent of the quicksilver in the tube, upon the first suck, to derive this advantage; that I should thence be enabled to give a nearer guess at the proportion of force betwixt the pressure of the air (according to its various states, as to density and rarefaction) and the gravity of quicksilver, than hitherto hath been done. For in our experiment there are divers things given, that may be made use of towards such a discovery. For first, we may know the capacity of the receiver wherein the experiment is made, since, by filling it with water, we may easily compute how many quarts, or measures of any other denomination, it containeth of air; which air, when shut up in the vessel, may be supposed to have a pressure equal to that of the atmosphere; since it is able to keep the quicksilver in the tube from falling any lower than it did in the free and open air. Next, here is given us the capacity of the brass cylinder, emptied by the drawing down of the sucker (its bore and height being mentioned in the description of our pump) whereby we may come to know how much of the air contained in the receiver is drawn out at the first suck. And we may also easily define, either in weight or cubic measures, the cylinder of quicksilver, that answers to the cylinder of air lately mentioned, (that mercurial cylinder being in our engine computable by deducting from the entire altitude of that cylinder of quicksilver, the altitude at which it rests upon the first exsuction). But though, if this experiment were very watchfully tried in vessels of several sizes, and the various descents of the quicksilver compared among themselves, it is not improbable, that some such things, as we hoped for, may thereby be discovered. Yet, because not only the solid contents of as much of the glass-tube as remains within the concave surface of the receiver, and (which is more difficult) the varying contents of the vessel containing the mercury, and of as much of the mercury itself as is not in the tube, must be deducted out of the capacity of the receiver, but there must also an allowance be made for this, that the cylinder, that is emptied by the drawing down of the sucker, and comes to be filled upon the letting of the air out of the receiver into it, is not so replenished with air as the receiver itself at first was; because there passeth no more air out of the receiver into the cylinder, than is requisite to reduce the air in the cavity of the cylinder, and in that of the receiver to the same measure of dilation. Because of these (I say) and some other difficulties, that require more skill in mathematics than I pretend to, and much more leisure than my present occasions would allow me, I was willing to refer the nicer consideration of this matter to some of our learned and accurate mathematicians, thinking it enough for me to have given the hint already suggested....

[*Works*, I, 1–3, 18–20, 33–36]

18. Boyle's Law

This famous law of physics is that which Boyle suggested when considering the Torricellian experiment (cf. p. 335), as a desirable hypothesis which someone ought to work out. It was published in the second edition of the *New Experiments Physico-Mechanical* in 1662, in the addendum called *A Defence of the Doctrine Touching the Spring and Weight of the Air*, answering the opinion of Franciscus Linùs, S.J., who insisted that air could not possibly support so much mercury as would be contained in a twenty-nine-inch cylinder. Boyle apparently thought that no one had taken up his suggestion and performed the experiment described below on compressed air. Meanwhile, he found out that Richard Towneley (an able amateur instrument-maker) had worked out the hypothesis for rarefied (dilated) air; when he discussed this with Hooke, he found that Hooke also had worked on this problem independently, as had Lord Brouncker. Boyle included a discussion of their work after the detailed discussion of his own. There is no reason to assume that Boyle was not ·telling the truth in describing the work on compressed air as his own; certainly neither Towneley nor Hooke expressed any dissatisfaction with his statements. What we call Boyle's law, he called "the hypothesis, that supposes the pressures and expansions to be in reciprocal proportion." His notes on the experimental difficulties and precautions are extremely good, and a wonderful example of the problems of good experimental technique.

We shall now endeavour to manifest by experiments purposely made, that the spring of the air is capable of doing far more than it is necessary for us to ascribe to it, to solve the phaenomena of the Torricellian experiment.

We took then a long glass-tube, which, by a dexterous hand and the help of a lamp, was in such manner crooked at the bottom, that the part turned up was almost parallel to the rest of the tube, and the orifice of this shorter leg of the siphon (if I may so call the whole instrument) being hermetically sealed, the length of it was divided into inches (each of which was subdivided into eight parts) by a straight list of paper, which containing those divisions, was carefully pasted all along it. Then putting in as much quicksilver as served to fill the arch or bended part of the siphon, that the mercury standing in a level might reach in the one leg to the bottom of the divided paper, and just to the same height or horizontal line in the other; we took care, by frequently inclining the tube, so that the air might freely pass from one leg into the other by the sides of the mercury (we took, I say, care) that the air at last included in the shorter cylinder should be of the same laxity with the rest of the air about it. This done, we began to pour quicksilver into the longer leg of the siphon, which by its weight pressing up that in the shorter leg, did by degrees straighten the included air: and continuing this pouring in of quicksilver till the air in the shorter leg was by condensation reduced to take up but half the space it possessed (I say, possessed, not filled) before; we cast our eyes upon the longer leg of the glass, on which was likewise pasted a list of paper carefully divided into inches and parts, and we observed, not without delight and satisfaction, that the quicksilver in that longer part of the tube was 29 inches higher than the other. Now that this observation does both very well agree with and confirm our hypothesis, will be easily discerned by him, that takes notice what we teach; and Monsieur *Pascal* and our English friend's experiments[38] prove, that the greater the weight is that leans upon the air, the more forcible is its endeavour of dilation, and consequently its power of resistance (as other springs are stronger when bent by greater weights). For this being considered, it will appear to agree rarely well with the hypothesis, that as according to it the air in that degree of density and correspondent measure of resistance, to which the weight of the incumbent atmosphere had brought it, was able to counterbalance and resist the pressure of a mercurial cylinder of about 29 inches, as we are taught by the Torricellian experiment; so here the same air being brought to a degree of density about twice as great as that it had before, obtains a spring as strong as formerly. As may appear by its being able to sustain or resist a cylinder of 29 inches in the longer tube, together with the weight of the atmospherical cylinder, that leaned upon those 29 inches of mercury; and as we just now inferred from the Torricellian experiment, was equivalent to them.

We were hindered from prosecuting the trial at that time by the casual breaking of the tube. But because an accurate experiment of this nature would be of great importance to the doctrine of the spring of the air, and has not yet been made (that I know) by any man; and because also it is more uneasy to be made than one would think, in regard of the difficulty as well of procuring crooked tubes fit for the purpose, as of making a just estimate of the true place of the protuberant mercury's surface; I suppose it will not be unwelcome to the reader, to be informed, that after some other trials, one of which we made in a tube whose longer leg was perpendicular, and the other, that contained the air, parallel to the horizon, we at last procured a tube . . . ; which tube, though of a pretty bigness, was so long, that the cylinder, whereof the shorter leg of it consisted, admitted a list of paper, which had before been divided into 12 inches and their quarters, and the longer leg admitted another list of paper of divers feet in length, and divided after the same manner. Then the quicksilver being poured in to fill up the bended part of the glass, that the surface of it in either leg might rest in the same horizontal line, as we lately taught, there was more and more quicksilver poured into the longer tube; and notice being watchfully taken how far the mercury was risen in the longer tube, when it appeared to have ascended to any of the divisions in the shorter tube, the several observations, that were thus successively made, and as they were made set down, afforded us the ensuing table. [See following page.]

For the better understanding of this experiment, it may not be amiss to take notice of the following particulars:

1. That the tube being so tall, we could not conveniently make use of it in a chamber, we were fain to use it on a pair of stairs, which yet were very lightsome, the tube being for preservation's sake by strings so suspended, that it did scarce touch the box presently to be mentioned.

2. The lower and crooked part of the pipe was placed in a square wooden box, of a good largeness and depth, to prevent the loss of the quicksilver, that might fall aside in the transfusion from the vessel into the pipe, and to receive the whole quicksilver in case the tube should break.

3. That we were two to make the observation together, the one to take notice at the bottom, how the quicksilver rose in the shorter cylinder, and the other to pour in at the top of the longer; it being very hard and troublesome for one man alone to do both accurately.

4. That the quicksilver was poured in but by little and little, according to the direction of him that observed

A table of the condensation of the air

A	A	B	C	D	E
48	12	00		$29\,\frac{2}{16}$	$29\,\frac{2}{16}$
46	$11\frac{1}{2}$	$01\,\frac{7}{16}$		$30\,\frac{9}{16}$	$33\,\frac{6}{16}$
44	11	$02\frac{13}{16}$		$31\frac{15}{16}$	$31\frac{12}{16}$
42	$10\frac{1}{2}$	$04\,\frac{6}{16}$		$33\,\frac{8}{16}$	$33\frac{1}{7}$
40	10	$06\,\frac{3}{16}$		$35\,\frac{5}{16}$	35
38	$9\frac{1}{2}$	$07\frac{14}{16}$		37	$36\frac{15}{19}$
36	9	$10\,\frac{2}{16}$		$39\,\frac{5}{16}$	$38\frac{7}{8}$
34	$8\frac{1}{2}$	$12\,\frac{8}{16}$		$41\frac{10}{16}$	$41\frac{2}{17}$
32	8	$15\,\frac{1}{16}$		$44\,\frac{3}{16}$	$43\frac{11}{16}$
30	$7\frac{1}{2}$	$17\frac{15}{16}$		$47\,\frac{1}{16}$	$46\frac{3}{5}$
28	7	$21\,\frac{3}{16}$		$50\,\frac{5}{16}$	50
26	$6\frac{1}{2}$	$25\,\frac{3}{16}$		$54\,\frac{5}{16}$	$53\frac{10}{13}$
24	6	$29\frac{11}{16}$		$58\frac{13}{16}$	$58\frac{2}{8}$
23	$5\frac{3}{4}$	$32\,\frac{3}{16}$		$61\,\frac{5}{16}$	$60\frac{18}{23}$
22	$5\frac{1}{2}$	$34\frac{15}{16}$		$64\,\frac{1}{16}$	$63\frac{6}{11}$
21	$5\frac{1}{4}$	$37\frac{15}{16}$		$67\,\frac{1}{16}$	$66\frac{4}{7}$
20	5	$41\,\frac{9}{16}$		$70\frac{11}{16}$	70
19	$4\frac{3}{4}$	45		$74\,\frac{2}{16}$	$73\frac{11}{19}$
18	$4\frac{1}{2}$	$48\frac{12}{16}$		$77\frac{14}{16}$	$77\frac{2}{3}$
17	$4\frac{1}{4}$	$53\frac{11}{16}$		$82\frac{12}{16}$	$82\frac{4}{17}$
16	4	$58\,\frac{2}{16}$		$87\frac{14}{16}$	$87\frac{3}{8}$
15	$3\frac{3}{4}$	$63\frac{15}{16}$		$93\,\frac{1}{16}$	$93\frac{1}{5}$
14	$3\frac{1}{2}$	$71\,\frac{5}{16}$		$100\,\frac{7}{16}$	$99\frac{6}{7}$
13	$3\frac{1}{4}$	$78\frac{11}{16}$		$107\frac{13}{16}$	$107\frac{7}{13}$
12	3	$88\,\frac{7}{16}$		$117\,\frac{9}{16}$	$116\frac{4}{8}$

(In column C, running vertically: MAKES $29\frac{1}{8}$ ADDED TO)

AA. The number of equal spaces in the shorter leg, that contained the same parcel of air diversely extended.

B. The height of the mercurial cylinder in the longer leg, that compressed the air into those dimensions.

C. The height of the mercurial cylinder, that counterbalanced the pressure of the atmosphere.

D. The aggregate of the two last columns B and C, exhibiting the pressure sustained by the included air.

E. What that pressure should be according to the hypothesis, that supposes the pressures and expansions to be in reciprocal proportion.

below; it being far easier to pour in more, than to take out any, in case too much at once had been poured in.

5. That at the beginning of the operation, that we might the more truly discern where the quicksilver rested from time to time, we made use of a small looking-glass, held in a convenient posture to reflect to the eye what we desired to discern.

6. That when the air was so compressed, as to be crowded into less than a quarter of the space it possessed before, we tried whether the cold of a linen cloth dipped in water would then condense it. And it sometimes seemed a little to shrink, but not so manifestly as that we dare build any thing upon it. We then tried likewise, whether heat would, notwithstanding so forcible a compressure, dilate it; and approaching the flame of a candle to that part where the air was pent up, the heat had a more sensible operation than the cold had before; so that we scarce doubted, but that the expansion of the air would, notwithstanding the weight that oppressed it, have been made conspicuous, if the fear of unseasonably breaking the glass had not kept us from increasing the heat.

Now although we deny not, but that in our table some particulars do not exactly answer to what our formerly mentioned hypothesis might perchance invite the reader to expect; yet the variations are not so considerable, but that they may probably enough be ascribed to some such want of exactness as in such nice experiments is scarce avoidable. But for all that, till such further trial has more clearly informed me, I shall not venture to determine, whether or no the intimated theory will hold universally and precisely, either in condensation of air, or rarefaction: all that I shall now urge being, that however the trial already made sufficiently proves the main thing, for which I here allege it; since by it, it is evident, that as common air, when reduced to half its wonted extent, obtained near about twice as forcible a spring as it had before; so this thus compressed air being further thrust into half this narrow room, obtained thereby a spring about as strong again as that it last had, and consequently four times as strong as that of the common air. And there is no cause to doubt, that if we had been here furnished with a greater quantity of quicksilver and a very strong tube, we might, by a further compression of the included air, have made it counterbalance the pressure of a far taller and heavier cylinder of mercury. For no man perhaps yet knows, how near to an infinite compression the air may be capable of, if the compressing force be competently increased.

[*Works,* I, 156–59]

19. The Astonishing Weight of the Atmosphere

This, from the New Experiments Physico-Mechanical, Touching the Spring and Weight of the Air *(a continuation of the* First Continuation, *published in 1669), is a dramatically striking experiment, as well as an important demonstration of the extreme force which the pressure of the atmosphere alone could exert.*

About a Way of Speedily Breaking Flat Glasses, by the Weight of the Atmosphere

For the more easy understanding of some of the subsequent trials, it will be requisite in this place to mention, among experiments about the spring of the air, the following phaenomenon belonging to its weight.

This is one of those that is the most usually shown to strangers, as a plain and easy proof, both that the weight of the incumbent air is considerable, and that the round figure of a receiver doth much more conduce to make an exhausted glass support that weight, than if the upper part of the receiver were flat.

To make this experiment we provided a hoop or ring of brass of a considerable thickness, whose height was 2½ or 3 inches, and the diameter of whose cavity as well at the upper as lower orifice (should have been just 3 inches, but through the error of the workman) was 3 inches and 2/10. To this hoop we successively fastened with cement divers round pieces of glass, such as is used by glaziers (to whose shops we sent for it) to make panes for windows, and thereby made the brass-ring with its glass-cover a kind of receiver, whose open orifice we carefully cemented on to the engine; and then we found, as we had conjectured, that usually at the first exsuction (though sometimes not till the second) the glass plate would be broken inwards with such violence as to be shattered into a great multitude of small fragments, and (which was remarkable) the irruption of the external air driving the glass inwards did constantly make a loud clap, almost like the report of a pistol: which phaenomenon, whether it may help us to discover the cause of that great noise that is made upon the discharging of guns (for the recoil seems to depend upon the dilation and impulse of the powder) I must not stay to consider. [*Works*, III, 192]

20. The Resistance of the Air

The two following experiments, the first from the 1660 *New Experiments Physico-Mechanical,* the second from the 1669 *First Continuation,* are important examples of the possible application of the air pump to quantitative measurement in physical problems. The resistance of the air was an important factor in both pure and applied physics, especially in confirming Galileo's law of falling bodies ($s = \frac{1}{2}\ gt^2$) and in exploring ballistics.

The Motion of Pendulums

It having been observed by those that have considered what belongs to pendulums (a speculation that may, in my poor judgment, be highly useful to the Naturalists) that their vibrations are more slowly made, and that their motion lasts in a thicker, than in a thinner medium; we thought it not amiss to try, if a pendulum would swing faster, or continue swinging longer in our receiver, in case of exsuction of the air, than otherwise. Wherefore we took a couple of round and polished pendulums of iron or steel, of equal bigness, as near as we could get the artificer to make them; and weighing each of them twenty drachms, wanting as many grains: one of these we suspended in the cavity of the receiver by a very slender silken string, of about seven inches and a half in length, from the cover of the receiver to which it is fastened. Then

345

(by including the engine) we made the pendulum swing to and fro in it, and describe as long arches, as in the capacity of so brittle a vessel we thought safe and convenient. And one of the assistants telling the recursions of the other pendulum hanging in the free air, by a string of about the same length, we shortened and lengthened this other pendulum, till it appeared to keep the same pace in its vibrations with that shut up in the receiver. Then having carefully drawn away the air, we did again set the pendulum in the receiver a-vibrating; and giving the other such a motion as made it describe an arch, according to one's guess, equal to that of the included pendulum, we reckoned, one of us, the recursions of that pendulum which was swinging within the receiver; and another of us that which was moving in (that which one would think a much more resisting medium) the air. But once, one of us reckoned near two and twenty recursions of the included pendulum, whilst the other reckoned but twenty of the pendulum that vibrated without. And another time also, the former of these pendula was reckoned to have made one and twenty recursions, wherein the other made but twenty: yet this experiment seemed to teach us little, save that the difference betwixt the motion of such a pendulum in the common air, and in one exceedingly rarified, is scarce sensible in vessels no bigger than our receiver; especially, since though during this experiment it held very well, yet we could not suppose it to be altogether devoid of air. We observed also, that when the receiver was full of air, the included pendulum continued its recursions about fifteen minutes (or a quarter of an hour) before it left off swinging; and that after the exsuction of the air, the vibration of the same pendulum (being fresh put into motion) appeared not (by a minute watch) to last sensibly longer. So that the event of this experiment being other than we expected, scarce afforded us any satisfaction, than that of our not having omitted to try it. And whether, in case the trial be made with a pendulum much less disproportionate to the air than steel is, the event will much better answer expectation, experience may be consulted.

[*Works,* I, 61–62]

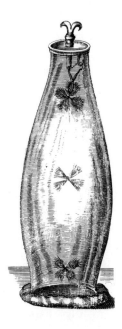

FIG. 3 FALLING BODIES IN VACUO

This illustrates the fall *in vacuo* of bodies so light that they float in air.

About the Falling, in the Exhausted Receiver, of a Light Body, Fitted to Have its Motion Visibly Varied by a Small Resistance of the Air.

. . . We took a receiver, which, though less tall than we would have had, was the longest we could procure; and that we might be able, not so properly to let down as to let fall a body in it, we so fastened a small pair of tobacco-tongs to the inside of the receiver's brass-cover, that by moving the turning-key we might, by a string tied to one part of them, open the tongs, which else their own spring would keep shut. This being done, the next thing was to provide a body which would not fall down like a stone, or another dead weight through the air, but would, in the manner of its descent, show, that its motion was somewhat resisted by the air; wherefore, that we might have a body that would be turned about horizontally, as it were, in its fall, we thought fit to join crosswise four broad and light feathers (each about an inch long) at their quills with a little cement, into which we also stuck perpendicularly a small label of paper, about an 8th of an inch in breadth, and somewhat more in height, by which the tongs might take hold of our light instrument without touching the cement, which else might stick to them.

By the help of this small piece of paper the little instrument, of which it made a part, was so taken hold of by the tongs, that it hung as horizontal as such a thing could well be placed; and then the receiver being cemented on to the engine, the pump was diligently plied, till it appeared by a gauge which had been conveyed in, that the receiver had been carefully exhausted; lastly, our eyes being attentively fixed upon the connected feathers, the tongs were by the help of the turning-key opened, and the little instrument let fall, which, though in the air it had made some turns in its descent from the same height which it now fell from, yet now it descended like a dead weight, without being perceived by any of us to make so much as one turn, or a part of it: notwithstanding which I did, for greater security, cause the receiver to be taken off and put on again, after which the feathers were taken hold of by the tongs; whence being let fall in the receiver unexhausted, they made some turns in their descent, as they also did being a second time let fall after the same manner.

But when after this, the feathers being placed as before, we repeated the experiment by carefully pumping out the air, neither I nor any of the bystanders could perceive anything of turning in the descent of the feathers; and yet for further security we let them fall twice more in the unexhausted receiver, and found them to turn in falling as before; whereas when we did a third time let them fall in the well exhausted receiver, they fell after the same manner as they had done formerly, when the air, that would by its resistance have turned them around, was removed out of their way.

N.B. No. 1. Though, as I intimated above, the glass wherein this experiment was made, were nothing near so tall as I would have had it, yet it was taller than any of our ordinary receivers, it being in height about 22 inches.

2. One that had more leisure and conveniency might have made a more commodious instrument than that we made use of; for being accidentally visited by that sagacious mathematician Dr. Wren, and speaking to him of this matter, he was pleased with great dexterity as well as readiness to make me a little instrument of paper, on which, when it was let fall, the resistance of the air had so manifest an operation, that I should have made use of it in our experiment, had it not been casually lost when the ingenious maker was gone out of these parts. . . .

[Works, III, 256–57]

21. Sound and the Air

This, from the *New Experiments Physico-Mechanical* (1660)
is a conclusive proof of what had been assumed since antiquity,
that air was necessary for the transmission of sound. That this
is a difficult experiment to perform successfully is indicated by
the fact that it had not previously been possible to make it in
a Torricellian vacuum. Once again, Boyle's patience and extraordinarily good experimental flair enabled him to devise
and carry through a difficult and important experiment.

That the air is the medium, whereby sounds are conveyed to the ear, hath been for many ages, and is yet
the common doctrine of the schools. But this received
opinion hath been of late opposed by some philosophers
upon the account of an experiment made by the industrious
Kircher, and other learned men; who have (as they assure us) observed, that if a bell, with a steel clapper, be
so fastened to the inside of a tube, that upon making the
experiment *de vacuo* with that tube, the bell remained suspended in the deserted space at the upper end of the
tube: and if also a vigorous load-stone be applied on the
outside of the tube to the bell, it will attract the clapper,
which, upon the removal of the load-stone falling back,
will strike against the opposite side of the bell, and thereby
produce a very audible sound; whence divers have concluded, that it is not the air, but some more subtle body,
that is the medium of sounds. But because we conceived
that, to invalidate such a consequence from this ingeni-

350

ous experiment (though the most luciferous that could well be made without some such engine as ours) some things might be speciously enough alledged; we thought fit to make a trial or two, in order to the discovery of what the air doth in conveying of sounds, reserving divers other experiments tryable in our engine concerning sounds, till we can obtain more leisure to prosecute them. Conceiving it then the best way to make our trial with such a noise, as might not be loud enough to make it difficult to discern slighter variations in it, but rather might be, both lasting (that we might take notice of what degrees it decreased) and so small, that it could not grow much weaker without becoming imperceptible; we took a watch, whose case we opened, that the contained air might have free egress into that of the receiver. And this watch was suspended in the cavity of the vessel only by a pack-thread, as the unlikeliest thing to convey a sound to the top of the receiver; and then closing up the vessel with melted plaister, we listened near the sides of it, and plainly enough heard the noise made by the balance. Those also of us, that watched for that circumstance, observed, that the noise seemed to come directly in a straight line from the watch unto the ear. And it was observable to this purpose, that we found a manifest disparity of noise, by holding our ears near the sides of the receiver, and near the cover of it: which difference seemed to proceed from that of the texture of the glass, from the structure of the cover (and the cement) through which the sound was propagated from the watch to the ear. But let us prosecute our experiment. The pump after this being employed, it seemed, that from time to time the sound grew fainter and fainter; so that when the receiver was emptied as much as it used to be for the foregoing experiments, neither we, nor some strangers, that chanced to be then in the room, could, by applying our ears to the very sides, hear any noise from within; though we could easily per-

ceive, that by the moving of the hand, which marked the
second minutes, and by that of the balance, that the watch
neither stood still, nor remarkably varied from its wonted
motion. And to satisfy ourselves farther, that it was indeed the absence of the air about the watch, that hindered
us from hearing it, we let in the external air at the stop-
cock; and then though we turned the key and stopt the
valve, yet we could plainly hear the noise made by the
balance, though we held our ears sometimes at two foot
distance from the outside of the receiver; and this experiment being reiterated into another place, succeeded after
the like manner. Which seems to prove, that whether or
no the air be the only, it is at least the principal medium
of sounds. And by the way it is very well worth noting,
that in a vessel so well closed as our receiver, so weak a
pulse as that [of] the balance of a watch, should propagate
a motion to the air in a physically straight line, notwithstanding the interposition of so close a body as glass, especially glass of such thickness as that of our receiver;
since by this it seems the air imprisoned in the glass must,
by the motion of the balance, be made to beat against the
concave part of the receiver, strongly enough to make its
convex part beat upon the contiguous air, and so propagate the motion to the listener's ears. I know this cannot
but seem strange to those, who, with an eminent modern
philosopher, will not allow, that a sound, made in the
cavity of a room, or other place so closed, that there is no
intercourse betwixt the external and internal air, can be
heard by those without, unless the sounding body do
immediately strike against some part of the inclosing body.
But not having now time to handle controversies, we shall
only annex, that after the foregoing experiment, we took
a bell of about two inches in diameter at the bottom,
which was supported in the midst of the cavity of the
receiver by a bent stick, which by reason of its spring
pressed with its two ends against the opposite parts of

the inside of the vessel: in which, when it was closed up, we observed, that the bell seemed to sound more dead than it did when just before it sounded in the open air. And yet, when afterwards we had (as formerly) emptied the receiver, we could not discern any considerable change (for some said they observed a small one) in the loudness of the sound. Whereby it seemed, that though the air be the principal medium of sound, yet either a more subtle matter may be also a medium of it, or else an ambient body, that contains but very few particles of air, in comparison of those it is easily capable of, is sufficient for that purpose. And this, among other things, invited us to consider, whether in the above-mentioned experiment made with the bell and the load-stone, there might not in the deserted part of the tube remain air enough to produce a sound; since the tubes for the experiment *de vacuo* (not to mention the usual thinness of the glass) being seldom greater than is requisite, a little air might bear a not inconsiderable proportion to the deserted space: and that also, in the experiment *de vacuo*, as it is wont to be made, there is generally some little air, that gets in from without, or at least store of bubbles, that arise from the body of the quicksilver, or other liquor itself, observations heedfully made have frequently informed us; and it may also appear, by what hath been formerly delivered concerning the Torricellian experiment.

On the occasion of this experiment concerning sounds, we may add in this place, that when we tried the experiment formerly mentioned, of firing gun powder with a pistol in our evacuated receiver, the noise made by the striking of the flint against the steel was exceedingly languid, in comparison of what it would have been in the open air. And on divers other occasions it appeared, that the sounds created with our exhausted glass, if they were not lost before they reached the ear, seemed at least to arrive there very much weakened. We intended to try, whether or no the wirestring of an instrument shut up into our receiver would, when the ambient air was sucked out, at all tremble, if in another instrument held close to it, but without the receiver, a string tuned (as musicians speak, how properly I now examine not) to an unison with it, were briskly touched, and set a-vibrating. This, I say, we purposed to try, to see how the motion made in the air without would be propagated through the cavity of our evacuated receiver. But when the instrument, wherewith the trial was to be made, came to be employed, it proved too big to go into the pneumatical vessel: and we have not now the conveniency to have a fitter made.

We thought likewise to convey into the receiver a long and slender pair of bellows, made after the fashion of those usually employed to blow organs, and furnished with a small musical instead of an ordinary pipe. For we hoped, that by means of a string fastened to the upper part of the bellows and to the moveable stopple, that makes a part of the cover of our receiver, we should, by frequently turning round that stopple, and the annexed string, after the manner already often recited, be able to lift up and distend the bellows; and by the help of a competent weight fastened to the same upper part of the bellows, we should likewise be able at pleasure to compress them, and by consequence, try whether, that subtler matter than air (which, according to those that deny a vacuum, must be supposed to fill the exhausted receiver) would be able to produce a sound in the musical pipe; or in a pipe like that of ordinary bellows, to beget a wind capable to turn or set on moving some very light matter, either shaped like the sails of a wind-mill, or of some other convenient form, and exposed to its orifice. This experiment, I say, we thought to make; but have not yet actually made it for want of an artificer to make us such a pair of bellows as it requires. . . . [*Works*, I, 62–64]

22. On the Nature of a Vacuum

Here is Boyle's earliest public discussion of the nature of the vacuum in his air pump receiver, in *New Experiments Physico-Mechanical* (1660). It 'is an extremely neat exposition of a difficult problem, for consideration of the nature of the Boyleian vacuum involved new 'and complex ideas. Clearly, as Boyle here points out, one could not speak of his vacuum as consisting of completely empty space, when light, magnetism and other forces (or bodies) traversed it. On the other hand, Boyle was averse to the Cartesian explanation that when the pump withdrew the air it left behind the ether; the Plenists he speaks of are Cartesians. He later (in the *First Continuation*, 1669) showed that it was impossible to detect the ether experimentally, and if the ether really existed it ought to be experimentally detectable.

What is a Vacuum?

Your Lordship[39] will here perhaps expect, that as those, who have treated of the Torricellian experiment, have for the most part maintained the affirmative, or the negative of that famous question, whether or no that noble experiment infer a vacuum? so I should, on this occasion interpose my opinion touching that controversy: or at least declare, whether or no, in our engine, the exsuction of the air do prove the place deserted by the air sucked out to be truly empty, that is, devoid of all corporeal sub-

stance. But besides that I have neither the leisure, nor
the ability, to enter into a solemn debate of so nice a
question; your Lordship may, if you think it worth the
trouble, in the Dialogues not long since referred to [on
heat and flame] find the difficulties on both sides represented, which then made me yield but a very wavering
assent to either of the parties contending about the question: nor dare I yet take upon me to determine so difficult
a controversy.

For on the one side it appears, that notwithstanding
the exsuction of the air, our receiver may not be destitute
of all bodies, since any thing placed in it, may be seen
there; which would not be, if it were not pervious to
those beams of light, which rebounding from the seen object to our eyes, affect us with the sense of it: and that
either these beams are corporeal emanations from some
lucid body, or else at least the light they convey doth
result from the brisk motion of some subtle matter, I could,
if I mistake not, sufficiently manifest out of the Dialogues
above-mentioned, if I thought your Lordship could seriously imagine that light could be conveyed without, at
least, having (if I may so speak) a body for its vehicle. . . .

. . . It also appears that the closeness of the receiver
hinders it not from admitting the effluvia of the load-
stone; which makes it very probable that it also freely
admits the magnetical steams of the earth; concerning
which, we have in another treatise endeavoured to manifest that numbers of them do always permeate our air.

But on the other side it may be said, that as for the
subtle matter which makes the objects enclosed in our
evacuated receiver visible, and the magnetical effluvia
of the earth that may be presumed to pass through it,
though we should grant our vessel not to be quite devoid of
them, yet we cannot so reasonably affirm it to be replenished with them, they as we may suppose, that if they were

gathered together into one place without intervals between them, they would fill but a small part of the whole receiver. . . . For (as elsewhere our experiments have demonstrated) both light and the effluvia of the load-stone
may be readily admitted into a glass, hermetically sealed,
though before their admission, as full of air as hollow
bodies here below are wont to be; so that upon the exsuction of the air, the large space deserted by it, may remain empty, notwithstanding the presence of those subtle
corpuscles, by which lucid and magnetical bodies produce
their effects.

And as for the allegations above-mentioned, they
seemed to prove but that the receiver devoid of air, may
be replenished with some etherial matter, as some modern
Naturalists write of, but not that it really is so. And indeed
to me it yet seems, that as to those spaces which the
Vacuists would have to be empty, because they are manifestly devoid of air and all grosser bodies; the Plenists (if
I may so call them) do not prove that such spaces are
replenished with such a subtle matter as they speak of, by
any sensible effects, or operations of it (of which divers
new trials purposely made, have not yet shown me any)
but only conclude that there must be such a body, because there cannot be a void. And the reason why there
cannot be a void, being by them taken, not from any
experiments, or phaenomena of nature, that clearly and
particularly prove their hypothesis, but from their notion
of a body, whose nature, according to them, consisting
only in extension (which indeed seems the property most
essential to, because inseparable from a body) to say a space
is devoid of body is, to speak in the schoolmen's phrase, a
contradiction *in adjecto*. This reason, I say, being thus
desumed, seems to make the controversy about a vacuum
rather a metaphysical, than a physiological question;
which therefore we shall here no longer debate, finding it

very difficult either to satisfy Naturalists with this Cartesian notion of a body, or to manifest wherein it is erroneous, and substitute a better in its stead. . . .

[*Works*, I, 36–38]

About an attempt to examine the motions and sensibility of the Cartesian Materia subtilis, or the Aether, with a pair of bellows made of a bladder, in the exhausted receiver.

I will not now discuss the controversy betwixt some of the modern atomists and the Cartesians; the former of whom think, that betwixt the earth and the stars, and betwixt these themselves, there are vast tracts of space that are empty, save where the beams of light do pass through them; and the latter of whom tell us, that the intervals betwixt the stars and planets, among which the earth may perhaps be reckoned, are perfectly filled, but by a matter far subtiler than our air, which some call celestial, and others aether. I shall not, I say, engage in this controversy; but thus much seems evident, that if there be such a celestial matter, it must make up far the greatest part of the universe known to us. For the interstellar part of the world, if I may so style it, bears so very great a proportion to the globes, and their atmospheres too, if other stars have any, as well as the earth, that it is almost incomparably greater in respect of them, than all our atmosphere is in respect to the clouds, not to make the comparison between the sea and the fishes that swim in it.

Wherefore I thought it might very well deserve a heedful inquiry, whether we can by sensible experiments (for I hear what has been attempted by speculative arguments) discover anything about the existence, or the qualifications of this so vast aether; and I hoped our

curiosity might be somewhat assisted by our engine, if
I could manage in it such a pair of bellows as I designed:
for I proposed to myself to fasten a convenient weight to
the upper basis, and clog the lower with another great
enough to keep it horizontal and immovable; that when
by the help of the turning-key . . . the upper basis should
be raised to its full height, the cavity of the bellows might
be brought to its full dimensions: this done, I intended to
exhaust the receiver, and consequently the thus opened
bellows, with more than ordinary diligence, that so both
the receiver and they might be carefully freed from air:
after which I proposed to let go the upper base of the
bellows, that, being hastily depressed by the incumbent
weight, it might speedily enough fall down to the lower
basis, and by so much, and so quickly lessening the
cavity, might expel thence the matter (if anywhere) before contained in it, and that (if it could by this way be
done) at the hole of a slender pipe fastened either near
the bottom of the bellows, or in the upper basis; against,
or over the orifice, of which pipe there was to be placed
at a convenient distance, either a feather, or (if that should
prove too light) the sail of a little windmill made of cards,
or some other light body, and fit to be put into motion by
the impulse of any matter that should be forced out of the
pipe.

By this means it seemed not improbable that some
such discovery might be made, as would not be altogether
useless in our inquiry. For if, notwithstanding the absence
of the air, it should appear by the effects, that a stream of
other matter capable to set visible bodies a-moving, should
issue out at the pipe of the compressed bellows, it would
also appear that there may be a much subtiler body than
common air, and as yet unobserved by the vacuists, or
(their adversaries) the schools, that may even copiously
be found in places deserted by the air; and that it is not

safe to conclude from the absence of the air in our receivers, and in the upper part of those tubes where the Torricellian experiment is made, that there is no other body
left but an absolute vacuity, or (as the atomists call it) a
vacuum coacervatum. But if, on the other side, there
should appear no motion at all to be produced, so much as
in the feather, it seemed that the vacuists might plausibly argue, that either the cavity of the bellows was absolutely empty, or else that it would be very difficult to
prove by any sensible experiment that it was full; and if,
by any other way of probation, it be demonstrable that it
was replenished with aether, we, that have not yet declared
for any party, may by our experiment be taught to have
no confident expectations of easily making it sensible by
mechanical experiments; and may also be informed, that it
is really so subtle and yielding a matter that does not either
easily impel such light bodies as even feathers, or sensibly resist, as does the air itself, the motions of other bodies
through it, and is able, without resistance, to make its
passage through the pores of wood and leather, and also
of closer bodies, which we find not all the air doth in its
natural or wonted state penetrate.

To illustrate this last clause, I shall add, that to make the
trial more accurate, I waived the use of other bellows
(especially not having such as I desired) and caused a
pair of small bellows to be made with a bladder, as a body,
which some of our former experiments have evinced to be
of so close a texture, that air will rather break it than
pass through it; and that the bladder might no where lose
its entireness by seams, we glued on the two bases, the
one to the bottom and the other to the opposite part of
it, so that the neck came out at a hole purposely made for
it in the upper basis; and into the neck it was easy to insert
what pipe we thought fit, binding the neck very close to
it on the outside. We had likewise thoughts to have another

pair of tight bellows made with a very light clack in the
lower basis, that by hastily drawing up the other basis,
when the receiver and bellows were very carefully exhausted, we might see by the rest, as the lifting up of the
clack, whether the subtle matter that was expelled by the
upper basis in its ascent would, according to the modern
doctrine of the circle made by moving bodies, be impelled
up or not.

We also thought of placing the little pipe of the bladder-
bellows (if I may so call them) beneath the surface of
water exquisitely freed from air, that we might see,
whether upon the depression of the bellows by the incumbent weight, when the receiver was carefully exhausted, there would be anything expelled at the pipe
that would produce bubbles in the liquor wherein its
orifice was immersed.

To bring now our conjectures to some trial, we put into
a capped receiver the bladder accomodated as before is
mentioned: and though we could have wished it had been
somewhat larger, because it contained but between half
a pint and a pint, yet in regard it was fine and limber, and
otherwise fit for our turn, we resolved to try how it would
do; and to depress the upper basis of these little bellows
the more easily and uniformly, we covered the round
piece of pasteboard that made the upper basis with a
pewter-plate (with a hole in it for the neck of the bladder)
which nevertheless, upon trial, proved not ponderous
enough, whereby we were obliged to assist it by laying
on it a weight of lead. And to secure the above-mentioned
feather (which had a slender and flexible stem, and was
left broad at one end, and fastened by cement at the other,
so as to stand with its broad end at a convenient distance
just over the orifice of the pipe) from being blown aside
to either hand, we made it to move in a perpendicular slit
in a piece of pasteboard that was fastened on one part

of the upper basis, as that which the feather was glued to was to another part. These things being thus provided, the pump was set a-work; and as the ambient air was from time to time withdrawn, so the air in the bladder expanded itself so strongly, as to lift up the metalline weight, and yet in part to sally out at the little glass-pipe of our bellows, as appeared by its blowing up the feather and keeping it suspended till the spring of the air in the bladder was too far weakened to continue to do as it had done. In the meantime we did now and then, by the help of a string fastened to the turning-key and the upper basis of the bellows, let down that basis a little, to observe how upon its sinking the blast against the feather would decrease as the receiver was further and further exhausted: and when we judged it to be sufficiently freed from air, we then let down the weight, but could not perceive that by shutting of the bellows, the feather was at all blown up, as it had been wont to be, though the upper basis were more than usually depressed: and yet it seems somewhat odd, that when, for curiosity, in order to a further trial, the weight was drawn up again, as the upper basis was raised from the lower, the sides of the bladder were sensibly (though not very much) pressed, or drawn inwards. The bellows being thus opened, we let down the upper basis again, but could not perceive that any blast was produced; for though the feather that lay just over and near the orifice of the little glass-pipe had some motion, yet this seemed plainly to be but a shaking and almost vibratory motion (to the right and left hand) which it was put into by the upper basis, which the string kept from a smooth and uniform descent, but not to proceed from any blast issuing out of the cavity of the bladder: and for further satisfaction we caused some air to be let into the receiver, because there was a possibility, that unawares to us the slender pipe might by some accident be choked; but though upon the return of the air into the receiver, the bases of the bellows were prest closer together, yet it seemed, that, according to our expectation, some little air got through the pipe into the cavity of the bladder; for when we began to withdraw again the air we had let into the receiver, the bladder began to swell again, and upon our letting down the weight, to blow up and keep up the feather, as had been done before the receiver had been so well exhausted. . . .

[*Works,* III, 250–52]

23. Air, Light, and Flame

Air was well known to be necessary for the production of fire, and it was only natural that Boyle should examine this fact in the air pump, together with the related question of light and air. This sounds an easy experiment to make, but in fact it was rather difficult, since it was not always possible to determine whether or how much residual air remained in the receiver; in some cases there was enough to make it appear possible that flame could exist in a vacuum. The first experiment is a careful test of the length of time a flame would burn under various conditions; it is taken from *New Experiments Physico-Mechanical* (1660). Later, in connection with his work on phosphorus, Boyle had occasion to examine the relation of the light emitted by both liquid and solid "Noctilucas" (phosphorus) under various conditions, which led him to some general considerations on flame and the air.

The Burning Candle

We took a tallow candle of such a size, that eight of them make about a pound, and having in a very commodious candlestick let it down into the receiver, and so suspended it, that the flame burnt almost in the middle of the vessel, we did in some two minutes exactly close it up: and upon pumping very nimbly, we found that, within a little more than half a minute after, the flame went out, though the snuff had been purposely left of that length we judged the most convenient for the lasting of the flame.

But the second time having put in the same candle into the receiver (after it had by the blasts of a pair of bellows been freed from fumes) the flame lasted about two minutes from the time the pumper began to draw out the air; upon the first exsuction whereof, the flame seemed to contract itself in all its dimensions. And these things were farther observable, that after the two or three first exsuctions of the air, the flame (except at the very top) appeared exceeding blue, and that the flame still receded more and more from the tallow, till at length it appeared to possess only the very top of the wick, and there it went out.

The same candle being lighted again was shut into the receiver, to try how it would last there without drawing forth the air, and we found that it lasted much longer than formerly; and before it went out, receded from the tallow towards the top of the wick, but not near so much as in the former experiment.

And having an intention to observe particularly, what the motion of the smoke would be in these experiments, we took notice, that when the air was not drawn out, there did, upon the extinction of the flame, a considerable part of the wick remain kindled, which (probably by reason of the circulation of the air in the vessel, occasioned by the heat) emitted a steam, which ascended swiftly and directly upwards in a slender and uninterrupted cylinder of smoke, till it came to the top, whence it manifestly recoiled by the sides to the lower part of the vessel. Whereas when the flame went out upon the exsuction of the air one time (when the flame retired very leisurely to the top) we perceived it not to be followed by any smoke at all. And at another time the upper part of the wick remaining kindled after the extinction of the flame, the slender steam of fumes that did arise ascended but a very little way, and then after some uncertain motions this and that way, did, for the most part, soon fall downwards. . . . [*Works*, I, 26–27]

Observations about the Aerial Noctiluca

I. The liquor, that afforded the aerial noctiluca,[40] (for which reason, and for brevity, I often call it the shining liquor) by daylight was not near diaphanous, and appeared muddy, and of a greyish colour, somewhat like common water, rendered opacous, by having a quantity of wood ashes mingled with it.

II. When no light appeared in the glass, we observed all the cavity of the vial, that reached from the liquor to the neck, to be transparent, as if there were nothing in the glass, save a spoonful of dirty water at the bottom.

III. But when the liquor was made to shine vividly, then all the cavity of the glass, untaken up by the liquor, appeared in an external light to be full of fumes. And this seeming smoke, being, in the vial that contained it, removed to a dark place, appeared lucid, and sometimes looked like a flame, that seemed to be reverberated, and to be made, as it were, to circulate by the close stopped neck and the sides of the vial. And the appearance of whitish fumes, when the glass was looked upon in an external light, was so usual a concomitant of its fitness to shine in the dark, that by looking upon the vial by daylight, I could readily tell, by the presence or absence of the whitish mist above-mentioned, whether the matter would, in a dark place, appear luminous or not.

IV. When this liquor had been kept for a competent time (as an hour or two, and sometimes much less) in some dark and quiet place, or even in my pocket; if in a darkened room my eyes were cast toward the place, where the vial was held, I could not perceive it to afford any light at all. And though I shaked the liquor strongly enough, to give it at least a moderate agitation, yet I could not discern, that this motion alone was able to bring the included liquor, or the vapour it may be supposed to have sent up, to be manifestly lucid.

V. But as soon as I unstopped the vial in the dark, there began to appear, as I expected, a light or flame in the cavity of it. I call it light or flame, because I dare not yet speak dogmatically of it; though it agrees with flame in divers particulars, and though also I am not sure, that all flames must agree in all points with common flames, experience having taught me the contrary; and particularly, that some flames will burn, and be propagated in close stopped vessels. I shall therefore on this account, and for brevity's sake, allow the aggregate of our shining fumes the name of flame (which Aristotle himself somewhere styles *fumus accensus*[41]) but without positively asserting, that it deserves it, unless further phaenomena shall be found to entitle it thereunto. But whatever be the nature and subject of this light, the light itself appeared to have, in great part, a dependence on the fresh air, as I judged it probable by the following phaenomena.

VI. First, I never observed the light to disclose itself first, either in the liquor, or upon the surface of it; but still the shining began at the upper part, which was first touched by the outward air, and made progress, quick indeed, but not so instantaneous, as that the eye could not follow it, from the top to the bottom of the vial.

VII. Secondly, the contact of the air seemed necessary to the propagation as well as production of this flame or light: for if, having shaken the vial, that the liquor might either wet the stopple, or communicate something to it, I warily bended the cork this way and that way, so that only a few particles of the outward air could insinuate themselves between the stopple and the neck of the glass; there would appear on the sides, and perhaps beneath the cork, little flames, as it were; which yet, though very vivid, were not able to propagate themselves downwards: whereas, when the cork was quite removed, and access was thereby allowed to a greater quantity of air, the flame or light (as was lately noted) presently diffused itself through the whole cavity of the vial, and reached as low as the surface of the liquor.

VIII. Thirdly, though oftentimes the light seemed more vivid near the surface of the liquor, than elsewhere; (whether because the lucid matter was there more dense, I now examine not) yet when by stopping the vial again, presently after I had opened it, I endeavoured to destroy the flame or light; I generally observed, that when it was ready to vanish (which in that case it usually did in no long time) it began to disappear first in the bottom of the vial, and seemed to shrink, as it were, more and more upwards, till it expired at the neck of the vial (where it was nearest to the air).

IX. Fourthly, but on the other side, when I kept it unstopped for some time, as for two or three minutes of an hour, though I afterwards stopped the vial very close, the air, that had more leisure than ordinary to insinuate itself, would so cherish the flame, that the light would continue sometimes an hour or two, and lasted once or twice no less than three hours.

X. Fifthly and lastly, it seemed, that some elastical particles of the included air, or some substance, that concurred to the maintenance of the flame, was wasted or depraved and weakened, by being pent up in the vial with the emanations of the liquor; since, when the vial had been kept stopped a competent time, and its cavity appeared transparent in the outward light, if I cautiously took out the stopple, the external air seemed manifestly to rush in, as if the springiness of the internal had been notably debilitated by the operation of the flame upon the matter, with which it was kept imprisoned.

Some of these phaenomena easily brought to my mind some of those of an odd experiment, that I formerly imparted to the curious. In which experiment I observed (among other things) that the spirit of urine, impregnated with copper, after the manner there prescribed, would continue limpid and colourless, as long as the vial, that contained it, was kept close stopped. But when once the air came to touch the surface of it, it would (sometimes in less than a minute of an hour) be so affected thereby, that in a very short time (for it was often within some minutes) the liquor would become of a transparent sky colour; and afterwards, the vial being well stopped, and kept in a quiet place, would by degrees grow diaphanous, and the air included with it was wont to have its spring weakened. And as the change of colour was first produced at the surface, where the liquor and air touched one another, and was afterwards thence propagated downwards; so when this ceruleous colour began to disappear, the liquor manifestly became limpid first at and near the bottom, that is, the part, which is remotest from the superior air.

But to return to our noctiluca, the five phaenomena last recited, and some others, seem to favour the conjecture or suspicion I lately proposed, about the interest of the air in our unburning flame. And to examine that suspicion, I thought it less proper to make the foregoing trials with a more vigourous noctiluca, than in a substance, wherein, as in that we have hitherto employed, the disposition to be kindled, or excited to shine, was but faint; so that being, as long as it remained, unexcited, opacous and dark, the absolute, or almost absolute, necessity of the concurrence of air to the actual shining (that constantly ensued upon its contact) of the disposed matter, seemed manifest enough.

But to what this concurrence or efficacy of the air ought to be ascribed, is a problem, that seemed to me so difficult, that my thoughts were put upon several conjectures for so much as a tolerable solution of it; for a taste of which, I shall venture to offer you one or two of these, that least displease me.

I thought it not improbable, that the admitted air, either by some subtle salt that it contained, or upon some such account, excited in the fumes, it mingled with, a kind of fermentation, or (if you please) a commotion, by which means the matter acquired so brisk an agitation, as to propagate the motion to the eye, and there make an impression, the sense whereof we call light: though it seemed also not unlikely, that some of the particles of the supervening air may so associate themselves with those congruous ones, they met with in the cavity of the vial, that, by that coalition, corpuscles were produced, fitted to be, by the subtle aethereal matter, that abounds in the pores of the air, so pervaded and briskly agitated, as to produce light. And it was not new to me, that the air should associate itself with invisible exhalations, and concur with them to make new concretions; since I have several times prepared a volatile sulphureous liquor, red as a ruby, which, when the vial has been kept close for some time, suffers the empty cavity of the vessel to be transparent; but upon the unstopping it, and giving access to the outward air, it appears presently full of white fumes, more opacous than a mist. And something like this, though in an inferior degree, may be observed, when we unstop glasses, that are but partly full of spirit of salt, or aqua fortis, provided those liquors be rectified as much, and no more, than is fit. For the contact of the air will presently make the former manifestly afford white fumes, and the latter sometimes red ones, and sometimes otherwise coloured. . . .

Such observations and reflections incline me to think, that, to speak in a general way, the light of our noctilucas depends upon a peculiar and very brisk agitation of some minute particles of the shining matter, in point of bulk, shape and contexture, peculiarly fitted to impel the contiguous aether to the bottom of our eyes; and made me think it not improbable, that the contact of fresh external air might contribute to this peculiar kind of agitation in the gummous noctiluca, as an helpful thing, and in the aerial noctiluca, as an almost necessary concurrent. But whether the air concurs to this effect, as it does itself excite a brisk commotion in the fumid matter it invades, or whether the air, or some fine substance contained in it, operates on this occasion, as a kind of vital spirit, such as is found necessary, not only to common flame, but to that which is supposed to keep animals alive; or whether the corpuscles of the admitted air so combine with those, that exhale from the grosser liquor, as to become fit to be vehemently agitated by some aethereal pervading substance; whether or no, I say, the agency of the air in our phaenomena be to be referred to one or more of the newly mentioned things, or to some other cause of a peculiar and very brisk agitation, which, to speak in general, seems to have the main stroke in the production of light, is left to further inquiry. [Works, IV, 385–89]

24. Respiration

Boyle's experiments on respiration were not intended to establish that air was necessary for life—a fact quite sufficiently apparent—but to find out more about the role of the air, to measure as accurately as possible the amount of air necessary for life, and to see what respiration did to the air. In general, the seventeenth century recognized the similarity between respiration and combustion. The following experiment (from the *New Experiments Physico-Mechanical,* 1660) is sufficiently representative of all Boyle's work, and clearly shows his desire to make quantitative experiments where possible. Hugenius is Christiaan Huygens, the great Dutch physicist, who was in close correspondence with English scientists even before his first visit to England in 1661; as a result of Boyle's books on pneumatics he interested himself in the subject.

To satisfy ourselves in some measure about the account upon which respiration is so necessary to the animals that nature hath furnished with lungs, we took (being then unable to procure any other lively bird, small enough to be put into the receiver) a lark, one of whose wings had been broken by a shot of a man that we had sent to provide us some birds for our experiment; but notwithstanding this hurt, the lark was very lively, and did, being put into the receiver, divers times spring up in it to a good height. The vessel being hastily, but carefully closed, the pump was diligently plied, and the bird for a while appeared lively enough; but upon a greater exsuction of the air, she began manifestly to droop and appear sick, and very soon after was taken with as violent and irregular convulsions, as are wont to be observed, in poultry, when their heads are wrung off: for the bird threw herself over and over two or three times, and died with her breast upward, her head downwards, and her neck awry. And though upon the appearing of these convulsions, we turned the stop-cock, and let in the air upon her, yet it came too late; whereupon casting our eyes upon one of those accurate dials that go with a pendulum, and were of late ingeniously invented by the noble and learned Hugenius, we found that the whole tragedy had been concluded within ten minutes of an hour, part of which time had been employed in cementing the cover to the receiver. Soon after we got a hen-sparrow, which being caught with bird-lime was not at all hurt; when we put her into the receiver, almost to the top of which she would briskly raise herself, the experiment being tried with this bird, as it was with the former, she seemed to be dead within seven minutes, one of which were employed in cementing on the cover: but upon the speedy turning of the key, the fresh air flowing in, began slowly to revive her, so that after some pantings she opened her eyes, and regained her feet, and in about ¼ of an hour after, threatened to make an escape at the top of the glass, which had been unstopped to let in the fresh air upon her: but the receiver being closed the second time, she was killed with violent convulsions within five minutes from the beginning of the pumping.

A while after we put in a mouse, newly taken, in such a trap as had rather affrighted than hurt him; whilst he was leaping up very high in the receiver, we fastened the cover to it, expecting that an animal used to live in narrow holes with very little fresh air, would endure the want of

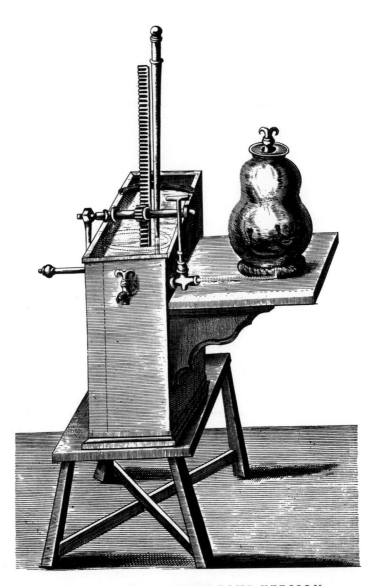

FIG. 4 AIR PUMP, SECOND VERSION

In this version of the air pump the working parts are submerged in liquid to make them more airtight, and the receiver is separate. Here a respiration experiment is in progress.

it better than the lately mentioned birds; but though, for a while after the pump was set a-work, he continued leaping up as before; yet, it was not long ere he began to appear sick and giddy, and to stagger: after which he fell down as dead, but without such violent convulsions as the bird died with. Whereupon, hastily turning the key, we let in some fresh air upon him, by which he recovered, after a while, his senses and his feet, but seemed to continue weak and sick: but at length, growing able to skip as formerly, the pump was plied again for eight minutes, about the middle of which space, if not before, a little air by a mischance got in at the stop-cock; and about two minutes after that, the mouse divers times leaped up lively enough, though after about two minutes more he fell down quite dead, yet with convulsions far milder than those wherewith the two birds expired. This alacrity so little before his death, and his not dying sooner than at the end of the eighth minute, seemed ascribable to the air (how little soever) that slipt into the receiver. For the first time, those convulsions (that, if they had not been suddenly remedied, had immediately dispatched him) seized on him in six minutes after the pump began to be set a-work. These experiments seemed the more strange, in regard that during a great part of those few minutes the engine could but inconsiderably rarefy the air (and that too, but by degrees) and at the end of them there remained in the receiver no inconsiderable quantity; as may appear by what we have formerly said of our not being able to draw down water in a tube, within much less than a foot of the bottom: with which we likewise considered, that by the exsuction of the air and interspersed vapours, there was left in the receiver a space some hundreds of times exceeding the bigness of the animal, to receive the fulginous steams, from which exspiration discharges the lungs; and

which, in the other cases hitherto known, may be suspected, for want of room, to stifle those animals that are
closely penned up in too narrow receptacles.

I forgot to mention, that having caused these three
creatures to be opened, I could, in such small bodies,
discover little of what we sought for, and what we might
possibly have found in larger animals; for though the lungs
of the birds appeared very red, and as it were inflamed,
yet that colour being usual enough in the lungs of such
winged creatures, deserves not so much our notice, as it
doth, that in almost all the destructive experiments made
in our engine, the animals appeared to die with violent
convulsive motions: from which, whether physicians can
gather any thing towards the discovery of the nature of
convulsive distempers, I leave to them to consider.

Having proceeded thus far, though (as we have partly
intimated already) there appeared not much cause to
doubt, but that the death of the forementioned animals
proceeded rather from the want of air, than that the air
was overclogged by the steams of their bodies, exquisitely
penned up in the glass; yet I, that love not to believe any
thing upon conjectures, when by a not over-difficult experiment I can try whether it be true or no, thought it the
safest way to obviate objections, and remove scruples, by
shutting up another mouse as close as I could in the receiver; wherein it lived about three quarters of an hour,
and might probably have done so, much longer, had not
a Virtuoso of quality, who in the meanwhile chanced to
make me a visit, desired to see whether or no the mouse
could be killed by the exsuction of the ambient air: whereupon we thought fit to open, for a little while, an intercourse betwixt the air in the receiver, and that without it,
that the mouse might thereby (if it were needful for him)
be refreshed; and yet we did this without uncementing the
cover at the top, that it might not be objected, that per-

haps the vessel was more closely stopped for the exsuction of the air than before.

The experiment had this event, that after the mouse had lived ten minutes (which we ascribed to this, that the pump, for want of having been lately oiled, could move but slowly, and could not by him that managed it be made to work as nimbly as it was wont) at the end of that time he died with convulsive fits, wherein he made two or three bounds into the air, before he fell down dead. . . . [*Works*, I, 97–99]

25. The Composition of the Atmosphere

This was a problem with which Boyle wrestled all his life. It was a peculiarly difficult question for the seventeenth century, which, though it discovered the physical properties of air, was baffled completely by its chemical properties. Air was generally thought to be chemically inert; if any part appeared to enter into a chemical reaction, this was because there were so many diverse substances carried by air in solution, as water vapor was. As the following selections show, it was on experimental grounds that Boyle decided that the permanently elastic air left when air would no longer support either respiration or combustion was the "true" air, and that the material used up in respiration or combustion was not air, but a quite different sort of substance. It was also for experimental reasons that he was so skeptical of the theory of Hooke, Mayow, and others that air contained "nitro-aerial" particles which were the active agents in combustion; as he points out, if they existed it ought to be possible to detect them, as it was not. The following selections are both taken from the *General History of the Air*, published posthumously in 1691; the first was obviously written before Henry Oldenburg's death, which occurred in 1677.

Of the Constant and Permanent Ingredients of Air A Short Answer to a Question about the Nature of Air, given by Mr. Boyle to Mr. Henry Oldenburg

As to your question, what I think the air to be? I shall in the first place take it for granted, that by the air you mean not, either the pure element of air, which some, nor that etherial or celestial substance, that others (upon what grounds I must not here examine) assert; but that, which I am wont to call the atmospherical air, which is that common air we breathe and move in.

But though I know you too well to suspect, that you design any ambiguity in your question; yet I shall not adventure to answer it, till I have premised a distinction that is not usual: for, according to my thoughts, the air may be taken either for that, which is temporary, (if I may so call it) or in a transient state; or that which is lasting, and in a permanent state. This distinction, which perhaps you looked not for, I shall illustrate by this example, that if you sufficiently heat an aeolipile furnished with water, and stay a pretty while to afford time for the expulsion of the aerial particles by the aqueous vapours, you may afterwards observe, that these last named will be driven out in multitudes, and with a noise, and will emulate a wind or stream of air, by blowing coals held at a convenient distance, like a pair of bellows, and by producing a sharp and whistling sound against the edge of a knife, held in a convenient posture almost upon the orifice of the pipe, whence they issue out. But this vapid stream, though in these and some other things it imitates true air, whilst the vehement agitation lasts, which the vapours it consists of received from the fire; yet in a very short time, especially if the weather, or the vessels it enters into, be cold, loses the temporary form it seemed to have of air, and returns to water, as it was at first.

This premised, I come to speak directly, but dare not do it confidently, to your question: for though possibly I may have made as many trials as another about the nature of the air; yet I freely confess to you, that I much suspect there lies yet something concealed in it, that needs a further discovery, which may perhaps be made by further trials. But in the mean time (not wholly to baffle your curiosity, since it is so modest as to desire to know of me, not what the true nature of the air is, but what I guess concerning its chiefest property or attribute) I will acquaint you with some of the thoughts I long ago had, and which I yet took upon myself, and desire to have them looked upon by you but as conjectures, entertained only till farther discoveries confirm them, or suggest better in their room.

It seems then not improbable to me, that our atmospherical air may consist of three differing kinds of corpuscles. The first is made of that numberless multitude and great variety of particles, which, under the form of vapours, or dry exhalations, ascend from the earth, water, minerals, vegetables, and animals, &c. and, in a word, of whatever substances are elevated by the celestial or subterraneal heats, and made to diffuse themselves into the atmosphere. The second sort of particles, that make the air, may be yet more subtle than the former, and consist of such exceeding minute parts, as make up the magnetical steams of our terrestrial globe, and the innumerable particles, that the sun and other stars, that seem to shine of themselves, do either emit out of their own bodies, or by their pressure thrust against our eyes, and thereby produce what we call light; which, whether we explicate it by the Epicurean or Cartesian hypothesis, argues a great plenty of a celestial (or some other very subtle) matter, to be dispersed through, or harboured in, the intervals of the stabler or grosser corpuscles of the atmosphere.

But because you expect from me a distinguishing (and as it were characteristic) quality, which may put a difference between the parts already named of the atmosphere, and those, to which most of the phaenomena of our engine, and many other pneumatical experiments seem to be due, I shall add a third sort of atmospherical particles, compared with which, I have not yet found any, whereto the name of air does so deservedly belong. And this sort of particles are those, which are not only for a while, by manifest outward agents, made elastical, but are permanently so, and on that account may be styled perennial air.

Of the structure of the elastical particles of the air, divers conceptions may be framed, according to the several contrivances men may devise to answer the phaenomena: for one may think them to be like the springs of watches, coiled up, and still endeavouring to fly abroad. One may also fancy a portion of air to be like a lock or parcel of curled hairs of wool; which being compressed by an external force, or their own weight, may have a continual endeavour to stretch themselves out, and thrust away the neighbouring particles, and whatever other bodies would hinder them to recover their former state, or attain their full liberty. One may also fancy them like extremely slender wires, such as those of gold and silver, that tradesmen unwind from some cylindrical bodies of differing sizes, on which they were rolled; which pieces of spiral or curled wire may be, as of differing substances and consistencies, so of very differing lengths and thicknesses, and have their curls greater or lesser, nearer each other, or more distant, and be otherwise diversified, and yet all have springiness in them, and (notwithstanding) be, by reason of their shape, readily expansible on the score of their native structure, as also by heat, gyrations, and other motions, and compressible by an external force into a very little room. I remember too, that I have, among other comparisons of this kind, represented the springy particles of the air like the very thin shavings of wood, that carpenters and joiners are wont to take off with their planers; for, besides that these may be made of differing woods, as oak, ash, fir, &c. and thereby be diversified as to their substance, they are usually of very various breadths, and lengths, and thicknesses. And perhaps you may the rather

prefer this comparison, because it may seem somewhat
to illustrate the production of the springy particles of the
air: for, to make these shavings, there is no art nor curious
instruments required: and their curls are noways uniform,
but many ways differing, and seemingly casual; and, which
is chiefly considerable, these shavings are producible out
of bodies, that did not appear, nor were suspected, to be
elastical in their bulk, as beams and blocks, almost any of
which may afford springy shavings, barely by having some
of its parts so taken off, as to be thin and flexible enough,
and commodiously shaped; which may perhaps illustrate
what I tried, that divers solid (and even mineral) bodies,
not suspected of elasticity, being put into corrosive menstruums, devoid of that quality, there will, upon the convenient comminution of parts ensuing the action and reaction that passes between them in the dissolution, result
or emerge a pretty quantity of permanently elastical air.
But possibly you will think, that these are but extravagant
conjectures: and therefore, without adding anything in
favour of them, I shall proceed, and willingly grant, that
one may fancy several other shapes (and perhaps fitter
than those we have mentioned) for these springy corpuscles, about whose structure I shall not now particularly
discourse, because of the variety of probable conjectures,
that I think may be proposed concerning it. Only I shall
here intimate, that though the elastical air seem to continue such, rather upon the score of its structure, than any
external agitation; yet heat, that is a kind of motion, may
make the agitated particles strive to recede further and
further from the centres of their motions, and to beat off
those, that would hinder the freedom of their gyrations,
and so very much add to the endeavour of such air to expand itself. And I will allow you to suspect, that there may
be sometimes mingled with the particles, that are springy,
upon the newly mentioned account, some others, that

owe their elasticity, not so much to their structure, as their motion, which variously brandishing them and whirling them about, may make them beat off the neighbouring particles, and thereby promote an expansive endeavour in the air, whereof they are parts. And though some of these may, in very cold climates and seasons, prove to be of those, which I not long since referred to temporary air; yet others of them may be so minute and agile, and so advantageously shaped, that, at least in our climate, the air will scarce be so cold, but that the causes, which entertain the agitation, and keep it fluid, may also give a competent motion to particles so well disposed to be kept in it.

Of Salts in the Air

I know, that divers learned men, some physicians, some chymists, and some also philosophers, speak much of a volatile nitre, that abounds in the air, as if that were the only salt wherewith it is impregnated. But though I agree with them, in thinking, that the air is in many places impregnated with corpuscles of a nitrous nature; yet I confess I have not been hitherto convinced of all that is wont to be delivered about the plenty and quantity of nitre in the air: for I have not found, that those, that build so much upon this volatile nitre, have made out by any competent experiment, that there is such a volatile nitre abounding in the air. For having often dealt with saltpetre in the fire, I do not find it easy to be raised by a gentle heat; and when by a stronger fire we distil it in close vessels, it is plain, that what the chymists call spirit of nitre, has quite differing properties from crude nitre, and from those that are ascribed to the volatile nitre of the air; these spirits being so far from being refreshing to the nature of animals, that they are exceeding corrosive: And even when I caused earth to be dug up in an old pigeon-house, because that is accounted the most nitrous sort of earth, and distilled it with moderate fires, I did not find the volatile saline parts, that came over, to be like that, which these learned men conceive the air to be stored with. Nor have I met with among them any positive proof, to evince the truth of their opinion; which yet, as I was saying, I am content to admit, as an ingenious supposition, until something be offered, that shall prove it to be more; which I think not impossible to happen, at least as to some times and places. But I am not yet sure, that the exhalations, that ascend from the subterraneal parts, and perhaps also the sunbeams themselves, may volatilize many of the nitrous corpuscles they chance to act upon, and elevate them into the air, without analyzing them, or destroying their texture, as our fire are wont to do. . . .

. . . It may be worth while to expose to the air such bodies, as we judge fittest to be wrought upon by the salt, that we think likeliest to be met with in it. So where we guess the air to be impregnated with nitre, we may expose lime to it, or some other body, that we think disposed to imbibe or retain such a saltness. We may also hang up in such an air clothes or silks dyed with such colours, that nitrous (for instance) . . . spirits . . . have been found peculiarly apt to make to fade or to discolour them. [*Works,* V, 613–15, 627–28, 630–31]

26. Some Consideration of Experimental Technique

The construction of gauges to measure the degree of vacuum in the air pump receiver was an important advance in the attempt to make pneumatic experiments more accurately quantitative. Boyle here describes several gauges with considerations on each. This is from the *New Experiments Physico-Mechanical* (the *First Continuation* 1669); it is rather surprising that he did not publish this account earlier, though it is possible that it was some time before he felt the need for gauges, or was able to construct any accurate enough to suit his needs.

The comments of Boyle on the problems involved in making the Torricellian experiment either in air or *in vacuo* are of interest as showing both the importance and the difficulty of having a good experimental technique. Boyle's appreciation of the niceties of technique is one of the things which set him above most of his contemporaries in experimental skill, and which enabled him to make so many more, and more fruitful, experiments than they could do with the air pump. It also indicates how right Boyle was to say at the beginning of the *New Experiments, Physico-Mechanical* (1660) (from which this is taken) that a certain prolixity of discussion was necessary if one wished to describe an experiment in such a manner that others could readily repeat it.

About the Making of Mercurial and other Gauges, whereby to Estimate How the Receiver is Exhausted

Because the air being invisible, it is not always easy to know whether it be sufficiently pumped out of the receiver that was to be exhausted, we thought it would be

385

very convenient to have some instrument within the receiver that might serve for a gauge or standard, whereby to judge whether or no it were sufficiently exhausted.

To this purpose divers expedients were thought on, and some of them put in practice; which, though not equally commodious, may yet all of them be usefully employed, one on this occasion, and another on that.

The first (if I misremember not) that I proposed was a bladder (which may be greater or less, according to the size of the vessel it is to serve for) to be very strongly tied at the neck, after having had only so much air left in the folds of it as may serve to blow up the bladder to its full dimensions, when the receiver is very well exhausted, and not before. But though . . . I yet make use of small bladders on certain occasions, in which they are peculiarly convenient, yet in many cases they do, when the glasses are well exhausted, take up too much room in them, and hinder the objects included in the receiver from being observed from all sides of it.

Another sort of gauge was made with quicksilver poured into a very short pipe, which was afterwards inverted into a little glass of stagnant quicksilver, according to the manner of the Torricellian experiment. For this pipe being but a very few inches long the mercury in it would not begin to descend till a very great proportion of air was pumped out of the receiver; because till then the spring of the remaining air would be strong enough to be able to keep up so short a cylinder of mercury. And this kind of gauge is no bad one. But because, to omit some other little inconveniences, it cannot easily be suspended (which in divers experiments it is fit the gauge should be) and the mercury in it is apt to be too much shaken by the motion of the engine, there was another kind of gauge by some ingenious man (whoever he were) substituted in its place, consisting of a kind of siphon whose shorter leg hath belonging to it a large bubble of glass, most commonly made use of at an illustrious meeting of virtuosi. . . .

But none of the gauges I had formerly used, nor even this last, having the conveniences that some of my experiments require, I was fain to devise another, which is that I most make use of, as having advantages, some or other of which each of the gauges already mentioned wants. . . .

To make the gauge we are speaking of, take a very slender and cylindrical pipe of glass of six, eight, ten, or more inches in length, and not so big as a goose-quill (but such as we employ for the stems of sealed weather-glasses) and having at the flame of a lamp melted it, but not too near the middle, to make of it by bending it a siphon, whose two legs are to be not only parallel to one another, but as little distant anywhere from one another as conveniently may be. In one (which is ususally the longer of these legs) there is to be left at the top either half an inch or a whole inch, or more or less than either (according to the length of the gauge or the scope of the experimenter) of air in its natural state, neither rarefied nor condensed; the rest of the longer leg, and as great a part of the shorter as shall be thought fit, being to be filled with quicksilver. This done there may be marks placed at the outside of the longer or sealed leg, whereby to measure the expansion of the air included in the same leg; and these marks may be either little glass knobs about the bigness of pins heads, fastened by the help of a lamp at certain distances to the longer leg of the siphon, or else the divisions of an inch made on a list of paper and pasted on, either to the siphon itself, or to the slender frame which on some occasions we fasten the gauge to.

This instrument being conveyed into a receiver (which for expedition sake we choose as small as will serve the turn) the air is to be very diligently pumped out, and then notice is to be taken to what part of the gauge the mercury is depressed, that we may know, when we shall afterwards see the mercury driven so far, that the receiver the gauge is placed in, is well exhausted. And if it be much desired to know more accurately (for one may arrive pretty near the truth by guess) what stations of the mercury in the gauge are answerable to the degrees of rarefaction of the air in the receiver, that may be compassed either by calculation (which is not so easy, and supposes some hypotheses) or, though not without some trouble, by letting in the water as often as is necessary into a receiver, whose entire capacity is first measured, and in which there may be marks made to show, when the water to be let in shall fill a fourth part, or half, or three quarters, &c. of the cavity. For if (for instance) when the quicksilver in the gauge is depressed to such a mark you let in the water, and the liquor appears to fill a fourth part of the receiver, you may conclude that about a fourth part of the air was pumped out, or that a fourth part of the spring that the whole included air had was lost by the exhaustion, when the quicksilver in the gauge was at the mark above-mentioned. And if the admitted water do considerably either fall short of, or exceed the quantity you expected, you may the next time let in the water either after the mercury has a little passed the former mark, or a little before it is arrived at it. And when once you have this way obtained one pretty long and accurate gauge, you will not need to take so much pains to make others, since you may then divide them by the help of that one; for this being placed with any other in a small receiver, when the mercury in the standard-gauge (if I may so call it) is depressed to any of the determinate divisions obtained by observation, you may thence conclude how much the air in the receiver is rarefied, and consequently by taking notice of the place where the mercury rests in the other gauge, you may determine what degree of exhaustion in the receiver is denoted by that station of the mercury in this gauge. . . .

. . . The ground of this contrivance was, that whereas in divers other gauges, when the pump came to be obstinately plied, the expansion of the included air would be so great, that it would either drive out the liquor, especially if it were light, or in part make an escape through it; I judged that in such an instrument as that newly described, those inconveniencies would be avoided, because that the more the air should come to be dilated, the greater weight of quicksilver it would in the shorter leg have to raise, which would sufficiently hinder it from making that heavy liquor run over; and the same ponderousness of the liquor, together with the slenderness of the pipe, would likewise hinder the included air from getting through in bubbles. [*Works*, III,211–13]

Some technical considerations on the Torricellian Experiment

First then, if in trying the experiment here or elsewhere, you make use of the English measures that mathematicians and tradesmen are here wont to employ, you will, unless you are forewarned of it, be apt to suspect that those that have written of the experiment have been mistaken. For whereas men are wont generally to talk of the quicksilver's remaining suspended at the height of between six or seven and twenty inches; we commonly observed, when divers years since we first were solicitous about this experiment, that the quicksilver in the tube rested at about 29 inches and a half above the surface of the restagnant quicksilver in the vessel, which did at first both amaze and perplex us, because though we held it not improbable that the difference of the grosser English air, and that of Italy and France, might keep the quicksilver from falling quite as low in this colder, as in those warmer climates; yet we could not believe that that difference in the air should alone be able to make so great an one in the heights of the mercurial cylinders; and accordingly upon enquiry we found, that though the various density of the air be not to be overlooked in this experiment, yet the main reason why we found the cylinder of mercury to consist of so many inches, was this, that our English inches are somewhat inferior in length to the digits made use of in foreign parts, by the writers of the experiment.

The next thing I desire your Lordship to take notice of, is, that the height of the mercurial cylinder is not wont to be found altogether so great as really it might prove, by reason of the negligence or incogitancy of most that make the experiment. For oftentimes by opening of the inverted tube into the vesselled mercury, you may observe a bubble of air to ascend from the bottom of the tube through the subsiding quicksilver to the top; and almost always you may, if you look narrowly, take notice of a multitude of small bubbles all along the inside of the tube betwixt the quicksilver and the glass; (not now to mention the particles of air that lie concealed in the very body of the mercury) many of which, upon the quicksilver's forsaking the upper part of the tube, do break into that deserted space where they find little or no resistance to their expanding of themselves. Whether this be the reason, that upon the application of warm bodies to the emptied part of the tube, the subjacent mercury would be depressed somewhat lower, we shall not determine; though it seem very probable, especially since we found, that, upon the application of linen cloths dipped in water, to the same part of the tube, the quicksilver would somewhat ascend; as if the cold had condensed the imprisoned air (that pressed upon it) into a lesser room. But that the deserted space is not wont to be totally devoid of air, we were induced to think by several circumstances: for when an eminent mathematician, and an excellent experimenter, had taken great pains and spent much time in accurately filling up a tube of mercury, we found that yet there remained store of inconspicuous bubbles, by inverting the tube, letting the quicksilver fall to its wonted height; and by applying (by degrees) a red-hot iron to the outside of the tube, over against the upper part of the mercurial cylinder, (for hereby the little unheeded bubbles, being mightily expanded, ascended in such numbers, and so fast to the deserted space, that the upper part of the quicksilver seemed, to our wonder, to boil). We farther observed, that in the trials of the Torricellian experiment, we have seen made by others, and (one excepted) all our own, we never found that, upon the inclining of the tube, the quicksilver would fully reach to the very top of the sealed end: which argued, that there was some air retreated thither that kept the mercury out of the unreplenished space. . . . [*Works*, I, 38–39]

Notes: PART ONE

CHAPTER 1: Life

1. The Publisher to the Reader, *History of Cold* (London, 1665).

2. Biographical material is mainly derived from Thomas Birch, *Life of Boyle* (London, 1744), which includes the autobiographical "Account of Philaretus during his Minority," supplemented by relevant correspondence.

3. *Memoirs of the Verney Family* (London, 1892), I, 206; this is Sir John Leake's comment on Boyle's sister Katherine.

4. Her life is recounted at length in Charlotte F. Smith, *Mary Rich, Countess of Warwick* (London, 1901).

5. "Account of Philaretus."

6. British Museum Add. MS. 4229, fol. 60.

7. *Lismore Papers*, 2nd series (1887–88), V, 19–24, 71–73.

8. B.M. Add. MS. 4229, fol. 68.

9. See especially G. H. Turnbull, *Hartlib, Dury, and Comenius* (London, 1947), and Hartlib's letters to Boyle published by Birch in the *Life* and in *Works*, Vol. VI.

10. The name is first mentioned in a letter to Francis Tallents of February, 1645/6 *(Life,* in *Works,* I, xxxiv–xxxv); the description is taken from a letter to Marcombes of October 22, 1646 (ibid., p. xxxiv); the letter to Hartlib of May 8 is printed in *Works,* I, xl–xli.

11. Letter to Tallents, *Works,* I, xxxiv–xxxv.

12. Cf. the dedication and the conclusion.

13. *Seraphick Love,* in *Works,* I, 262.

14. Letter to Lady Ranelagh of August 31, 1649, *Works,* VI, 49–50; p. 274.

15. Letter of May 8, 1647.

16. Cf. Boyle Letters (Royal Society Guard-Books), VI, No. 3, July 23, 1649, and Margaret E. Rowbotham, "The Earliest Published Writing of Robert Boyle," *Annals of Science,* VI (1948–50), 376–89.

17. Royal Society Boyle Papers, Vol. XVIII.

18. Letter of Petty to Boyle, April 15, 1653, *Works,* VI, 137–39.

19. Cf. Roger North's comment, *The Lives of the Norths*, ed. A Jessop (London, 1890), III, 187.

20. Copied by Henry Oldenburg into his commonplace book in 1660 (Royal Society MS. MM 1). Part was included in the *Usefulness of Natural Philosophy*, Tome I, Part II, Essay II. The essay lists and "Memorials" are in the Boyle Papers, Vols. XXVIII and XXXVI.

21. Version of 1696/7 in *Works of Thomas Hearne* (London, 1810), III, 150–64; it is quoted in many histories of the Royal Society.

22. Works, VI, 633–34.

23. *De Cycloide & corporibus inde gentis*, 1659.

24. A. Wood, *Life and Times*, ed. A. Clark, 5 vols. (Oxford, 1891–1900), I, 472.

25. Royal Society MS. MM 1, published as "An Early Version of Boyle's *Sceptical Chymist*" in *Isis*, 1954.

26. Cf. the dedication and conclusion of the *New Experiments Physico-Mechanical*, of 1660.

27. By Yonker de Bills, trans. by Pell as *A Tract Touching the Skill of a Better Way of Anatomy of a Man's Body* (London, 1659).

28. Cf. Pepys' "Diary" for April 11, 1660.

29. It was rumored by John Beale that Boyle was offered the post of Provost of Eton; but there is no evidence for this in spite of Boyle's biographers.

30. The relevant documents are given in Ornstein and in Birch, *History of the Royal Society*, Vol. I.

31. Cf. Weld, *A History of the Royal Society* (London, 1848), I, 146–49.

32. Letter to Hooke in *Life* (*Works*, I, cxix).

33. Entry for January 6, 1691/2.

34. Gilbert Burnet, *A Sermon Preached at the Funeral of the Honorable Robert Boyle* (London, 1692), p. 27.

35. "Diary," Surtees Society, LIV (1870), 21.

CHAPTER 2: The New Learning and Its Methods

1. Royal Society Boyle Papers, Vol. I.

2. Letter of December 23, 1665; Royal Society MS. B 1, No. 101.

3. "Diary," entry for June 2, 1667 (see also entries for April 28 and May 26).

4. *Nouveaux essais sur l'entendement*, in *Die philosophischen Schriften von Gottfried Wilhelm Leibniz*, ed. Gerhardt (1882), V, 437; letter to Huygens, January 8, 1692, *Œuvres complètes de Christiaan Huygens* (La Haye, 1882–1944), X, 228–29.

5. A "natural history" (collection) of experiments which Bacon thought a necessary preliminary to the devising of a sound scientific theory.

6. Birch, *History of the Royal Society*, III, 9, for February 8, 1671/2.

7. *Works*, IV, 235 ff.; cf. p. 179 ff. Though the passage in *Works* reads, "the more various the *particles*," *particulars* is the correct form.

8. *Works*, V, 427.

9. Cf. Sprat, *History of the Royal Society*, which reprints some of these accounts; others are to be found in the *Philosophical Transactions*.

CHAPTER 3: The Mechanical Philosophy

1. *De chymicorum cum Aristotelicis et Galenis consensu ac dissensu* (Wittenberg, 1619).

2. Cf. Stillman Drake, *Discoveries and Opinions of Galileo* (New York, 1957), pp. 273–79.

3. *Novum Organum*, Book II, aphorism III.

4. Ibid., aphorism VIII.

5. Cf. p. 281.

6. Cf. Part II, Section II, No. 11.

7. Lavoisier heated water in a closed glass vessel for many days and found that the "earth" formed came from the glass; this he reported in 1770 to the Académie des Sciences in a memoir "On the nature of water and on the experiments by which the possibility of changing it into earth have been alleged" (*Œuvres de Lavoisier*, Paris, 1862–93, II, 1–25). A similar experiment was independently performed by the Swedish chemist Scheele. Both were familiar with Boyle's discussion in *Origin of Forms and Qualities*.

8. Rey, an obscure figure, claimed in 1630 that the calx was lighter than the metal, but that it weighed more because air thickened by heating, became physically (not chemically) attached to it. His ideas were little noticed until Priestley discovered oxygen and Lavoisier explained its role in combustion. Rey's essays have been edited by Douglas McKie (London, 1951).

CHAPTER 4: Chemistry

1. There was a professional center in the two chairs at the Royal Botanic Garden in Paris: cf. J.-P. Contant, *L'Enseignement de la chimie au jardin royal des plantes de Paris* (Cahors, 1952), which contains brief biographies of the professors. Lemery, Homberg, and others gave private lectures. German chemists like Daniel Sennert and Oswald Croll were connected with university medical faculties.

2. Helmont's collected works, *Ortus Medicinae* (Amsterdam, 1648), translated as *Oriatrike or Physick Refined* (London, 1662 and 1664) were filled with a strange mixture of chemical experiment, vitalistic physiology, mysticism, alchemy and strange chemicomedical preparations.

3. N. Lefebvre was professor at the Botanic Garden before coming to England as physician to Charles II; his *Traité de chymie* (Paris, 1661) was published in London as *A Compleat Body of Chemistry* (1670). His successor, Christopher Glaser, wrote a *Traité de la chymie* (Paris, 1663 and many editions); it was printed in London as *The Compleat Chymist* in 1677, though by then Glaser himself was under a cloud, suspected of complicity in a notorious poisoning case.

4. 1645–1715; his *Cours de chimie* (1675) was the most popular of all the seventeenth-century textbooks and was read as late as the mid-eighteenth century.

CHAPTER 5: Pneumatics

1. See Part II, Selection No. 25.

2. Michael Sendivogius, whose *Novum Lumen Chymicum* (perhaps really the work of Alexander Seton) was highly popular in the seventeenth century, was a mystic Paracelsan who believed that a "universal salt" present in the air accounted for (among other things) combustion. Kènelm Digby, mystic, occultist, and original fellow of the Royal Society, read a paper before the Society on January 23, 1660/1 in which he discussed the role of air in combustion, also employing a universal salt: it is published as *A Discourse Concerning the Vegetation of Plants*. Hooke's theory was discussed in *Micrographia* (1664) and in the sessions of the Royal Society as reported in Birch's *History*. John Mayow's *Tractatus Quinque* (1674) is available in his *Medico-Physical Works*, Alembic

Club No. 17 (Edinburgh, 1907); Mayow has had a mixed press, but though his speculations are ingenious he had no better understanding of the real-role of air in combustion than did his contemporaries.

CHAPTER 6: Conclusion

1. I, 31–32.

2. Saverien, *Histoire des philosophes modernes* (Paris, 1768), VI, 63–92.

3. It was first described as a universal pneumatic "rule" in 1683 by Jacques Bernouilli in *On the Gravity of Air (Opera,* Geneva, 1744, II, 47–163). Of Rule IV in pneumatics he said, "The truth of this rule was made evident by two ingenious experiments on the subject made by the illustrious Mr. Boyle, which you may find in his Tract against Linus, chap. V, to which the author adds Tables of the different degrees of condensation and rarefaction."

4. *Œuvres de Lavoisier* (6 vols.; Paris, 1862–93), II, 105 ff.

5. Written c. 1728, published in 1748; 2nd ed., 1750, p. 64.

PART TWO : *Selections*

1. Gassendi (1592–1655) devoted the latter part of his life to reviving, modernizing, and Christianizing the philosophy of Epicurus. Boyle here refers to *Philosophiae Epicuri Syntagma,* 1649; he seems never to have read the later, much longer, *Syntagma Philosophicus* of 1658. Descartes' *Principia Philosophiae* was published in 1644 and widely read in England.

2. Boyle knew of Leucippus and Epicurus from Diogenes Laertius' *Lives of the Philosophers* (still an important source).

3. Bernardo Telesio (1508–88) was an anti-Aristotelian philosopher; Tomaso Campanella·(1568–1639), theologian and anti-Aristotelian, wrote a notable defense of Galileo's Copernicanism while a prisoner of the Inquisition.

4. Much used in seventeenth-century medical practice.

5. Columbus is Realdo Columbo (1516–59), who lectured on the lesser (or pulmonary) circulation at Padua. Andreas Cesalpino (1519–1603), best known as a plant physiologist, described the lesser circulation and had a confused idea that circulation might occur in sleep. William Wotton in *Reflections on Ancient and Modern Learning* (London, 1697) credited "Father Paul the

Venetian" (Paolo Sarpi, 1552–1623), publicist and an amateur of science, with discovering the valves in the veins before Fabricius, and some of his contemporaries thought he knew of the circulation (which he certainly did not). Warner is perhaps John Warner (d. 1565), first Regius Professor at Oxford.

6. Dasypodius designed the clock built by Isaac Habrecht in the late sixteenth century to replace a late medieval mechanism; only a cock which flapped its wings and crowed was retained. In the nineteenth century the clock was again rebuilt. Habrecht built a small model, now in the British Museum. For details, H. Alan Lloyd, *Some Outstanding Clocks over Seven Hundred Years, 1250– 1950* (London, 1958) is useful; see pp. 40–41.

7. Aristotle's conviction that the universe had no beginning and no end naturally posed a problem to devout medieval Christians committed to the belief that God had created the universe in time and would destroy it at the day of judgment. It was one of the doctrines which St. Thomas Aquinas had been forced to refute, and Thomism had become the orthodox doctrine of Scholasticism, the doctrine taught in the universities.

8. This refers to the plague years of 1665–66 and to the Great Fire of London of 1666; Boyle's papers were removed to the country for safekeeping at the time and he himself, like many others, stayed away from London.

9. Richard Reeves (fl. 1641–79) was a well-known instrument-maker. He worked for Pell and for Hooke; Huygens visited his shop; and Pepys bought microscopes and telescopes from him.

10. Drebbel (1572–1634) was a Dutch engineer and experimenter who made a great stir at the court of James I with his submarine, which performed on and under the Thames. He introduced the scarlet cochineal dye into England, and the secret of tin-mordants in dyeing.

11. Christiaan Huygens (1629–95).

12. For Pascal's work in English there is *The Physical Treatises of Pascal*, ed. J. H. B. and A. G. H. Spiers, Columbia Records in Civilization (New York, 1937).

13. Printed in English in *The Principal Works of Simon Stevin* (Amsterdam, 1955), Vol. I.

14. Stanton St. John, a pleasant village about five miles northeast of Oxford.

15. Not, of course, the famous disciple of Luther.

16. In 1665.

17. The Cartesian aether, which accounted for the properties of terrestrial bodies.

18. Plato's all-pervasive world soul.

19. Helmont's version of the alchemists' universal solvent.

20. Mysteries.

21. Fl. c. 1600, of Italian origin, though active in Germany as a physician and chemist; his collected works, in Latin, were published in 1648. Boyle often referred to him as "the experienced Sala."

22. It was a commonplace to compare jestingly "luciferous" (light-bearing) and "lucriferous" (money-grubbing) experiments.

23. Ammoniacal solutions.

24. Fluorspar.

25. Iron. Alchemy associated planets with all metals; only mercury now remains.

26. Minium is lead oxide and a "vitreous Saturnis," a glassy compound of lead.

27. Rosin.

28. Anything "per se" was made by heating (and frequently distilling) the original substance without any addition.

29. Small broken surfaces.

30. To dryness. The result was silver chloride, which blackens on exposure to light.

31. Though the least parts.

32. The element or principle.

33. Sugar of lead (lead acetate).

34. A magistery is composed of the original elements of a body with the impurities removed; hence it is a mixture of pure "elements."

35. By absorbing moisture from the air.

36. Balaustium is the flower of the wild pomegranate, used medicinally as an astringent. Myrobolans (ben nuts) are fruits of the species Terminella, used as a drug and dye.

37. Neutral (properly a theological term).

38. The Puy-de-Dôme experiment.

39. Dungarvan, eldest son of Boyle's brother, the Earl of Cork; the treatise was "in the form of a letter."

40. A liquid containing enough phosphorus to shine.

41. A rising fume.

The standard editions of Boyle's works are those edited by Thomas Birch, *The Works of the Honourable Robert Boyle*, 5 vols. fol. (London, 1744); 6 vols. large quarto (1772). The latter edition has been used for all references here. A number of Boyle's minor works not included by Birch and often not previously published have been made available in learned journals; e.g., Marie Boas, "An Early Version of Boyle's *Sceptical Chymist*," *Isis*, XLV (1954), 153–68, contains a transcript of "Reflexions on the Experiments Vulgarly alledg'd to evince the 4. Peripatetique Elements or 3. Chymical Principles"; and R. S. Westfall, "Unpublished Boyle Papers Relating to Scientific Method, Part II," *Annals of Science*, XII (1956) 103–107, gives another version of "Requisites of a Good Hypothesis" than that published here.

Almost all of Boyle's surviving manuscripts are in the Library of the Royal Society, some fifty ill-arranged volumes, the legacy of Birch's collaborator Henry Miles, but badly bound in the nineteenth century. Some material used by Birch, especially letters, is now in the British Museum, MS. Add. 4228 and MS. Add. 4229. Most of Boyle's correspondence, including that not published by Birch, is in the Royal Society's Guard-Books; there are a few letters in the Malet Collection of the British Museum, MS. 32,093. A catalogue of Boyle's correspondence has been published by R. E. W. Maddison, *Notes and Records of the Royal Society*, XIII (1958), 128–201. Boyle's correspondence with Oldenburg is published in *The Correspondence of Henry Oldenburg*, ed. A. R. Hall and M. B. Hall (Madison, Wisc., 1965)

The best biography of Boyle is still that by Birch, prefixed to his editions of Boyle and also published separately (London, 1744); this includes Boyle's autobiography and many letters, and is the chief source of most of the information in later biographies; even Birch's errors have been faithfully reproduced. A more modern work is Louis T. More, *The Life and Works of the Honourable Robert Boyle* (New York, 1944); it is more readable than Birch, but adds little and is unreliable. For Boyle's family and boyhood the best source is the delightful *Life and Letters of the Great Earl of Cork* by Dorothea Townshend (London, 1904).

For the scientific background of the seventeenth century, see A. Rupert Hall, *From Galileo to Newton* (London and New York, 1963) or *The Scientific Revolution* (London, 1956 and 1962; Beacon Paperback, 1956). For the mechanical philosophy, see Marie Boas, "The Establishment of the Mechanical Philosophy," *Osiris*, X (1952), 413–541. The best general survey of chemistry in this period is Hélène Metzger, *Doctrines chimiques en France au XVIIᵉ siècle* (Paris, 1923), which includes Boyle; a more specialized study is Marie Boas, *Robert Boyle and Seventeenth-Century Chemistry* (Cambridge, 1958). For the scientific instrument-makers and physical scientists of London, an indispensable reference work is E. G. R. Taylor, *Mathematical Practitioners of Tudor and Stuart England* (Cambridge, 1954). For the early history of pneumatics, see Cornelis de Waard, *L'Expérience barométrique* (Thouars, 1936); for an analysis of scientific method and technique, see J. B. Conant, *Robert Boyle's Experiments in Pneumatics*, Harvard Case Studies in Science (Cambridge, Mass., 1950).

The standard account of the development of the Royal Society is readily found in Martha Ornstein, *The Role of Scientific Societies of the Seventeenth Century* (Chicago, 1938); Thomas Birch, *The History of the Royal Society* (4 vols.; London, 1756–57), reproduces the minutes of the Society's meetings in Boyle's day; Thomas Sprat, *History of the Royal Society* (London, 1667; facsimile ed., St. Louis, Missouri, 1958) contains some early papers. For the various informal societies before the Restoration see especially R. H. Syfret, "The Origins of the Royal Society," *Notes and Records of the Royal Society*, V (1948), 75–137; G. H. Turnbull, "Samuel Hartlib's Influence on the Early History of the Royal Society," *Notes and Records*, X (1953), 101–30; and H. W. Robinson, "An Unpublished Letter of Dr Seth Ward Relating to the Early Meetings of the Oxford Philosophical Society," *Notes and Records*, VII (1950), 68.

Boyle wrote too many separate treatises for listing here. The following gives, in chronological order of publication, the complete titles of works from which selections have been taken, together with date of publication and (where known) the approximate date of composition. For a complete list see John Fulton, *A Bibliography of Robert Boyle*, 2nd ed. (Oxford, 1961).

Seraphick Love, 1659 (written 1648).

New Experiments Physico-Mechanical, Touching the Spring of the Air and its Effects, 1660 (written 1659).

Certain Physiological Essays, 1661 (completed by 1657).

The Sceptical Chymist, 1661.

A Defense of the Doctrine Touching the Spring and Weight of the Air, 1662.

Considerations Touching the Usefulness of Experimental Natural Philosophy, Tome I, 1663 (first part written 1647–49).

Experiments and Considerations touching Colours, 1664.

Hydrostatical Paradoxes, 1666 (written 1664).

The Origin of Forms and Qualities, 1666.

New Experiments, Physico-Mechanical, Touching the Spring and Weight of the Air, First Continuation, 1669.

The Usefulness of Experimental Natural Philosophy, Tome II, 1671 (written ca. 1665).

New Experiments to Make Fire and Flame Stable and Ponderable, 1673.

The Excellency of Theology, 1674 (written 1665).

The Excellency and Grounds of the Corpuscular or Mechanical Philosophy, 1674.

Experiments, Notes, &c. about the Mechanical Origin and Production of Divers Particular Qualities, 1675.

The Aerial Noctiluca, 1680.

The Icy Noctiluca, 1681.

Short Memoirs for the Natural Experimental History of Mineral Waters, 1685.

A Free Inquiry into the Vulgarly Received Notions of Nature, 1685/6.

A Disquisition about the Final Causes of Natural Things, 1688.

The General History of the Air, 1691 (partly written before 1677).

INDEX

(Boldface nos. refer to selections from the writings of Robert Boyle.)

air pump, 3, 4, 24, 96, 98, 323 et seq., **380, 385–91**
Aristotelianism, 57–59, 68, 70-71, 96, 157, **168, 177–79, 183–86, 189, 190–91, 204–5, 211, 233, 248**
Aristotle, 16, 60, **129, 183–86, 188, 191,** 367
Atomism, *see* Epicurus, Gassendi, Mechanical Philosophy

Bacon, Francis, 22, 42, 44, 52, 62–63, 85, **124, 163, 178**
Becher, J.J., 31
Beguin, Jean, 71–72
Boyle, Mary, 8, 11, 15
Boyle, Robert
  and chemistry, 15, 16–17, 41, 78–79, 81–93, 112–14, **247–50, 273–322**
  and combustion, 78–79, **264–72**
  and ethics, 15–16
  experimental principles, 44–45, 73–74, **119–31**
  his health, 17–18
  life, 3–33
  and mathematics, 22–3, 55–6, **123**
  and medicine, 17–18, 41, 79–80
  method of work, 34–47, **173–76**
  reputation, contemporary, 3–5, 6, 29–33, 43, 70
  reputation, eighteenth century, 111–12, 114–15, 220
  and utility, 51–54, **155–65, 304–5**
  see also air pump, mechanical philosophy, pneumatics, theology
Boyle, works of:
  The Aerial Noctiluca and *The Icy Noctiluca*, 90–91, **304–19, 366–71**
  Certain Physiological Essays, 25, 44, 65–66, **119–31, 179, 246–47, 280–85**
  A Continuation of New Experiments, Physico-Mechanical, 98, **343–44, 347–49, 358–63**
  ————, The Second Part, 30, 99
  A Defence of the Doctrine Touching the Spring and Weight of the Air, 98, **336–42**
  Dialogues on Heat and Flame, **356**
  A Discovery of the Perviousness of Glass to . . . Flame, 78, **268–72**
  Enquiry and Experiments about Electrical Bodies, **252–55**
  Essay on Gems, 79
  Essay on Nitre, see *Certain Physiological Essays*
  "An Essay of Turning Poisons into Medicines," 19